NOTES FOR AN ATLAS

SEAN BORODALE

Notes for an Atlas

isinglass

First published in 2003 by Isinglass

Printed in England

A CIP record for this book is available from the
British Library

ISBN 0-9533273-2-9

ACKNOWLEDGEMENTS
I am grateful to the Elephant Trust and to the Arts
Council of England for financial assistance which
has made the printing of this work possible, and to
the Rijksakademie van beeldende kunsten/ Stichting
Trustfonds Rijksakademie for the provision of time
and space in which to work.

I am indebted to the generous support of
Henry and Deborah Abercrombie,
and to Mathilde Heyns, Gerry Hughes,
Bruce McLean, Avis Newman
and Jane Borodale - S.B.

The Elephant Trust

'And walken as wide as the world lasteth.'
WILLIAM LANGLAND

For Alfred Please

A man walks and he speaks, and every word   I
warps in the wind in the street. See brambles, a
blackberry still as a boulder suspended among
thorns. Leaves broken as sawdust, curled and
torn. A man wearing black clothes walks to a
car, see lips clamped. See clouds reflected on
car doors. See brown eyes and clouds banked,
knotted and ripped. Wind ticking a maple,
scratching the leg of a twig. See cracks in grey
tar. Hear a tattered blue and white flag, the
shrug and the quiet crack of its cloth in a turn
of the air. See chains from crane arms. A brown
and white spaniel, the crook of its leg cocked,
drops of spray fly. Walk, see an old man and
woman with hands in big pockets and heads

crouched on shoulders like parrots. Turn and
see sky pink as a dog rose, pale as the skin of a
labrador under the hair, like snow flushed with
soft sun in winter. A can in a brown bag lying
on black grass. See pylons and wires on sunset
like skeletons of cinder. Read SCARE WAS.
Air brown as mackerel. See the eye of a
chestnut. See grey leaves on bone stems. Read
WELCOME. Hear, "Rewards are sweeter
than." A man counting coins in the palm of his
hand. See towers of pink like the ears of dogs in
the sky pink with sunset. Sky from the hump of
a bridge. Docks brown as horses, scarred black
at their edges. See pylons like fir trees. See red
lights and wires. A woman alone, eyes wide as a
calf's. See the cauldron of a white bindweed
flower. Hear the click-clack of a bike changing
gear. And hear, "I've got a bit of experience in
that area." And see yellow flowers with long,
grey ragged leaves, grey as goats' legs, and leaves
like torn hearts. See a brown bottle neck.
Leaves groggy with dust. Read TEMPLE
MILL. Green apples and marjoram flowers.
And pale hairy leaves like the backs of pigs. See
black leaves. In the sky's furnace, the horizon, a
band of glowing iron. Red apples in leaves black
as bats. See the grey steel legs of a pylon mid-
stride. A clutch of red rowans. Read Jack Smit.
Pass under the ribs of a bridge. A mallow's
bruised crease in the rag of a petal. A bread
crust curled up. Hear the murmur of cars. See

two headlamps beaming like daggers. See a
shadow's dark face in a car and two shadow
faces and two shadow hands fanning out. Pass a
gap in a wall where six men are heaving a white-
netted metal-framed goal across a flat field.
Pass three fire-scorched truck cabs like
dynamite boulders heaped in a quarry. See level
grass fields and two red lights among trees, like
two giant eyes. A crow flies. See broken green
glass. Read WHEN THE. Tick of a bike. Hear
the growl of a bus. A turbo's pitch falls. Hear a
jitter of wind crashing in. See a leaf like a
joker's hat. Read DANGER. Read letters in
black. Hear shouts and hear, "Don't." Hear the
slap of a ball. Clack of a drain grate driven
across. Speed of a car and the road's emptiness
hangs on the wind's move for the length of
three steps and a maple leaf claps. Read
Trident. See pale chips and a seeded white bap
in a brown polystyrene tray on the tar. Read
SPITAL. See brutal hewn rocks in grey. Rust
brown and smashed horse-brown pieces of
earth. Shards of a window and music in a car
falling like snowflakes from the mouth of a
window. White daisy flower. Bent scrag-end of
tin-grey tubing, a leak of red wires. Read
GROOVER IDER. Open land with fringes of
trees. One blunt metal bar and you walk onto
mower-clipped grass. A pigeon flies like a
blown plastic bag. Three crows in clockwork
walk-tick. Netted goals gape. Flying gull and a

cry of two sirens. See the head of the flying gull
swivel. Look into a storm of swarmy
mosquitoes. See brown tape wrapped over goals
like carnival bunting in tatters. A light in the
sky, small on a plane's wing. Maple leaves
flicked by the wind, maple-black, maple-red, a
tree chequered. Stream of warm wind. Two
grey ears of a rabbit and its white tail flashes
like teeth in a laugh. Rabbit crouched on short
grass listening, turns and runs, listens, turns,
runs with its head thrown in lollops. A V of
geese fly dark over blown red cirrus and rush
over black, leathery crowns of near trees. Man
behind tree. Sandpit ahead and you walk
scuffing sand. Troubled coils of a plane's jet
thunderingly. And leaves flip up shaking like
African dancers. Whitish clouds bubble and
wobbly leaves on a black river, oaks span like
big men clambering off. Reeds reflected are
spiders half submerged. Yellowed leaves shake
like wind tambourines. Sweet slime, the gasp of
a river, the ooze of mud, a sheen's trickle in the
dark light of sundown. A heron landing, wide as
two men shoulder to shoulder. Open flat space
with white metal frames. Crows in their quiet
blacks like men round a newly dug grave. A
blackbird tying knots of sound. Five yellow
grass stems broken. Grass yellow with dust.
Sweet trampled grass. The long-nosed body of a
plane. A moon risen in a bonnet of rainbow, a
full squashed circle of fat-cheeked moon-

yellow. Cloud like a womb. Trees black as
witches on broomsticks. See mountains and
seas of the moon. Your ear in a crow's chak-
chak. Your ears in the water ticking itself
through the mat of the grasses. Moon smudged
like albumen in water. Scruffy dandelions dead
in their petals, hubs of seedheads like miniature
doorknobs. Pink, rose pink and blood-in-water
pink of the moon's sky. Blood orange among
grey over the top hat of a squat grey tower.
Men behind trees. Three figures walking and
you turn. See the green mat of fields and the
shortened grass and pink light like blooded
urine. Dandelion's hat like a sorcerer's, cut
from the stem intact in the ruffled pith of its
seeds. Curled brown leaves like men reclined on
a field in the sun of the moon. Orange dark
light and alder leaves glint like gold coins on
earth. Smell dead leaves and they shout kicked
by the walk of your feet and rise like a mob of
crackles and fall down clattery as dinner plates,
dead. Square of a car slicing the ray of its
headlights through railings like cheesewire.
Duck on green water. Flatness by a bridge is
stalled water. Read MARSHGATE. Read
WILD. Read DRAGON. Read USTRIES.
Grey long ears on the moon's dust. Hear,
"Really intimidated by a thirteen year old."
Voice of a girl like a creek into sea by
moonlight. Feet scraping leaves. Beams of light
between walking legs. Faces in shade. Squeak of

[11]

brakes and see knees rising and falling with pedalling bikes. Cry of a child. A man sweeping stops in the road. Hear, "Sheez, fucking." Man and woman talking. Hear, "I'm the one who brought them you know." Hear, "Were you at football today?" A cry of a girl. A start of a car. A diesel clanks to a standstill. Fall of a whistle. A woman and a brown dog. The beep of a horn. And light on leaves and leaves like scorched lanterns. Read WING LEE. Head in a hood. Read CHEAP CALLS. Cry of a man. Shivering shadow of a leaf on a wall like a fly in the sun afloat on its legs. Alder leaves. Gold rings on a turbanned man's hand. Hand sprinkling salt over chips glinting like feldspar. Read £1 per hour. Man taking his cap from his head. Read IF VOTING CHANGED ANYTHING it Would Be illegal. Read V649 KTW. Man leaning on a window holding cut flowers. Read THE JACKDAW AND STUMP. A salty chip smell. Watermelon cut like raw flesh. Glints on black windows. Read BRINGING ENCOURAGEMENT TO THE PEOPLE OF HOMER. Two men in a long, neon lit corridor. Rumble of engines. Hear, "Check out that girl dancing." Read STAR FOOD. Man with a black beard. Click of a handbrake. Read SHEPHERD'S LANE. Man on a counter sitting alone. Read CRASH REPAIRS. Cry of a horn. TV crying in a room. Man leaps in the dark sky, falls behind low wall. Two fighting men. A head wrapped in hands. Read IF YOU WITNESS A VEHICLE. Square of police blue. Read MORNING. See a door opens. A woman steps into the dark with her head in her hands and her hair wrapped up in a bayleaf green headscarf. Read ABUSE THROUGH PROSTIT. Hear, "D'you want one what I got it, yeah." Read COME IN FOR YOUR PLATTING BRAIDING & CORN ROW. Seven men in a hairdresser's shop in a circle talking over and round a man sitting, a man cutting hair talks to them all. Eighteen eyes look and you turn in the dark. Bricks in a barrow. Planks under black plastic sheeting, quiet as raindrops hanging from thorns. Three figures in a tunnel without light like rocks in a cave. Clouds tabby as cats. Men with heads tilted up high in a pub. Pass windows of bright light. Shift of a man on his feet. Smell of a man's sweat. A wind passes like tapwater over your hands. Tower standing in a group of squat broad trees, like a man among toddlers. A train pulling the strength of its freight. Read FRESH FISH. A car slows to a standstill. Lion's mane of a tree's shadow, necks of its roots. Read FISH SHOP 020 8985 3271. Read BLESSED AFRICAN FOOD CENTRE. A woman's eyes spark. Hear, "It's just like." A woman slotting a pale prawn cracker into her mouth. A red bus roars like a panic. Hear, "Oh." A man's face yawns wide on its jaws. Hear, "Yeah, good, isn't

[13]

it." A woman speaks words you cannot decipher. A man in the road singing loudly, his mouth to the sky like a mineshaft. Little black pigtails over his shoulders lying on his back, like a head with two anchors. Hear, "Got this is what I think yeah, a girl, sort it out cruising yeah." A boy sits to speak. Read DOMINION TO LET.

Pass a sign. Read OPEN 24 HOURS. Read II MERSIN. Read Clean Tiapia. See pink fish scales and smell fish. See women in chairs having haircuts. See a corner of mud at the foot of a building. See the ribbed, crescent bodies of green plantain leaves. See a pale, whitish room behind glass. Smell sweet fat. See a woman in a crumpled shirt move. See four cars swing. Car car. Car car. See a girl with a brown monkey held in her arms. Read INVEST IN HACKNEY. See a girl with a small leather bag. Read w. Read TOILETS. See a golden cup in an alcove. See a driver leaning on a steering wheel over his knees, all crouched in a man-sized cab at the front of a bus. A door opens and a foil wrapper slides across paving like a tanker at sea drifting sideways. See a man lifting up a glass of beer from a square mat, he laughs in a tight way. See two small tub-shaped candles on a table, each flame floating above its wick, each wick threaded blackly, each like a single root through a pool of clear wax, each flame reflected on its pool clearly. On a white board read YOU ARE NEVER SAFE. Read MARE STREET. See gold beaks cluttered with pollen on trees. See black branches in air. Look up to an almost round moon as two children run. There is the smell of petrol beneath the shadows of trees, and you see the thinner shadows of tree twigs like cracks over paving. See paint peeled on the wall of a porch and hear the double-toned whine of a bus and the burble of an exhaust like a pig in its body. Read 222. Hear, "On Thursday." Hear, "Yeah." And you pass bin liners full and tied shut. See a shop of lights. Read QUAKE HORROR. See the squashed orange globes of mandarins and walls of a pale wooden crate like a doll's fence. See black scabs on green-yellow bananas and see glossy magazines and a man in a room containing bottles leans on the frame of a door. Read BUN PHO. See beaks of green and white blossom. Read CAT UON TOC NAM NU. See a fluorescent jacket on the torso of a woman and you see she is pedalling. The wet nose of a baby in a pram and the air is cold in a corner you pass. See orange lights flash and see faces, eyes under the caramel light of a bus shelter. Read LAS VEGAS TATTOO. You turn to see a car turning and rims of glasses reflect orange light round the eyes of a man. Read LIBRARY. See a man writing, crouched.

See a caravan parked. See a group of gas bottles.
See a ripped green sofa. See screwed-up pieces
of paper-based rubbish. A train like a chain-
link-horizon along the setting sun's sky. Read
INSANE AND. Pass a torn latex glove. Pass a
dried leaf and you hear distant voices. Hear
voices. See a smashed van window and opened
dark doors. See a cat crying at the face of
another cat and see the four dark eyes of the
cats as you pass. Read PUB ON THE PARK.
A man passes and voices rise up like rooks into
flight. There is the sheen of a light on cast iron.
See a dark space of trees quietly standing like
police at a scene. A cycle wheel ticks as the
cycle creeps pedalled by a figure among the
shadows of trees. See one stone, like a star
kneeling on earth. See a nose. See the bent
frame of a bicycle left and see one bent post of
metal beside it. Hear the clamour of hoarse
crows. See daffodils flopped in many directions.
Three figures in the shade of a tree. See a
bench. See a tower of lights far away. Hear
traffic. See a bench under the glare of a light
above and you hear the twisting roar of a
plane's jet like the gurgle of oared water slowly
and you are deaf in the roar. See the smooth
fuselage-nose of a moving plane like a bomb's
muzzle. See grass cut. See the dark grey body of
a cloud on a grubby horizon of cyan. Hear the
single beep of a car driven through traffic and
turn to see cars moving and cars beyond trees

like black sheep at dusk with dark glinting eyes.
Pass small blue flowers and dark leaves like
shields. Read POOL OPENS. Read LONDON
FIELDS LIDO. See quiet, black broken
windows and the dark pots of chimneys. A car
without wheels and its windscreen dented and
smashed into mosaic and the crazed glass is
green with crackles like a sea. See the glitter of
glass over tarmac and a car passes and the
glitter grows fast in the light thrown before the
road of the passing car. Feel a faint breeze
running. Read J850 GGO. Read B385 PLC. See
a clear plastic box left on the pavement. See
razor wire and bits of sharp metal across it like
the claws of squirrels. Read PMT 144R. See an
overturned gas bottle. Read SHOE REPAIRS
WHILE U WAIT. See a woman crossing the
road. See three children behind a window and
the fling of arms and bodies like fighting and
one girl is crying. Read CATV. The note of a
whistle rips through the air and a car horn cries
twice. See a man climb up from the door of a
car and walk and turn up his head and shout
towards windows and sky on the face of a
building. Read C471 OCX. See the shouting
man turn and climb down into the body of a car
and see the door close. See long leaves behind
frosted glass panes. See a car pass with a dented
door. See grit on the pavement you walk. See
shiny leaves. See the map of the world on an
upstairs wall. See a blonde-haired woman in the

frame of a dark window involved in a room. See variegated, three-pronged and waxy leaves of ivy. See cast ironwork. See a pollard tree without leaves and a full bloom of pink camellia. See two tarpaulins over two motorbikes. Look up to stars over houses and down to a figure standing in a low basement room. See three figures on the street talking like corners of a triangle. Hear, "Really, would be opened, but the thing is, again." Read 138. Read ZONE. See ten children gathered by a grey phone box door. Read ST PHILLIPS ESTATE. A woman walks fast, her head is cast down. See winks of glass on tar pavement skimmed by a light. See green lights ahead. See a tower of lights as you pass two dark houses and five cars pass in a row. Read NO. See red lights ahead and you smell the bitterness of car fumes. Hear the buzz of a doorlock and a woman passing bags into an opened doorway makes the bags huss in and out like the leaves of an oak in a wind. Hiss of a bike chain, three ticks pinch air into sound. Click of a handbrake. See a hawk of white stone and see seven squares of white paint laid across the dark grey-orange hues of the road. Read E8. Read 10 HOUSES FOR RENT. See the fronds of bushes weep to the ground with the weight of leaves like black daffodils. Hear a chuckle in the dark. See wires and pipes emerging from the ground and see palettes of bricks. Five cars stop together. Read BT. The letters are iron. And the air is thick with the fumes of burnt petrol, like the colour of pondwater's haze. Cry of a car's horn and a woman passes with rustling bags and you listen to the diminishing rustle as you walk. Smell the dry, pointed smell of washing powder burn on the walls of your nose. Read CELANDINE DRIVE. A woman walks wearing a white top and she carries a black shiny bag like the crown of a buffed crocodile. Hear music distantly like birds at dawn as a woman walks crossing the cambered road surface and opens a gate and walks though and turns back delicately closing the latch behind with a metallic click and turns again to where she is going and walks to a door and with one thumb to lips presses a black button with her other thumb beside the doorframe and you hear a bell ring from the body of the house. Pass a small shrine lit by candles in the brick box of a shed made for bins and a red cloth laid out and two twigs of incense give bluish smoke which smells deep-brown red like a spice and you see pictures of many-armed beings with the heads of elephants. See houses and trees in the dark amber light of a streetlight. Cross sunken space like a gorge with railway lines. Pass a sack trolley. Read PLEASE RING. See two green stems and leaves growing from purple-grey mortar. See two men in a dark room and a man kicks-up a motorbike engine into its growl.

Read Dyslexia Breath Test. Pass a man looking
hard at a paper held in his two hands. See a
man writing fast in a shop. See two women
leaving a doorway, dragging a big box between
them. See three dark boys in a shop of phones
and a man passes slowly and turns to walk back.
Smell cooking bread and a phone rings. Three
figures pass. A black face framed by a doorway
speaks as you pass. See scissors closing onto
hair streaks and the steel blades meet and
lengths of hair fall to the floor of a shop. Pass
bananas in a window. Hear, "Twenty minutes
only." Hear the duo-tone of an alarm. Shutters
pulled over a window. A hole in the pavement.
A girl passes quietly and you hear steps of feet.
Pass a man wearing a black tie under the light
of a shop. See four figures, like a family seated
to eat at a table in a bright room. See clothes
pinned to the shapes of human figures painted
on a board. See a building with black gloss walls
and a cream ceiling and figures inside with tall
glasses holding red, gold-yellow liquids, each
with a head of cooked-codflesh-white froth. See
the four eyes of two faces looking. See four
padlocks. Two arms folded under flesh-filled
fabric. Read 5 LITRES INDUSTRIAL
SEWING MACHINE OIL. See a man tilting
a bottle to his mouth and up over his head and
you see clear bright bubbles rising through the
liquid within the bottle and the level of the
liquid lowers and his throat moves with a

motion up and down swallowing. See spools of
cotton. See a shop of bright African clothes and
the colours are orange and lime-green and black
and cadmium yellow and deep ochre yellow. See
a man's hair cut by the hands of a woman
yawning a pair of scissors open and closed as
she talks flashing a comb and her legs are
visible, she wears a short skirt. Hear two tones
of a door alarm cry 'open'. Pass a white,
microwave oven lying on the pavement. See
palm leaves behind glass. See a man in a black
jacket and black trousers watch from a
doorway, the whites of his eyes are grey with
the tone of the streetlight. Read ORIGINAL
JERK. See a hand pull away from a pocket. See
carpets. See beds. See carpets and a bus passes
and the brakes of the bus are applied to a
pointed squeal. See a picture of a man with a
missing tooth. Read Clothing Bank. Read
TROPICAL SHIPPING SERVICES
LIMITED. A polythene bag moved by a tusk
of the air. A man walks to a door. See a white
stick. A boy runs fast from a shop. See bottles
of green and green-brown and brown and
clearer stream colours. See clocks and the
hands of clocks moving behind a window. See a
shop of shoes all on shelves. See a plump-
fingered hand carrying keys swinging from a
ring pushed over the first joint of the right
hand's crooked index finger. See two girls
examining a page of a newspaper held between

their four hands. A girl passes you with a
headscarf and you hear the hum of tyres
winding to a nearby halt. See chipped paint. See
cracked stones. A hand places a long cigarette
into a mouth and the lips clasp the body of the
white cigarette. Read DHKC. See a man
operating a bus and he wears a white hat. See a
car with faces and a car's horn bleats once.
Read WILLOW TREE. See a cracked
windowpane and a door with no handle. See the
open door of a shop. Read DRY CLEANERS.
See the bobbled surface of bubble wrap and a
bus moving fast. Smell burning tobacco and it is
a dark brown liquorice smell. A tissue dances
into the gutter part of the road. See a woman in
a fur jacket scratching her nose with two red
fingernails. Read OMELETTES. See a man
locking a door and a key pulled from the slot of
the lock and hear the jangle of keys on a key-
ring. See a small mound of earth the size of a
crouched child. See a man alone at a sewing
machine in a room of half-upholstered chairs
and pieces of cloth bigger than the shapes of
seat cushions. See an old face and see lines over
the skin of the cheeks and the bright light of a
room and glints of glasses, there are drinks in
the room. See white petals of blossom. See a
man in a dark car pulling a seatbelt across the
breadth of his shirt. Pass two cars parked and
there are small trees with new leaves shaking in
the air full of dark sky. See a man facing a

[22]

woman and hear a man's voice spoken. Read
NEW EAGLE. Sudden loud click of a voice.
See men in white clothes and a doorway into a
steel-and-ceramic-lined kitchen. Pass a broad
lady walking with a small grey dog. Pass a pile
of boxes. A lorry alongside boarded-up
windows. Read EAST. See a courtyard with
black rusty railings and wide opened gates. See
an area of grasses clipped short. Pass a hooded
man standing at the post of a bus stop. Slivers
of shadow and light intersected like sharp ends
of wicker. See a black woman enter a church.
Hear a door rattle woodenly and knock like the
glung-noise water through stones in a fast
shallow river. Read OUR LADY & SAINT.
And the letters are in gold on maroon. See the
figure of a man stretched out in a cross on pale
stone. Read Fri 25th Jan They Came From The
Sea. Read ANGELS (5) £1.50 + VAT. A woman
passes wearing an orange jacket. See a shop of
bottles and two men crouched behind a
wooden counter. A woman walks slowly. Pass a
man's arm around a woman's shoulders and the
two figures are walking side by side and both
are smiling. Pass a man and a young boy
choosing large green apples from apples laid out
inside a black box. See a black bed in the
window of a basement. See a shop of white
ceramic sinks and mirror-polished taps. See the
figure of a man made of red light. On the sign-
board of a passing red bus read NOT IN

SERVICE. Pass an iron grate rusted and pass
red tomatoes. See a woman leaving a doorway
holding a bag and you smell the fume of passing
cars and the fume of stationary cars with
engines running. See a stomach move under
white, stretched tight cotton. A gaunt and grey
face with orange frizzed hair above eyes yawns.
See infant leaves on a black twig. See the shiny
surface of a flattened can. See a floral design on
net curtains like a ghost of flowers, like
transparent insects sewn into cloth. Pass a man
saying one word calmly you cannot decipher.
See the shadows of railings and pass a man
rolling a thin cigarette. See a bag hanging from
a strap hooked over the spear of a railing. Hear
the voices of boys and the words, "Get it up
like that." Pass the black building of a stone
church. See leaves illuminated by light. See
leaves in sets of three and see pads of moss like
cats' feet on a wall. Read ST. PAULS. And the
letters are in black. Read RING O' ROSES.
Read OUR HIGHEST ENDEAVOUR MUST
BE TO DEVELOP FREE HUMAN BEINGS.
See shadows of leaves and a crack in a wall and
the burnt umber blackness of walled-up corners
in orange grey shadow. You pass steps and pass
bins. There is the damp scent of cut grass like a
river you wade with your nose. Read SHUNA
WALK. See the wrinkled faces of old posters.
Pass the lit interior of a blue hallway and there
is a road strewn with debris and you pass. See

short grass worn to a baldness by the passing of feet. Pass a grey hood concealing a head. Hear footsteps. Read FURLONG. Read CROWLINE. Read BUS STOP. And the letters are in yellow script on tar. Scrape of a foot and you turn to see a figure behind and you turn back. A white van passes. Read POLICE. Hear the breathing of a man and see the man stops and unlocks the door of a car and climbs slowly into the case of the car like a hermit crab entering an empty shell. Walk on and hear the door of a car slammed shut and with a muffled click like the sound of locked-in. There is a slight gradient to the road and you walk. Pass a dull blue interior. A door shuts. See red tail lights. An engine starts-up with a squeal and you turn to see the face of a man behind a windscreen is chewing. Pass pale berries like minute coconuts and you hear the rasp of a cough. A man jogs alone. A man sings to himself a song you do not know. Smell hot plastic and music spills from a car. There is lacy white blossom like opened drawers full of strewn knickers. Read SERVICES EVERY SUNDAY. Read HOLY WEEK. See pine fronds curled over like small dogs' ears and a hooded man walks fast singing. Pass the dark spaces of gardens and windows overlooking dark gardens. Read C180 VOX. Read BUILDERS ARMS. See a wooden door shutting. See a man feeding himself and walking towards you until you have passed him. See low buildings like houses and dark streets bisecting buildings. Pass a man emptying a plastic bin of grey water into the mouth of a drain and he beats the upturned base of the bin once like a drum with the flat palm of his hand, and yells once a sound like the word 'yeah', his lips are thick and dark like dates. Pass a pale man carrying a single A4 sheet of white paper in both hands, he walks with a briskness. The shadows of two hands close a sash window and draw together curtains till the hand-shadows meet at the crack of the curtains and you see the crack in the curtains tugged thin and only the shape of the window is visible like a blood-brown ghost of its former light. Pass a woman smoking on the steps of a house and a man you watch jogging to a door. See a tuft of grass brightly in the turn of a headlamp. Basket of tree shadows. A cyclist. See a white mark splattered. A lady walks slowly, her left hand to her throat. Pass a full green plastic binbag with a grey-yellow sheen. Read ON THE SPOT QUALITY DRY CLEANING. See a driver's arm on the thin ledge of a wound-down car window. See a man leaving the door of a pub talking to himself. See a mobile phone and look up to see the grimy moon and look ahead to a man reading a book and the man stands up and holds his book high and a bus slows down and he jumps on the backstep. See he wears a grey

herringbone tweed and smell engine oil. Read
CTRL WORKS TRAFFIC 2H. Letters in
white on red. See the orange eye of a woman's
lit cigarette like a small portable lion's mane of
light. See a woman hold up a finger and a black
car slow to a halt alongside her. Read THE
NORTH A1. See a taxi pass and the rear
compartment contains a woman. Cypress trees
like black feather dusters and see figures
waiting beside a thin post. Read FREE
DELIVERY. Hear the high tweet of a car
alarm flying and three lights flash before your
eyes. A girl eating. See a shop of bras and
underwear. See a shop of jewels and see
coloured stones like the phosphorescent bodies
of tropical fish. See hair braided. See a room
containing faces drinking and smiling. Read
COMEDY. See the screen of a TV. See a
square of green behind bars of black railings
and see yellow flowers roaring their colours to
your eyes. See there are green stems like the
legs of miniature giraffe, see stems like the
necks of geese. See a yellow hat on a long
window ledge. A woman passes. See legs. See
legs splayed like the back legs of a birthing ewe.
Read Delice. Pass through a choke of rubbish
bin smells. Pass the hand of a man holding a
bunch of bananas. Hear, "There's three of
them." Pass round concrete tubs filled with
concrete, containing brown flints. See the
surface of an eye encased in a gauze of dark

violet light. A blonde cycling man. Hear, "I'm
meeting Harry." See a man in a flat cap smiling
alone and a blue sleeping bag hanging from one
arm. Smell a dusty underground smell. See a
grey interior and long poles of striplamps and
the air is warm and heavy as dead dogs. Pass
iron grilles over a doorway and windows of an
unlit building. A door shakes. Smell the bleachy
sharpness of a fluid. See a woman in a doorway
drinking red substance clear as rubies. Read
MINI BAR. See thick leather clothes behind
shutters of metal. Read WINE. Read
MANUFACTURERS OF WEYLUX. See a
man's torso and face in the dark high window
of a lorry's cab, see his mouth move with words
you cannot hear. See files on shelves behind
windows in uninhabited rooms. A building with
a doorway lit like a gloom and three rows of
black windows. A paving stone tilts up like a
suddenly waking man. Read CHICKEN AND
RIBS. Read FER on a woman's top. Pass two
plants growing among blades of grass. See a
patch of cigarette butts scattered like curled
sleeping grubs, or children strewn sleeping in
curled sleeping bags. A glossy zone of oil-
blackness. Pass the window of a room and see
sheltered faces moving through the room. See
an arm gesturing itself in a circle. Hear, "It's
really cheap as well." Music of drums passes in a
black car and you hear the clack of metal on a
passing bicycle. The chewing mouth of a

[28]

woman is closed. Read SOCIAL CLUB
MEMBERS ONLY. See the hands of a man in
an upstairs window feed folded papers into an
envelope and the man walks across the visible
space of the room from the window, see he is
wearing a long dark coat, the collar turned up
on his neck. Pass two men leaning on a red
varnished counter, like boiled sugar the deep
colour of stewed Kenyan tea, they are talking.
See a man brushing crumbs of pale grey from
the white cloth of his jeans. Music falls from
the wall of a house like a cat leaping down on
its front paws. See the face of a man smiling
before a monitor screen, his lips apart and a
white car bearing blue lights passes and a siren
rises and falls like a cry. Read ZONE ENDS.
Hear, "Hi, is that Katy." See pale stone stained
dark with a fur of soot and the sky is unbroken
in a dark orange of grey. Three cars in a row
with men alone in each of them. A car with two
men. Read FANTASY CENTRE. Two men
walking, a hand dips into the square glove of a
crisp packet, a hand holds the cone of an ice
cream to the mouth of a face and a tongue curls
over one side of the rounded top of the ice
cream in a half-spiral fashion forming a point.
Pass a foil wrapper lying on the pavement and
air twitches and shakes it like a fit. Read
BEWARE OF THE DOG. Pass a woman
placing a nozzle into a hole in the rear wing
part of the body of a car and there is the sharp,

sweet stink of petrol fumes. Pass two figures huddled close together at a machine with buttons in the wall of a building. See the long face of a short-legged and long-haired dog looking up. Clear plastic bags of potatoes in the window of a shop stretched over the bulge of potatoes in places. See the slow walk of two men swaying at the hips with the weight of bellies, close in grey jumpers of a similar hue. Hear, "The phone." A man talks in the space of a dark car, his visible hand tapping the rim of the steering wheel. Pass two women lifting a small dark child from the back door of a car. Hear from the mouth of the child, "Let go." A man talking words you do not know. Hear a voice in the body of a building of brick walls, and the words, loudly. Read METHODIST CHURCH. The oily salt-smell of chips. Read 100% free. See the image of a red man light up. Car headlamps skewed through the round ribs of railings. See a wall of light within a room and condensation scored by threads of run-away water beads. There is tapping. Hear the shape of a voice in a dark space of trees. See dandelion leaves and the green teeth of their edges. The plastic body of a white bag bloats up with air, like a goat's udder full, then sags to a wrinkledness, like old potatoes. See the metal cages of wheeled shopping trolleys on the flatbed of a lorry. A woman in red cloth inside a room of marigold light, there are no curtains,

and giant paper flowers. Daffodils about you
with down-pointing heads like trumpets held
down, and some like trumpets beaten awry.
Keys jangle. Picture of a man shovelling. Read
LOUGH ROAD. Read Hello. See rooms
within houses. See electric appliances with the
tails of cords. Pass the anxious arrangement of a
woman's face, the brow concentrated to a
double wrinkle and a knotted furrow between.
There is the pad of footsteps and the gritty
cement clunk of a paving slab. Hear a tinny hiss
of chords and a shout sung from a black muff
on the ear of a man. Read KELLOGGS. Box in
a window. See three figures at a table eating
and one is a child. See a kitchen uninhabited
and one lightbulb bright at the filament like a
shrimp's nerve. A green bottle gleaming like a
pond's shallow. Hear the voice of a television.
See boards of wood leaning about and a man
exiting the open space of a doorway. Hear,
"Yeah." And the single word rises in pitch like
the tone of a question. Pass yellow flowers
illuminated by grey-orange light. Read
ROMAN WAY. See plastic yellow plates and
the ambient light of a dim room turns angelica
green from grapefruit pink. See fronds of a fir
tree black as burnt iron wires softly bent and
with needled tips like bronze slivers. Pass the
open mouths of sacks of rubble rolled back at
the rim like the thick lips of a fish you cannot
name. See plastic flowers composed of five

segments each. Read NOTICE BEWARE OF
UNEVEN STAIRS. A stack of pallets to man-
height. A quiet forklift. The soapy rancid-sweet
smell of orange peel. See the grey stone of a
building's wall lumpy on the outer edge. A
woman steps from a bus, the handle of a pram
gripped in each hand. The open gate of a
garden, she passes and you hear tiny wheels
growl on the pram as they turn. Pass a small
bull's head of cast iron. Hear, "I finished
eating." A woman passes swinging a tennis
racquet in her left hand. Pass the open palm of
a glossy fig leaf. The leaf turns. Hear, "And I
didn't even see you. Obviously I didn't say
nothing to." Read TENNIS CENTRE. See a
dark tower with the pale face of a clock set
close to its top and the clock face illuminated,
grubby like the wax of cheese. Pass a large-
windowed hall where the floor is green, and
figures are leaping and bearing racquets against
the force of flying yellow balls. The clock face
reads twenty-to-nine. See a room of cross-
legged women sitting and lowering their torsos
flat to the ground before them, heads curled
into laps, legs folded to X's. And see a broad
room of men jogging on the spot, see black
moving belts on machines beneath feet and
screens emitting moving images from one wall
of the room. See green tennis courts, shady as
caves, and hear cries and claps and the sharp
smack of a ball hit to air from the strings of a

[32]

racquet. See black gates of iron locked. See a
football kicked up into darkness over a team of
flood spotlights. Men running in black and
white shirts as a team. Men running in blue and
white shirts as a team. The cry of a whistle.
Men run towards the white portal of a goal.
Hear, "Way. Way. Way." Clap of two hands. A
man leaps and kicks. Hear the thump of a ball
kicked. Hear, "Hurry. Hurry. Hurry." And the
voice is strained to a hoarseness. Pass a woman,
a pink scarf about her head. Hear, "Jesus,
fucking play." Men stand about and one man
points talking fast. Three figures sit silent on
the slats of a wooden bench. Hear the bright
laugh of a girl and a clap of hands sharply. See a
white van parked and read AMBULANCE. See
two figures within the yellow light of the cab.
Lace of tree shadows over the white body of a
van. Hear, "Tony. Tony. Tone." See a bearded
man footing a ball before him forging a
zigzagged path between the paths of other men.
See a foot shepherd a football away from
opponent feet, they are dark as dogs. And men
running fast over the floodlit green of the pitch.
Men crying out sounds which are not words.
Voices herd all together into a unified yell. A
white ball rolling itself into a corner without
men. See a man's hand dipping into the mouth
of a bag. Read CORPORATION OF
LONDON. Look up to the face of a man
watching from a window and a red bus passes.

See a long-haired woman silent as a horse in
rain who stands by the torso of a man with a
talking face with a cap crowning the head. Pass
a long car body under tarpaulin, low parts of
the tail and bonnet. See a doorway into the
cube of a factory. See a man in the cube of an
office holding out papers, a yellow and black tie
striped like a wasp. See the shape of a girl in a
phone box. Read PENTONVILLE RUBBER.
And two figures pass leaving behind them the
tar-smell of cigar smoke. Read Ignite Your
Passion. See fake flowers standing behind
warped glass. See a man and guitar. Look up to
one star flickering red to green in its white
light. See a ball of gum greyish and dents of
toothmarks in its bitten and rolled-up surface.
See a star of grasses spread from a tuft. Glint
on the face of a crystal in the skin of a stone. A
car. Read GUINNESS. And there is a black
umbrella twisted shut and upturned. Pass two
men in black with white bags. A dark blue
folded paper. Hear the crunch of grit under a
passing tyre. Pass under the spanned shade of
two concrete bridges like two ribs over the road
meeting the ribs of their shade forming a
diaphragm of dark echoes merging. See the
image of a man in white. Pass a hangar of
parked red buses. Pass a compound of white
vans closely parked. See a scape of dark
buildings like a dark marsh. Red and blue lights
on the face of a tower, see towers that seem

crouched beside it. Dust in the air as you pass
the squat form of a cardboard box and see the
ribs of the corrugation. Dust shifts like the
foamline of a wave in wind and you see grains
of various sands rolling over the pavement. See
a shrub of black twigs trussed down by two
ropes to the flatbed of a van. Haze of white
lamps. Gold foil of a crushed cigarette packet
gleams and dulls as you walk. The low hoot of a
train's horn falls in pitch. See two clouds
moving. Read TRANS EUROPEAN. Look up
to a blinding moon. Look down to coloured
lines printed on glossy card and there are the
flashing blue lights of an ambulance casting a
blue sheen over the gloss of white card. Hear
the juddery revving of a petrol engine climb to
a sleek roaring-away. See a herd of plastic bags
ahead and you pass among them. Hear the
crease of semi-inflated bag bodies and see the
sluggish collapse of a floating binliner crash-
landing, and scuff the chin of its bulk. Smashed
grey green glass of a monitor screen. A man in a
yellow hat and jacket. See the yellow man
cycling. A black-haired woman exits a car like a
crow stepping. Read THE OLD SCHOOL.
Pass a stationary car, hear the purr of its engine
at idle and see in the square of one window the
shape of two faces kissing and the dark hair of
one half over the cheek of the other like the
wing of a blackbird. Read PRIVATE ROAD.
See a twisted snake of polythene in a black bed

[35]

of ivy. See an overturned sofa. A heap of swept
particles of sand and grey dust like a tidemark
around it. See pieces of cardboard, the ripped-
off flaps of boxes like placards discarded. Read
LORRIES TURNING AHEAD. See two
pieces of wood, one long, one round. See metal
bollards girdled with red lines. See the cracked
bark of a tree and the cracks are like ropes and
then deeper like chasms as you pass. See the
arched shadow of a tree. Read CTRL WORKS
TRAFFIC 4J & 5J. See leafbuds like opening
beaks of parrots and the moon is among them.
See canal water and reflected lights extended
down like plumb lines. A yard containing a
caged stack of white sacks. See the single spine
of a steeple on a clocktower and the clock is
round, lit yellow. See red traffic lights. See half-
circles of grey glass in streetlight. See grey
struts under the barrelled vault of a building's
roof. See ochre bricks in the barrel-roofed
space. See girders of steel. A lorry clatters
deeply, and the two struts of its chassis grow
visible as the brakes grind to a tapered squeal.
Read GEORGE'S RESTAURANT. See train
carriages and the oblong lights of carriage
windows. Lichen on the capping of a stone wall
like countries. See dark faces over the counter
of a bar and clear, golden and red drinks at the
level of chests. Hear a repeated beeping and the
pitch sharpens towards the end of each beep. A
round wall. Read RAILWAY STREET. Read

MAXIMUM HEIGHT 11ft 6ins. Read JAHN.
Two headlamps blind you for a split-blink
second with concentrated dazzle and a broad
man in black leather coughs. Look up to stars
in the darkness above buildings. Pink plastic
flowers in a vase on the dashboard of a coach
without passengers or any driver. See the figure
of a man sitting at a varnished counter, one
elbow leaning. A hand twists up into the
scorpion posture of a violinist's hand on strings
and four fingers move. Read It's rude to stare.
Six women standing and a lady leaning on the
spliced stick of one crutch. Hear, "O,
fantastic." Long hair and an arm pulling a
wheeled suitcase behind a body leaning
forwards with the strain of it. And a man is
beside the suitcase-dragger, moving his mouth.
Smoke-pale face of a woman smoking and four
girls laugh at once in different directions like
faces turning aside to whisper. Read
PEDESTRIANS. See a hook hanging from a
crane made of yellow. A man sweeps cigarette
butts into a coned pile. Hand touches a
shoulder. Hear, "Same road there." A hand
points. See an eel of smoke wind upwards from
a mouth. See two figures lifting cigarettes to
mouths at once. See the narrow, triangular
peaks of a brick building's roof. Hear, "Oh
yeah, fussy mate." A hand pulls a cap down over
a forehead. See the belly of a man in the
unbuttoned space of a shirt. Hear the clacking

strut of a woman's heels and the swish of
automatic doors sliding apart, pausing, and
sliding together. Girl with a fur-lined hood. See
figures queued at a kiosk.

See light between legs and light on a dark pane
of glass like a foil. See large lips on a face and a
finger bent back hooked in the slit of a pocket
sliding up and down in the crevice within. Look
up to see a three-quarter moon like a circle
rubbed away along one side. Hear, "That's erm,
that's." Hear a deep horn. Hear music like
cicadas ticking. See the dark eyes of a man
fixed on a scene of two girls passing. A pigeon's
fluttery flight. See road reflected on a window
of glass and a mouth moving. Hear a minute
clack of gummy saliva between lips. See light
through a fine netting of green around a
construction site. A man steps from a bus and a
woman in black cloth steps with him clutching
his arm in one hand. See curls of broken glass.
See lines on a face like the bark of an alder and
eyes are narrowed to a sharp look like the
squint of a cat. Hear, "Know what I mean." See
freckles over smooth skin. Pass a two-pronged
black beard. A green hue over paving stones.
There is the ragged beep of a horn and you pass
windows pointed at the top. See cigarette butts
and there is the sharp stink of grazed rubber
tyres burnt in a skid over tar. See an arm

[38]

leaning on glass. A woman with tanned skin walks up out of the ground. Read EMMA PELL 2002. See one leg leaping up and down and see eyes that turn and scan something in front. Hear, "Come on." See dark lips and lipstick smeared like a bruise. See three flies in the air and their flight is a spiral pillar upwards like the path of buzzards. Hear 'tick' muttered four times. Smell the reek of ammonia and the smell is flat like the hiss of a snake. See a fast strutting blonde-haired woman and the mouth is chewing gum and her plaited hair is thick and golden and the mouth besides chewing is talking. See she turns left and turns right like a distracted body and turns to walk straight on strutting with a black bag swinging at her hip and there is a lamp post close to her for a few steps. See an arm lifted and a black cab slows to a halt. See a hand held up and hear the drumming of engines. Read BUREAU DE CHANGE. See orange cones stacked and hear the cry of a car's horn. See the butt of a cigarette burnt and held between two yellow fingers of a hand trembling. Hear three beeps of a car's horn. Pass squares of translucent glass the jelly-grey colour of fish-eyes. Smell dampness of paper. Read HEALTH AND SAFETY LAW. Hear a cry of voices and six men pass. Hear a crying whoop of a voice like a bird. A woman walks alone. See a red hue of skin. Hear, "Straight place." Hear, "No." And

the word is cried out. Hear, "Yes" in chorus.
Pass a man and woman standing face to face
and see one mouth kissing the mouth of the
other and see a tongue pass between and enter
the cave of a mouth. A green hose gripped in
the hand of a man. Hear water splashing and
the sound is a sharp hiss like thin paper torn.
See a figure in the space of a window in a room.
See two hands of a sitting woman extend
outwards and a circle gestured by their motion
and see eyes watching the hands complete their
circle, one hand with a cigarette. See figures of
a family on a doorstep and their language is not
yours. An old man leans on an orange stick. See
a white arrow on a blue circle pointing ahead.
There are leaves of green and shadows of leaves
projected onto the translucent bodies of leaves
and intersections of leaves like the irises of cats,
pointed at both ends, and some like the ears of
cats, and some are cut in half also at various
angles making smaller round-edged triangles
and curved segments like claws or the horns of
goats. There is a coppery red hue and the red of
roses embodied in a sheen at the tips of leaves.
Hear, "Shippen, give it to Rachael." Hear, "Mo
sha heed." See women together all in dark,
blood-red shawls and cocoa-dark garments
descend to the ground. See the appearance of
walking with no feet visible. See two elders with
greyish beards of great length. A grey bird floats
earthwards and flies under the moon which is

white with watermarks of pale blue. See a crow
landing on one top corner of a building. See the
shadow of a crow on the wall of the building
rise up and attach itself to the feet of the crow.
Turn to see a rod of silver light along the lip of
a window sill. See there is redness, like a graze
red with blood. Two women lead children
through the gates of a park. A hand rubs the
point of a hipbone and you see gold rings on
fingers and semi-transparent cloth wrapped
opaquely around bodies. See air lift a corner of
fabric back from a woman like a tail. Wheel of
a pram jolts on a kerbstone. See a pink coat
shrugged from the bucket of the pram and the
coat is pushed briskly back by a dark hand. A
woman watches. See a woman standing by black
railings and see a pale blue sky reflected on the
darkness of upstairs windows. See the hood of a
bird's head. Read FIRE CONTROL. Letters in
bold script are red. Read NEIGHBOUR-
HOOD CENTRE. See a smashed globe of
concrete. Read CCTV in operation. See the
grey body of a camera mounted on a thin grey
mast like a bird's leg. Hear, "Trinity FM." Hear
the clatter of laughs and arms shake up into air.
Hear from the gape of an open window the
voice of a radio and you see the red-going-away
of two tail lights. A woman walks alone. See the
grey pavement stained by a red hue. See trees
above buildings. Read FOOD AVAILABLE.
See heads and the hair of men shaved to a

stubble. Hear, "Fucking hell." And see smiles. See the circles of nipples in the body of a T-shirt and there are pale leaves across paving slabs. A newspaper printed with script you do not know. See mirrored glass and a milky foil of light makes a cyan flash and a rose tinge over the surface of the glass as you pass, colours like two fish. See a woman alone. Read NEON PLASTIC SIGNS. See lips pursed on a dark face. See a dark red turban. Read HALAL. Look up four storeys of a building and you see smashed glass. Hear the dull thrum of a muffled music like music wrapped in cloth and then the shrill sustained notes of an electric guitar like music stinging. Smell the aroma of hot spice. See grey and black stubble on the chin of a man. Star of a thistle at the foot of a tree. An illuminated plane passing close to the disc of the moon. See curled-over grasses. See an apricot frock on a small girl. Hear, "Mummy," cried up and turn to a small boy leap-frogging a bollard. See ivy binding the trunk of a cherry. See white blossom containing dark structures like the antennae of insects. See a long grey coat and a white hat. Read RICE KRISPIES. See a chromed wheel rim and green and pink hues over the gleam. Pass railings of murky green colour and in recesses see blue among shadows like men in the dark. See soot-blackened tombstones and leaves glowing with sunlight between the flat stones. See scrolls of

leaves and black roses of iron. See a chain
passed through the gates of the graveyard and
the two ends of the chain clasped in the D of a
padlock. Pass a face looking down to the
ground and smell cooking pasta. Pass an opened
window and hear the sound of a small voice
behind the fabric of curtains. See a window
beyond a window. See a woman seated with her
back to the window and the face of the woman
is turned, looking out through the window, see
the shape of her body. And see the room about
her is swept with dark shadows and there are
colours of green with hues of blue like the
phosphorescence of bluebells and the colour of
yellow over grey like the colour of goldcrests
and four lamps lit with red shades the colour of
redcurrants, like Chinese hats standing on
sideboards black as treacle. Hear a double
cough and a long fringe of black hair like a
raven falls over a face. See glass lampshades in
the form of winged angels. Hear a cough
gripped by a throat to a muffle. Read The
Open. Letters in yellow on a blue-screened
television in a dark grey-walled room, and see
the dark shape of a curly-haired man sitting
near to the screen, see a spoon lifted up from a
bowl. Read 16. Pass flowered net curtains
hanging against glass and the glass is dusty. See
three men crossing the grey surface of road. See
the sheen of a light on a surface which reflects,
and dulls as you walk. Hear the soft whistle of a

music and turn to see a white and pink van, a large plastic ice cream on the round of its roof and the cavity of the street between buildings is filled with a gluey and syrup music. In red letters read WARNING. Read UNITED REFORMED CHURCH. See shelves mounted behind a window and see plastic tulips on one of the shelves of varnished pine. See an arm twisted at the wrist and a watch looked at. See a woman in black heels leaving the space of a doorway's shade and see a black leather jacket slung across one shoulder. See a van round a bend in the road, a building of bricks with tall and dark windows. See nettle flowers like strings of dusty green beads and see sections of cracked earth among stems of nettles. Two bright yellow dandelions and two halves of a broken brick scabbed with crusts of lime mortar. A green gate padlocked. Pass tree fronds swaying in a slow way and see two rows of tombs against the length of a brick wall and see grass like giraffes' necks. Croo of a pigeon. Pass a figure of stone. A blackbird runs on two legs. A blackbird stands like a man with arms behind back. See dark leaves with red corners like the corners of eyes. A towel draped over a window sill. On the sill of a window see a fat red candle. A face talking into the handset of a phone, net curtains. Read POST-OFFICE TELEGRAPHS. In letters of iron. The stain of a wetness on concrete. Pass a crack in a slab of concrete. See water and foam floating like icebergs on a dark mass of water. Smell stagnant drains like a warmth in your nose. Pass a fly, silver wings and a blue-black abdomen. A sound of leaves moved by the air is a hiss, as of onions thrown into warm oil. Hear the roller and scrape of a sash window lifted. See leaves shaken and dropped and a blue-shirted man leans from the square of a window. A steel-grey lock about the frame of a bike linking to the slender trunk of a young tree. An arm about a shoulder. A single laugh. A bike tyre and two boys serious with sucking green ice lollies and you can smell the sweetness of the ice as you pass. A single squeal. Read Keyholders Only. Smell the tar of roast coffee and a grey-red mottled face with beard and glasses is a grey-red face talking. And blue light moves over the curl of a leaf. Black-framed windows and screwed-up eyes thin in wrinkles pry from the shields of their glasses. Hear, "Yeah, been busy ... that's not bad then." See teeth pointed out over lips. Hear, "But in all, honestly though ... because of everything that happened." Hear, "Frowned upon." And the voice is a man's. Pass black-gloved hands held one over the other at the entrance of a mouth. A long white cigarette held between lips. See tweed hats and thick glasses and the red-pinkness of beer within a glass and look up to see a pale blue moon and walk on to see the figure of a man at railings

and two cans beside him on the grey ground.
Read STELLA. And the man's skin is dark and
his face still without a sound. See the cliff of a
building's face above you and look down to
pebbled concrete and walk on seeing the glint
of windows above. Hear, "I thought." See
folded interiors of a pink blossom and there are
black railings like painted spears. A wide-
hipped man wearing a yellow tie strolls. A gauzy
cactus in the face of a window. Read MAS1
GBY. Three women pass by. Read TOTAL.
Dark blue tiles, each an inch square. See lights
at the front of a car and there are red lights.
Dark leaves against black like beetles' wings.
Variegated lacquer, gloss of leaves of laurel.
Pale dusty-skinned berries like the eyes of a
dead rabbit. Figure seated before a glass table
above your head and one red glass of beer
transfers a honeyed light down through the
glass of the table like the colour of straw. A
mouth chewing. A woman seated with curly
grey hair. Black eyes below look up to your eyes
and meet and turn. See fans of leaves shaking.
An open square of grass clipped short. See
lights on the bodies of cars. A car without
lights and you see the plastic containers of
headlight-buckets. Smell the resin-sweetness of
pine. Four stone figures of dark rose-greyness.
Pass a red and white and blue flag and look
down to a white rectangle of card lying flat on a
flagstone. Read Haleys Naughty Massage

Stunning English Blonde Genuine 18 yrs 020
7691 2367. See a golden tie. Hear, "Pretending
he's still going to work." Rose light on a
building's face and tree forms carve sky into
sections between, and the blue of sky is tinged
with sulphurous yellow weakly and you look up
to darker sky like the pink colour of sandstone
and then down a bit to the lights of rooms
within buildings and see the parallelograms of
windows and reflected trees like wobbly trees
of water. Dusty green bark of an alder. Glinting
eyes of an old woman, the turned down corners
of her mouth. Hear, "I'm afraid get your shoes
and socks on." Water emerging from a circle of
water. Pass figures on benches leaning against
the slats of benches. See the throat of a woman
clenched with the action of swallowing and in
her hands she holds a single pen and a pad of
paper. Hear the bass-hum of traffic on all sides
about you. A man head down with the lozenge
of a silver phone to his ear. A man and boy and
two trees interlocked. Hear, "She had someone
then." Pass the face of a man looking up into
the branches of a tree and the mouth of the
man talking with a voice gently. See the hand of
a man in the cave of a plastic bag and look up
to see two squirrels. Hear, "Hello ... poopoo
poopoo ... hello ... poopoo poopoo." See the
movement of squirrels downtree and hear the
rustling of a hand within the body of a bag. See
two squirrels at faces like a mirror-mime-act on

[47]

the surface of black bark. See a man pull a bag
from a bag, throw bread up to descending
squirrels. See the body of a squirrel grow long
stretching and the zone of its mouth open wide
gently to take bread from the hand, the hand
held upwards, the bread on the palm. Hear the
noise of trousers and turn to a woman jogging
with curly black hair. Read SYNTAX HOUSE.
See the moon on the head of a man and the
man looking up to see as a hand pulls a black
seatbelt over a shoulder. See the face of a small
golden lion on a black door. A concrete lion
crouched on a doorstep. Pass a concrete dog
chained to a railing. Hear the beat of a
helicopter and look up to the dark bell and tail
of a flying machine and its flashing tail-light.
Turn to see a photograph of three figures and a
man in a pale jacket. The space of the street is
a quietness you walk. Slam of a door to a frame
and the flat sound of heels on stone and look to
see feet climbing steps to a door and the door
is opened and closed without sound to a click
of the latch. See a rough yellow line painted on
tar parallel to the stones of the kerb and birds
cry and the cries of the birds fall from the
direction of green leaves above you. A pale
redness to the green of leaves. See heads below
through a grille of iron. A bike passes and you
hear the ticking of a chain and ratchet
mechanism. Read The Poetry of Nature. Read
by John. Read Ulysses. Three notes of a bird. A

man in a black jacket passes, lank strand of hair
fallen like the mane of a pony to the level of his
eyes and his eyes look imprisoned and you hear
the note of a tenor bell struck and the space of
the street is filled with one wobbling note
growing weaker continually back to the bass-
hiss of traffic all streets away and the sounds of
feet moving. See orange light over golden.
Hear, "Oh yeah, yeah." See a stone pediment
marked with figures and gilded objects in the
hands of the stone. Gates of black iron. A hand
wiping the surface of a car's interior mirror.
Hear the note of a bell. And a bristled noise
ticking across stone paving. See claws of iron.
Read JOHN WALKER YORK. Letters in
iron. Read McBacon. Letters in red on yellow.
See light reflected, two rhomboids wreaked on
the bowed lenses of glasses. See strands of
cobwebs. See the faces of three lions of stone.
Hear, "And, er." See a mouth in the process of
eating. See the face of a television covered in a
greyish agitated speckle like a dense cloud of
gnats. See a man of green light. Hear the chord
of engines at idle. Look up to a rose sky and see
a lone bird. Turn to a red man. Read Cyprus.
See a man walk from the door of a building. See
red bricks of a wall. Read LEAGUE WANTS
TO BUY IT. Read The MOMENT and other
essays Virginia Woolf. Read Tradition and
Crisis. Read The Zulus and MATABELE. Read
THE PIG BRITISH HISTORY. Read MAO

[49]

A. Read SISLEY. Read POETS &
PALADINS. Read Planning Professionals. See
a green sheen over the surface of a milky violet-
grey reflected on a dark window. Orange to
yellow light. There is the smell of hot exhaust,
dry and poison-sharp. Pass a small-bodied
woman and see her shoulders raised up like a
tension and she carries a wicker basket over
one arm. Read JAMES SMITH & SON WHIP
MAKER. Read MOUNTER. Pass a rose
window, a dark circle of glass, unlit colour
almost to a blackness of various hues like boiled
sweets in a black bowl. See men in the saloon of
a swish mirrored car. Pass a triangle of figures
leaning and drinking and see the eyes of each
swap glances with another and one pair of eyes
looks from the triangle's intimate trio for a
second and all heads turn to the ground and are
quiet. Read STRATEGY CONSULTANT. See
a painted face on a brick wall. The photograph
of a woman. Turn to see pink light reflected.
Neon striplamp glowing a pale moth-yellow like
the colour of pollen. Pass a window reflecting
black leaves and lamps between leaves glowing
dimly. A girl with black hair pushed up over the
rims of her ears and her ears bending out with
the bulk of her hair. Hear, "See you Marigold."
Read SHOE REPAIR. See four men. Hear,
"Working out." A woman heaving a bag and a
hand out before her shaking like a dancer. A
warmness of air. Hear, "Four dot two dot six."

[50]

Hear, "For the short periods of time." Pass a figure seated cross-legged on a bench, smoking, and you see the orange eye of a cigarette flare. See thumbs placed together and hands splayed, butterfly-winging. See smoke pale and green move like pondweed up from an O-shaped mouth. See one hand move to another and you turn in the direction of a siren to see blue lights. A roar of engines and the siren grows faint and a flash of blue light like a flare of lit condensation across a night window happens and dulls on the gloss of a vehicle's body. See car shadows and turn to see the skin of a woman's face shadowed under the nose and lower lip and in two crescents under the eyes. Men wearing black turbans, the walls of a mustard-coloured room around them and tables and chairs between them. Pass the darkness of a room behind glass and no-one is there. Hear, "Shall we go back and cry our brains out." See shiny leather shoes in the window of a shop. See rags clothing the body of a stark mannequin. See a man painting, see the lozenge of a silver phone in one hand and brush in the other, and about him the space of a new painted room, a man in the back of the room staring out, a case open before him on a white counter. Hear, "I'm like ... she does not know me at all." A woman crying and you see her face red and two streams of tears flowing from eyes, her cheeks wet and hair clinging flat like a

scribble on one corner of her cheek. Hear, "I'm
sorry." Hear, "You haven't changed." See a
woman climbing stairs with a broom in one
hand. See dingy orange lights and a round fish-
tank lit from the blue, pale and clear bubbles
rising up through. Hear, "Like private rooms
only." See figures standing about with bottles
and glasses of wine. See a fingernail running
around the rim of a nostril. Read TOILETS
ARE FOR THE USE OF OUR CUSTOMERS
ONLY. See the white butt of a cigarette
hanging from a mouth. Hear "Yeah" seven
times. See a football kicked along the street.
Hear, "Yo ... please." See a man beckoning a
man with a football wedged under the tip of his
right foot. Hear, "No." See the beckoning man
move to the ball. See the ball is a white ball.
Two figures pass as a couple. See a tall woman
taking and clasping tightly the ball between her
ankles. See four women seated on an area of
cobbles. See a man sitting. See the white ball
kicked by the foot of a man. Hear, "My God,
it's St. George's." Hear the buzz of an electric
drill crying like the word 'we' distorted to a
whistle-scream like that of a firework. Hear,
"Smile ... nice to smile." See a man poised
upright, smoking. Hear the 'clok' of a drip of
water landing. Hear a second 'clok' of landing
water. Look into red light and turn and see a
halo, the disc of the moon of greenish hue
extending to violet, red into blue and the

darker blue of the sky affected with a black-greenness. See the mouth of a woman open a yawn and close it slowly. See a man's mouth extend across his rough face like a smile. Hear, "Somewhere else." Hear, "Probably will because he's done well." Hear, "She's afraid of Irene." Hear, "We're on the right track ... it's amazing." Hear, "She was married once." Hear, "It's life out the way." Hear, "How did we get here." And a man coughs with his hand balled-up in a fist like a boulder at the mouth of a cave and the flush of blood is like sunlight and you see the green of veins like a jade beneath the milk of the hand's skin. A stone with veins of four tones. See a man eating a banana. Hear, "It sounds like." Read MACHINE SAYS YES. Pass a black broad-rimmed hat and a walking stick and a man attached at the hand, see the man limping. Part of the surface of a stone glints as you pass, see the stone cut with flat faces and mounted at a woman's ear. See colours floating through the surface of a cut glass like a section of rainbow. See wispy hair and a beard and two women pass. A voice intones, "Well, I'm here." Read EA SHAW HHY. See letters etched into brushed steel. See dark tables and a glint of eyes like black glass. A knife and fork raised in the hands of a sitting woman. Read LA BELLERINA SPECIAL PRE-THEATRE MENU £12.95. Hear the roar of a bike and a slapping noise flying through the space of the street. See a cream-white bandage wrapped round the hand of a man. Hear, "It's just desperate." Read La bohème. Two men, maroon jackets. Hear, "This side out." Hear, "Cheers." Look up to see a red haloed moon like a bearded moon and small dim lights in the bodies of trees. Pass two men walking arm in arm. Pass a man dragging a cordon from a roadside. Read The Search is on. Pass alongside the smooth face of a building. Read Dry rise inlet SPRINKLER STOP VALVE INSIDE. Read DRURY. See a group of figures gathered, a canopy of cloth. Two men in jackets pass and arms are all opened to wave. Read ESTABLISHED 1870. Pass a woman talking to the handset of a phone. Pass a dome of green copper and a blue jumper and cream trousers. There is the tone of a whistle two times and lights pour over the dark street and bricks are dark. Read FISH AND CHIPS £5. Hear, "It's open now is it." You see figures in twos and threes walking beneath a canopy of striped colours and white. Hear, "Seen many shoes then." Hear, "There's more people outside this time of night." Hear, "Really, do I have to pay for it ... well I never." See the dim orange flush of a cigarette tip. See white cuffs about wrists and hands, one hand bearing a cigarette in the peg of two fingers. See the long hair and beard of a man who does not move. Hear, "God bless." Hear, "It's God's game ... it's God's game everywhere." See a man of long hair and beard pass quickly and see strength in his shoulders and his spine is twisted and his shoes are worn flat and his shirt is French blue and his trousers black and one bag in one hand and a jacket in the other. Hear, "No, but sometimes you feel like an idiot." Pass a woman of white-hair. Hair on a chin. See a blue-black sheen on well-polished steel. A car draws up and doors open and figures climb out from the body of the car and close doors and the car moves away. See a man seated in the shade of an alcove and his shirt is blue and his hair long and his face bearded and his eyes meet with yours. See an open space into blue-black and the blue is sky and there are no buildings in the dark space below but a thick-flowing water. Orange into blue light over the surface of oil-black water and green-gold glints over troughs of shadow. Hear creakings of iron. See the edge of water rising and falling and upstream, figures at tables on a boat's deck. See a red cross of light above the arch of a bridge. See a clockface pale as milk, a green yellow hue. See the clockface tells nine o'clock. There are dark cones of buildings and green fragments of light over curls of dark river, see none of them still. Orange into blue light over the surface of oil-black water and green-gold glints over troughs of shadow. See yellow lines of a tower picked out by light like the lines of a drawing of a tower. There is a

bright, small light moving across sky. Turn to
see a grey dome sitting on a building of
darkness and metal framed cranes, skeletal, like
inky scratches into the sky. See numberless
lights and a curved, pale blue pediment above
the face of a building. See a waxy sheen on the
lips of a woman and see she wears black boots
that shine and her eyes are fixed ahead and
marked with reflections of amber. Hear the hiss
of a passing boat and hear the lick of a wave of
water hitting the shore. Canary of a green glint.
A red lick of water like a tongue of flame. Blue
rhombus stretched to a triangle and the blue
darkens to violet and flashes green and daylight
blue like the eyes of a dying dog and a wave like
snow-toothed pikes and crags after sundown. A
wind rolls the butt of a cigarette the length of a
foot along paving. Hear, "And then people got."
Hear, "But." And two men in black clothes pass
together. Read Please Forward To. Read OXO.
Three letters of red light. Hear the rumble of a
train on a metal-ribbed bridge. Read RIBENA.
Read KFC. Hear, "They demolish it." See the
grey skeleton of a wheel, spoked like a bicycle's.
Hear the gritty click of a camera's shutter and
there is a flash of green-white light intruding
onto the green-black surface of water which is
snakes and serpents coiled in the mass of
movement and see worms of paler green and
gold-pinks slipping sometimes to the surface
and squirming in and marks like red incisions at

[56]

the edges of scales of reflected light curling up
like the greens of a fish refracted through all of
its scales and scales of water are colour afloat
and black spreads a blot and is unpicked to
colours of light afloat. Pass a man with a
camera in both hands and one finger raised like
a spider's leg up, on the metal button of the
shutter. See he rests the camera on the flat top
of a white metal post. See a flank of grey gritty
shore protruding out of the water below like
the belly of a whale. Look up to see pointed
turrets and there is a small light moving across
the sky in flickers. Figures stand between two
benches. Pass a woman in black, mounted
astride a man seated on the thin slats of a
bench and his back and buttocks curved into
the curve of the bench like the letter 'J'. See the
orange pip of a cigarette's tip alight in the dark.
See the curve of a round building ahead and the
flat wall of a grey building is next in sight. The
bulb of a grey dome to your left and a woman
in black passes down steps to your level of
pavement like the glide of a raven flying down
to carrion. And then the gentle trot of her heels
is like hooves of a wooden tone. See a ripple on
water flow and flow from sight into general
dimness. Fading blue horse-eye of water on the
black. There are boxes of buildings and you see
rectangles of grass-green and primrose light
among them. There is a dark burning yellow
and a small wind moves. Read FALLING

FROM OR THROUGH THIS ROOF
COULD RESULT IN FATAL. See the surface
of the road brighten and darken with the body
of a red bus passing. Three laughs of a man like
the sound of three pigeons. Furrow of a
woman's forehead. The ticking of an engine at
tickover breaks and repeats a sound like a
dotted line. A footway descending into the
ground and you knock something small with
the walk of your foot and it sounds like metal
which scrapes over ground. Hear a clicking of
small metal parts and a drone like stag beetles'
flight. Pass under a globe of milk light and walk
over broad concrete slabs. There is a green
bottle, empty, perched like a canary on a
banister rail. See a hand dipping into a packet
of crisps. See a stone figure and the arms of
that figure holding a cup high overhead and two
figures enter the mouth of a subway before you.
See shadows lean over a wall and shrink and
pass shadow back in arms of shadow like a
stone handed up. See figures reflected on tiles.
See pieces of cardboard and there are black
letters printed on white boards. Read I AM
AFRAID NOT AS I DESCEND OF ROMAN
GLASS AND WOLF BONE ITS ECHOES
TANGLE LIKE BRIARS IN MY THICK
HAIR A DAMP SMUDGE FOR MY EYES
STILL. Hear, "What isn't." Hear, "Well she
says that, but I don't believe it." There is a
tangle of the sounds of footsteps with the

[58]

echoes of the sounds of footsteps. Hear, "It's not the effect." See a pert nipple under the cloth of a ham pink T-shirt. Hear, "The last couple of weeks." And you see three figures ahead in clothes, black and white, and you climb steps and enter into the large space of a hall and there is a giant of voice saying a word you cannot catch but you hear the words echo through the space of the hall like flickering bats. See banks of blue monitor screens above heads and see dark cabinned engines of trains lined-up like black visors. Read 19 17 18. See a sitting man conveyed on the body of a small blue vehicle travelling quietly across the smooth floor of the hall and it stops with a jolt as the giant voice yawns on its words. See a man slumped low down in an armchair. See figures standing about like flamingoes on the polished floor's shine and reflections drop vertically as plumblines. Read TRAIN DEPARTURE. See two figures seated together. Hear the ticking of a bicycle pushed. Read BURGER KIN. Read LAW OF TORTS. Read THE HUNT FOR BIN. Hear, "Of course man." Read ULTIMATE INDULGENT TREAT. See a man in a long black coat walking. See a foot pull backwards out from a shoe and shake once and slip toewards back to the horn of the shoe. Three figures step from a tall rectangular shadow. Two women kiss at the cheek and stand back.

A giant voice speaks and echoes spill back and words you cannot make out move slowly as armies over the air. And words like shadows involved in shadows. See dark windows like eyes which are black and the sky is beyond with the orange of flames ascending to violet black and you see the black is a dark blue amazing with colours below. Hear, "Boring, isn't it." And see two figures leaning against railings and the figures are dressed in blue garments with white letters printed over their backs. Read Station Security RAILTRACK. Hear, "The twenty-one twenty-six service to Gatwick will depart from platform." And you hear a faint and soft, reed-like whistle passing into you.

Cry of a laugh in falling pitch and three figures smoking. Pass a line of nine black cars and a woman sitting. A finger pressing a button. Hear, "Hello." Rattle of a machine. Read UNLOCKED OUVERTE ABIERTA. See figures ahead. A voice. The tail of a dog. A hand pulling hair. Hear, "As you said, I." A rising-in-pitch and repeating beep. Stains of oil on a man's grey trousers. A man and woman say quietly together, "Yeah." Read Pay before you board. Hear the voice of a radio pass. Hear, "This is Jeff." Hiss of pressurised gas released and a smell of rubber and you see a woman reading a plastic sign and read In the interest

IV

of. Man with a black briefcase. Grit under a heel, a scrape. Figures of stone standing together. Arms folded, of a woman. See broken parts of an upholstered chair. Croon of two women forming an agreement and you see smiles and read daylight robbery. See a temple front of white fluted columns and an arch. Read Select Service Partner please press 3. Man at a grey metal door. Eyes of a man smoking. A grey feather and you read MEPHAM. Pimple on a face and a frown. Half a smile on a man's face and a freckle on the skin of a stomach revealed. Three figures behind glass and a voice drowned by a roar of traffic. Hear, "I know." See shade and smell smoke and a hand lifts up a clear blue plastic bottle and beyond clear glass see figures eating. A man with a camera. A dog and hear, "Good dessert wine." Hear reply, "O fantastic." Hear, "Having Tom?" Man in an alley. Hear, "And, er." Man in an alley climbing through bent-apart railings into a soft space of vegetation. A woman reading out to herself. A woman driving a bus, see a pink tongue. Hear, "O did you ... did he?" Man with a green bottle and a rug with tassels and hair clumped into tassels. See the rose-pink feet of a pigeon. A man with a hand in a pocket and hear the laugh of a black-haired man crossing the road. The pocketed-hand man passes quietly and you see a thin brass line running along paving, set into stones and hear the voice of a man, turn left,

the man smoking without a shirt on and the
top button of his trousers undone. Hear,
"Hopefully I'll get the keys and I'll get it done
by tomorrow night." Face of a woman behind
glass smoking. Read ALIVE FROM
PALESTINE. See a clockface, read a quarter to
three. Read Stories Under Occupation. Two
woman talking, see white teeth and a woman
leans her head forwards on its neck and laughs a
low note. Two boys run towards two boys
seated on wooden fencing, see the passing of
coins from one to the next tipped from the
palm of a hand to the palm. Hear, "Orange."
One boy runs to a shop, in through a glass door.
Hear, "She said, 'Oh, you tell me.'" Cry of a
blackbird in fast succession and men handling
breezeblocks up from a stack of many and see
feet at the left corner of the stack of grey
blocks and a woman passes and you see white
scratches on the skin of the calves. See the blue
skirt of a passing woman skewed to the left.
Read The Rig. Smooth steps descending. See
two red-box vehicles with crowns of flashing
blue lights and look up to see smoke belching
black and rising from windows eight floors up.
See figures on the street with hands above eyes
like the cowlings of caps. A man reading text
on a white sachet held in his right hand. A blue
jumper slumped over black railings. See dust on
the paint of railings. Black hair of a man's head
upright. Read HELP A CHILD TO THRIVE.

A boy with a book. A wheel with spokes higher
than buildings. A dark room containing figures
like dark birds. A blonde woman dressed in
black clothes. A crack of noise like the shot of
a gun. Hear a siren behind the back of your
head. A man sweeping with keys in one hand
clenched like rags of glistening meat in a bird's
bony claws. Tongue licking lips. A woman steps
up. A man steps down from a shop with a can
in a hand. Hear, "I could've gone in about two
months." Cry of a siren. Read Working with
Emotional Intelligence. Crumb of expanded
polystyrene. A man with a picture of flames on
a red T-shirt. Drone of a passing bus. A
cigarette butt. Two doors open. The cry of a
phone. A man bent over picking up boxes with
one hand only. Perfume from a woman, the
woman listening to the voice of a man. Pass
two men with laces untied, one drinking from a
blue and white can, you pass, hearing, "Two
fak." Hexagonal iron plate on the ground. An
obelisk of pale stone. Read ONE MILE CCCL
FEET from FLEET STREET. Look up to arms
and leaves of trees, in faded letters read NEW
MILK fresh from the COUNTRY twice daily.
Look back to see two men together and pass
bouquets of dried flowers attached to railings.
Cigarette burning in the hand of a man and you
read AROUND MIDNIGHT, A MALE WAS
SERIOUSLY ASSAULTED OUTSIDE THE
NEST. See many chairs on wheels and there is

a smell of dust. See straw-pale grasses. See small leaves of horehound. You hear, "The decimens, who were completely disenfranchised." And read SLOW. A bus passes and there are fumes and see the picture of a man at work and read ENTRANCE NOW CLOSED. A bus passes. A car door opens. A man walks to a phonebox with a box of cigars in one hand and an upward look from his lowered down face to a man drinking from a golden can with his blue eyes closed with swallowing to a squint, face up into sky. See a passing bus attracts many people to run as a herd and see figures boarding the red bus. See a man in a high lorry's cab drinking water, the lorry is white. Read WOMAN KILLED BY POLICE CAR. A man with the road reflected on the curves of his eyes and a finger held out extended on an arm extended. Pass a woman running with a smile and she cries, "See you." A man with grey stubble standing still with a small grey elephant of stuffed fur on a string around his neck and his head looks down and you turn to see rough skins of unwashed potatoes with scabs of clay earth and see two stacks of folded newspapers. And turn, see an elephant of stuffed fur hang from the neck by a string with a small black bead eye either side of the trunk. Hear, "Is it that way?" And two women with bright red and gold headscarves tied at the chin and with pleated scarlet dresses with gold parts

[64]

embroidered, both are dark-haired. Man with a
stoop carrying a brown bag. Hear, "Fifty quid."
See rivets in steel and a cigarette in a mouth
and see broken curls of brown glass strewn like
dead leaves and read for Gold. Hear a car
starting and see a leaf rolling over the tar road
after the passing of a car. Hear, "You know, I
tell you something." Hear a door close and a
door locked. A man leans on elbows of folded
arms against railings, feet in black slippers. See
an orange rose flowering against the shape of
his torso. See his torso is dressed in black fabric
tucked into grey trousers. See the hairs of his
legs like black stitch ends from skin. See the
bone of the ankle's protrusion and the trousers
clamped to the leg by elastic hems. See the toes
of the slippers frayed and you pass, as a pigeon
pecks the tip of an ice cream cone. See the
cone roll one part of a circle over the ground,
the cone dressed in blue foil paper. Hear,
"German and Korea, they play." Read Do what
it takes. And turn right to see three women
wearing white head scarves seated in the back
of a car and a child on the lap of one. Hear the
long note of a siren through a squeak of brakes.
Man with a finger in his left nostril seated in
the room of a black glossy car with purple and
green in the black like the black of a beetle's
carapace. Burble of engines together into a din
of hums and see pink dreadlocks on a man's
head in the body of a car and four lanes of

stationary cars with engine sounds and a woman standing before three men like sacks on a bench and the woman drinks from a gold can. Hear, "We draw two games." Man asleep on grass, curled like a small boy on his side and his stomach protruding from a gap between his shirt and trousers. See a man on cut grass with his eyes closed by a golden can, a woman beside in a black leather jacket with tassels at the arms and curled hair the colour of cedar with greys and her skin with sharp lines with a can in one hand leans on an elbow and you read I hate this girl. Sets of eyes in a passing red bus. See three clam shells on a black tie worn by the throats of children from school. Hear, "Janet's coming." Hear, "No, I'm not ... just the whole class." And hear, "I just said come this way." A girl with pink lipstick. And a boy's voice says, "Cher's my wife." And arm in arm. Hear, "This always happens." And hear again, "This always happens, yeah." And a bright laugh of many boys with clam shells on black ties at their throats. And hear, "Oh, you lot." A boy alone and two policemen in black and white wearing helmets. Hear spoken, "You got a, er ... bill score." And men in black and white clothes wearing helmets stand watching children walk from the gates of their school. And the children pass like a chattery energy and creep and jump in directions like starlings together at crumbs. Turn to the image of a man with arms

[66]

stretched flat out on the wall of a narrow brick building. A lorry passes and there is thunder in the road and the cry of a horn is the air for a moment. A boy's face scurries into a laugh. Man with hair in a square formation. See a car parked with figures seated within and a door open and many children are beside the body of the car, which is black. Man in a yellow T-shirt walking, pulls a small boy aside, walks on and raises his thumb. Hear, "Oh wait, let me talk to her." Dove grey handwriting scraped over dark bricks. See railings and a padlock and chain binding a gate to its post. See a blackbird dead in a space of short grass like a collapsed black marquee and there is a sour smell of old blossom dying. See a girl spit foamy phlegm onto nettles. Descend a ramp out of daylight into a tunnel. Read South Subway, North Subway, East Subway. And you walk. A curved ramp up under trees with the palms of their leaves green with light and pointed tips and accents of stutterings out of the air in among leaves fluttering. See an empty cardboard packet and a ball of scrumpled pink tissue. Read Debbi + Vicki ST OLAVES PIGS IN PLEATED BLUE SHIRTS. Pass a man walking and he looks up to the sound of the rumbles of traffic and step by step you regain the broad daylight and a pigeon lands and many red leaves shake on the hill of the sky and you turn to a man reclined on a grassy mound like a

[67]

Gulliver sleeping. Read controlled ZONE M1.
See two girls ahead. Hear, "Must have some
jokes." Large flat leaves and five women
pushing prams. And a boy slouched in the shell
of one pram. Read COMING SOON
SUPERCLUB COMPLEX. A broad woman
with a bag in each hand and pass a red and
green blurred tattoo on an arm. Hand of a man
places a clear glass bottle into a bag. Read THE
WORLD IS TURNED UPSIDE DOWN.
Read REID'S STOUT. A shirtless man sitting
on a plastic crate. Read DYNAMIC GOSPEL
MINISTRIES. Woman in a black doorway
with tight jeans. A man with a gap for his two
front teeth. And see bandages wound on the
fists of the man without teeth. Eyes of a
woman squint. See pieces of fried chicken with
surfaces gnarled, with blistered batter jackets.
Read EAT AS MUCH AS YOU. Girls in a row
wearing maroon. A woman mopping black and
white squares of a cafe floor. See a counter and
a man's shoulders and face behind a metal mesh
at the counter. Hear, "What's up?" See blue
plastic angels. Read OMMERCIAL E IDE
TIAL SALES LETTINGS &. See a boy eating
one chip. Man of red light. Plaster ornaments
and see dirt-shiny paving. Man seated by the
door of a shop on a red milkcrate. Man
spooning a treacle tart to his mouth from a
white plate at a table alone. Squawk of a man
clearing his nose. See white cuffs and collars.

Meat wrapped in clingfilm. See straps of twined clingfilm like watery tendons pinching the meat. A wooden crate of fat, smooth watermelons. Read THE DUN COW. Man seated in a room. Stare of a man's eyes from a dark doorway. See sacks and boards of wood. See a space of open land and a grey tower with a pale pyramid of grey. Hear, "Are you going through tunnel ways." Woman at a table with a needle sewing. Man and boy on a doorstep, the boy by fingertip pushing crumbs over the edge of the step. Smell car wax. See suds of soap and bubbles. A shop of wheel rims and black rubber tyres. Read 4444 W44. Read LET & MANAGED. A green space of short grass. Boys with hoods. Look up to a fence of sharp curled pieces like banana skins of torn metal. See the pale, weeping skeleton of water from a fountain. Hear, "What's the man." Read Southwark Council. See rubble flooring through a house. See comfrey leaves' thick furs. Read HUSBAND AND DAD. See a lavender shrub. Read BAGSHOT. Read CARIBBEAN AND WORLDWIDE. Bucket, shoe, packets. Read ROAD CLOSED. A boy running over a concrete walkway like a squirrel. A crackle of soles over bright broken glass. See a long high building of windows. A crackle of glass glints like a giggle. A woman with long white hair, watering roses. Hear, "Mummy." Hear reply, "We wanna cross the road." See three boys entering a long high building of windows. Blackbird on grass. See an image of a man crying on green grass. See brown iron shears without handles. Read TO BE KEPT LOCKED SHUT. See a man leaning still in a gaze on a balcony and clothes out to dry. Read PARKS RANGER SERVICE. Hear the body of a siren and see blue lights flashing and you pass and read the word POLICE. Man in a car reading. Man in a white shirt. Moustache on a man and his eyes look up and down. Read FOR SALE 1988. Pass a wooden horse with white eyes. Scrag of tissue on cracked asphalt. Cry of a child. Two horn-beeps of a passing car. Read FOR SALE £600 NO OFFERS. A leaf folded in parts like two wings and wood chips and pale flowers, see yarrow. Look up to a pigeon. Two women stroking their hair in a car with the harps of their hands. See a brick pub's carcass with windows boarded. Meadow of tall grass. Read WILLIAM THE FOURTH. See hanging parts of material as makeshift curtains. And two men smoking together in sunlight like two fish suspended. See two men walking in quickness and the cry of a car starts, see freckles of white clover flowers among grass. Hear music pouring from an open window and see dark trees and a girl with fingers pressing buttons on a small silver phone. Hear, "Fucking." Pass a boy singing loud and three knocks of a hammer and fifteen clicks of a

mallet striking a chisel to stone, by the sound.
Dead leaves of ivy like dried black tongues.
Read SC60 REFUND. Pass a red bus. Read
RML 2302. See the belly of a driver folded over
the rim of a wheel. White-haired woman with a
walking stick. Read FRESH GOAT LEG. See a
triangle of meat on the bone with grey, creamy,
fatty damp skin. See a building with a broken
face of smashed windows. Read AFTER
SCHOOL CHILD COLLECTION. Hear,
"Oh, what have you got and gone." Three boys
in the room of a telephone box. Boy laughing
like a crow with his mouth wide and head
forwards and a hand throwing a turn. Hand
curled over a boy's shoulder clamps and uncurls.
Hear, "I ain't walking far." Black tie knotted at
a boy's throat. An old lady lifted by two to a
chair from the door of a car. And her hand is
long with fingers and shakes. Dark stain on a
woman's magenta blouse. Hear, "You can take."
Man pulling up his flies. Man with a shuffle.
Woman with a knee darker than her face. A
woman runs, skips, lands on the footboard of a
moving red bus. A man with a bottle of pickled
onions pours. Hear, "Oh, she's had a baby."
Hear, "You can only have one marriage." And a
woman before you with five black-spined books
talking to a man. And the spines of the books
read Agamemnon for Beginners. Three girls
with chips and ketchup. Read CARING
MEMORIES. Big lips of a serious face. See a

[71]

man sigh but do not hear. Hear, "It was really funny." A shop of electrical equipment. A shop of trays of flat cakes. Hear, "Okay boy, quickly to the middle." A woman with blonde hair at the handles of a pram. Woman in a car places a green wine bottle with a gold foiled neck into a silver ice bucket. A long face and a hand at a stomach. Leaning to the left, the body of a woman heavy with a bag. Hear, "Well I mean ... it's been our intention." Hear, "She's given up her office." Hear reply, "Has she?" Man with a white envelope gripped at its corner in his mouth. Area of trees. Read Chaplin Centre. Two cries of a car's horn and hear a car beginning. Two ticks of a lighter at a cigarette end. A woman walks fast, her hair twisted back like a watery flame. You see sky and turn and see a waiting man wailing with his mouth to the sky open like a bite-mark into an apple and a white man stops walking and you hear, "She's flirting all around." See a woman's mouth tightened and her lips thin with tightness and you pass seeing two women with red and gold headscarves tied under the chin and pleated red skirts with gold parts embroidered and both dark-haired and both eating, both seated on grass. The sky is dark grey with curls of grey cloud turning around. Two dark men ahead clasp hands and unclasp and part different ways. Man cleaning teeth with a finger and you pass seeing sandals of blackness with broken buckles

and a woman carrying the sack of a punctured
football by the pinch of its skin, like the yolk of
an egg. Iron gates with scrolled leaves and roses
of iron. Red spots on a woman's face and hear,
"Probably good." And hear, "Er, still nothing ...
well yeah." A boy walking like an arms-behind-
back kind of man. A woman seated with lips
together like a closed case. Gold in a woman's
ear and you hear her cry "O" and she runs. Read
The Northe is closed. Look up to leaves
glowing with light in green and see two pigeons
and in a dark room the box of a lit television.
Hear, "You never use it." Face pushing lips on
the mouth up. You hear, "I just telling you
now." A street of dark houses. Clicking clack of
billiard balls leaps from the door of a dark room
with big green tables lit from above like green
island stages set in the dark. Hear, "Oh my
God." Girl with a broom of green bristles
sweeping turns with the broom and drags its
bristles bent back into a garden and up the
damp path. Hear, "No one's going home." And
read BOYS. Cut in stone letters above a gate of
wrought iron. Read OF LOVE. Thin face of a
woman with ringlets and see a woman arm-
cradling a baby and walking slow and the baby
is dressed in a blue knitted hat and a white
knitted shawl and see a white-haired woman
bending and she lifts up a plastic yellow flower
from the flatness of pavement and turns to a
white-haired man beside her and holds the

flower and she smiles. Pass a garden of pink,
yellow, red and peach orange roses. Read
A3203. And turn to a green copper dome and
turn to see orange shutters behind windows.
Hear, "I like." Smell of sweet perfume, you pass
a woman. And a man ahead in a black shirt
with a green heart tattooed on the back of his
left hand. Read GEORGE MYERS 1803 - 1875
Master Builder lived here. Dark half-circles
beneath a woman's eyes. Hear, "We're all
surrounded by." A man's cough twice. Read
Morley part-time. Look up to men standing on
a platform and the whole platform moving at
the side of a building. Look up to a spire of pale
stone. Hear, "Another corner of the jigsaw." A
man wearing gold-rimmed glasses eating an ice
cream. Picture of a woman sunbathing on a flat
beach of sand. Man with a red face and stubble
smiling. Read SAVE 1/3RD. A man passes and
see dust flecks over the fine corduroy of a black
coat. Man with a green cap and glasses makes a
gesture with a hand like writing and passes.
Two notches of green on a woman's cheeks like
a tally. Hear, "What do you mean, Mark?" Read
SPECIAL OFFERS FOR 1ST TIME. And two
women walk from an arch of shade. Read
MARSH. Walk into shade and into the
rumblings of big trains passing and see
blackened arches of steel and brick and look up
to see the body of a pigeon folded dead and the
body of a pigeon alive beside it is quiet and a

mesh of thin black wires scarfing the neck and
body of each and the eye of the alive pigeon
turns and the body is folded, shut as a book.
About forty engines beat in the cave of a tunnel
to a molten dry roar and you see orange lights
in the dark like small fires. In letters of green
light read 16:38. Read VISIT. And see green
leaves with cracked veins in the throat of a
soot-dark tunnel and the air and the space of
the tunnel are filled with echoes passing and
the curled cries of sirens and blue lights are
flashing over the black walls and hear the roar
of an engine like a harsh sound and look up to
see black girders like the ribs of a giant and
turn and you read Long & Short stay. A pigeon
flies. And you read Assembly. Read station
security. Sky in mottled grey opens translucent
like the flesh of skinned grapes as you walk
from the tunnel, light is close-up and grows
faint. And two men stand by the door of a car
agitatedly looking. Read TRAFFIC LAYOUT
CHANGED. See three pigeons and one plane
swiping through the sky slowly and read
Domestic. Pass the blade of a white feather
curling down through the air and a sweet smoke
twists dryly from the stick of a cigar and a man
with the image of an eagle in green lines under
the fine hairs of his forearm turns. Black and
white square of a man's jacket fabric. A woman
wipes her lips with the thumb-length of her
hand and you see writing on her hand's back

[75]

but cannot read. And hear, "Is Ray not
coming?" Hear reply, "No." And you see many
black cars together and hear, "Meeting Paul on
the escalator." Hear "Your attention please ...
service to Portsmouth Harbour, this train will
now depart from platform." And see many
figures running together like a herd driven.

A shrieking lulls. Tick-tick of a woman's walk.   v
Green circles of cloth wrapping a head.
Headlamps. Flapping rag of plastic like an
irritable polythene. A tapping of feet. The far
sky red like copperplate. Red light. Read
LOOK RIGHT. Turn to look right. Hear a
clink of coins tumbling together. A car door
clunks and rattles. Read Chianti Clasico. Eyes
pierce. Grey-coated man the colour of a heron.
Stubble on a man's face. See a biscuit pushed
whole into a mouth, stretching lips wider as it
slots through. Lips close together. Pass a man
and woman together. Read Hercules Road. A
man, grey-haired adjusts his coat looking down
pushing each of six buttons through
corresponding holes. Read Oriental Bar. See
reflected lights. See a black hat, gold hair, see
leaves that do not move. Hear voices behind
leaves. See a swept pile of sticks. Red lights like
warnings far at sea. Four rings linked together
like a symbol on the grille of a car. Shadows
stoop and the sky is the colours of bluetits. See

[76]

pages ahead held in arms and smell the curling
vapours of car fumes, a dryness curling up in
your throat. Hear a clang of wrought iron hit
against iron of a gate being shut. A man's face
quietly. Hear, "Toilets." See a painted yellow
iron flap and read ALPHA. Read The
Pineapple. Creases on a man's grey clothes as
he strides in a mechanical fashion. See a girl
laugh, hissing towards the end of the laugh-
burst and two men sandwich a woman. Hear,
"We must be close to Waterloo." Read SCRAP
METAL. A face, narrow eyed, the skin sallow.
See a shaded lightbulb and a bulb of shade on a
near wall. High shoes clack like clopping
hooves. Read OVENBAKE. Two eyes of light,
a contorted face with triangles, eyewhites open,
eyes like the mouths of toads. A hand holding
money. Hear the flat hiss of water sprayed. See
the red lantern of a lit cigarette. A dog's face
serious at a window. Read DHL. A black dog's
nose lifted. A leather jacket in shadow. A leaf
facedown. Read Pimlico Plumbers. Rattle of a
diesel van passing. Dark archway. See rags of
paper glued and see brickwork in mottles.
Thump of metal on metal, a hammer-clunk
knocking a vibration through girders above.
Pass engines of traffic. See a woman's hand slap
the forearm of a child. Hear, "I think it
happened last, erm." A white van moves
forwards and a bird of exhaust fumes flies up to
your face. Hear the rattle of a steel wire cage. A

woman's face lowered, she walks. A stream of
cars and glasses flash with strewn carlight. Scuff
of a foot. A coach moves and coach panels
shake. Yellow leaves like leopards and air
moves. A face looks up, each eye bright as a
moon. Click of metal and you see a strap-
buckle. A leaf is dragged across stone with a
scrape. Sniff of a nose. Bridge of blue, cream,
red colours shaking like thunder. Dark face
moves. Pass the pole of a bus stop. Five figures
alone. A child cries. Hear, "Stay here." Hear,
"No." Hear, "No no." Two men shaking hands.
Read This Gateway to be Kept Clear for
Emergency Vehicle Access. Read Read Only.
See a head wrapped in wool. A woman striding
with bags in each hand and the arms long with
the weight of them. Two lions of metal
rampant at each others' throats. Three lit
windows in a row. One scrape of a footstep.
Cool air stalks like a cat. Read Release Fee £30.
Read Random Security. See a scar-faced man
with a dark jacket over his shoulders. Three
leaves dance in a circle and a bus pulls up
squeakily. Lights in pairs on approaching
vehicles. Read AD1 238. Hear, "You follow my."
A lemon-scented detergent. Pass the mouth of
a gaping bin. See a light turned on in an upstairs
window. Hear five ticks of a green bicycle.
Read J81 DJ1. An arched door, painted green as
bluebell leaves. A brick passage with a curved,
illuminated ceiling. Read Rosemary. Read

Fairley House Upper. Read Mon - Fri 7am - 10am 4pm - 7pm. Thunder of engines moves on all visible roads. See a blind pulled down on a window. Corrugated card, rotted to apple-rot brown. Cracks of paving. Bricks mortared to bricks. Orange lights flood a dimness. Bent rod of iron. Planeleaf dragged scraping like a boat onto pebbles. A ripped paper plate, the corrugated edge flat with wetness but creased. Flowers of iron. Squeak of a car's brakes once. Two boys playing together. Glint of light on a creased earlobe. Hear, "So one can pass." See a flashing orange sphere mounted on a black and white striped post. See blue lights ahead rising and setting on a white roof. Read Emergency Ambulance. The sky, dark ahead. See windows lit, a lit room empty. Light and a splash sound of water falling from water into water. And then like the ghost-sound of water, the sound of its falling grows louder and fades. A black face with steel-rimmed glasses. A bearded face. Blue lights. A wide-rimmed hat and beard beneath. See a woman at a desk, a phone in one hand, see a coiled cable leading to the handset. Turn to see a building set with a clockface illuminated to a porcelain-white like a moon. See glass the colour of coal-smoke, a whitish glare shielding the space beyond the glass from view. Leopard skin gloves over moving hands with their fingers. Read CCTV in operation. A man and woman in smiles. White cyclamen flowers like the heads of still lambs small at foot-level. Cigarette butt lying in a crack between paving. See the bow of a boat. A man leaves a building by swing doors and the doors flap in and out after him, and flap in diminishing arcs to a standstill. Read IMO Publications. See a man busy with walking and see the man busies and speeds up his walk till you no longer see him. A tower girdled with lights. Read 01895 466466. A white and blue jacket. Read Sky Net. See tail lights of a car light and go out. Traffic flows, passing. Cars of varying heights move like a merry-go-round. See an obelisk backlit. Four spires in one square above trees. A crown of trees. Sky lit with stars like spoors of light. A fox face of a dog's face. See strings of lights suspended between posts. A scrag of grass ripped at the foot of a lamp post. Read Cleansing Hotline. Read Albert. See an area of sky lighter above. Flat scabs of chewing gum trodden smooth to the ground. Read Bus Lane. Read Cross. Tremor conveying low-pitched vibrations of music. See firemen of stone. Read London Fire Brigade Head Quarters. Read Return. See water flowing and flocking in a mass breaking apart and flowing. Tick of a bicycle passing. See traffic cones sitting in silt. See lights reflected scattering on trembling water. A skirmishing breeze. The rumble of engines. Turn and you read SEAWHEEL. Hear the scuff of a foot. The

metal cage of a trolley abandoned. See the face
of a woman gasping and yawning, the face the
appearance of a dried apricot with a hole
pressed in for a mouth, and you look to the
figure of a very old lady in high, black boots.
Read SEAFISH. Pass a black iron fish. An old
man's bearded face like the face of a river cast
in black iron. Read 18170. Read LIFEBUOY.
See steps up and down and you feel the river-
cold air against skin and a smell of the sea from
far in the river. Hear, "Massey Shaw." See
lightbulbs like dark eggs. Eye of a black fish of
iron. Look up to a light flashing in sky. Read
TELEPHONE. Red scarf on a craned neck.
Pass bony leaves of a ragwort. A blonde woman
trots like a fox in black, lean-legged clothes. See
diamonds of iron painted pillarbox red. Read
HOUSING. See smooth lips of a fish of black
iron and the sheen of a lightbulb's light over the
fish head like an electric milk. Ballerinas of
light dance across the water's black stage.
Crow-feather green and crow-feather black are
the colours of water. See water like a gelatinous
ice skating rink and you turn to a tug ploughing
upstream through the dark and a wake of froth
curls from the bow of the boat and smears ribs
over the skin of the river. A small green light
visible on a moving boat and the boat slides
under the yawn of a bridge. See orange lights
rigged on a vehicle's flank. Hear a chuckle.
Turn to see obelisks of dark merging with the

dark of the sky and all darknesses assembled
like the moving parts of a fog. Hear, "O that's
not." Hear, "If he gets delayed I'll get a taxi and
I'll phone you." Hear, "Yes, exactly." Hear the
passing away of footsteps and the scuff of a foot
and a scrape of grit under a sole. See ripples
wrinkling through water. Hear the clip-clip of a
tidy footstep. A suddenish chatter of water like
voices almost starting together. And you climb
over steps. Man listening to a box strapped by
the belt of his hand to his ear. Eyes look ahead.
Read Lambeth. A paper waved by a hand
urgently. Ribbed stones like the bark of
cedarwood in slow-moving shadow. Read
POLICE. Letters in blue. Black spikes of iron.
Glint of a mineral's crystal. Face in a blue hood.
Sky dark as the skin of a whale. Water dark like
the skin of a whale. Mid-bridge pale shadow
moving within a grey shadow like a woman's
foot trying on a shoe. Water screwed-up and
uncrumpled like a sheet of grey silk. Drumming
of a helicopter straightens the pulse of its noise
to a fading bee's drone. Hiss of a pneumatic
valve on a lorry like the rearing-up of a hissing
cobra. Rattle of light. Glint of dusty black-
painted iron. Noise of a helicopter sinks.
Movement of a bridge under your foot with
traffic like uncontrollable excess shaking the
fabric of the bridge. Tree in dark on the shore
as you walk. Two walking women. Huff of a
breath. Match-burning noise of a heel's scrape.

[82]

Sinew of a laugh snaps and falls silent between two faces. Hood with the wings of a crow. Black coat flares like a black willow unfolding, and folding again over the body of a woman passing. Red gloves alive with hands in the puppets of their fingers. Dull violet-grey construction of metal and plastic, like a house. A movement of turquoise and a flash of the colour like a gleam on glass in a small-windowed room in the dark red minutes of the setting sun. Paper torn and cast down by two hands. Blazing electric lights. Two hands held up over a face. Spikes into air. Flowers of iron painted gold. Read Victim. Read Parliament Square. Paving stone rocks with a see-saw motion and rocks up and down. Oblong of polished iron like a beached fish. Look down to shingle at the shore's lip. Rocks and water splashing like children among rocks and water, and the rocks green and soft with strands of weed. Wind sharpens to many points like a shoal of fish. Black pupils of a woman's eyes set like a distance. Hair of tight ringlets. Palm fronds swaying at a hip are pictures on a printed dress. Rectangles reflected up onto shore-stones from dully gaping holes in water like yawning mouths. A cold iron handrail. And you walk. Tree branches segment the visible face of a stone carved as a man. A shadow falls and walks joined to a man. Read OPENED BY H.M. KING GEORGE V ACCOMPANIED.

A shaved head passes, green with new stubble. A man tugs at his beard and runs. Leaves circle leaves. Black butterfly of shadow on a wall twitching black wings. Read MILLBANK. A horn blows softly like somebody hunting. Traffic moves and stops like the big wheel of a giant fairground, each car dressed up in glosswork and plastic decoration and bright name badges. Two faces of stone. See arms left and right. Tall man with a dark plastic bag and the appearance of no face. Read gifted. A leaf falls into the stream of passing traffic, ekes forwards. A car passes. A line of lights is vertical and traffic slows. One cry of a horn. Read Advanced Warning Major Road Works. See arched windows in row upon row. See the images of faces behind bars and faces in front and heads and bodies with hands made of panes of clear glass. Hear the scream and the extended hoarse sound of a slipping fan belt. Tree glanced all over with lights for a second. Read millicent. See a grey rose window and see black glass panes like sheets of obsidian and a pepper of stars over you. Herd of feet, shufflings pass all at once. Hear, "O right, are you talking." A ruffled lion's mane of hair, head of a man. Tree roots dive at a square of earth bound by four paving slabs. The rise and fall of a siren's pitch. Hear, "That last thing." Fur-collared girl. Man with dark eyes like conkers. Read Black Rod's Garden. Read OUT. Read

[84]

SOVEREIGN'S ENTRANCE. See falling and turning. Arch of roses and crown in stone. Leaves and buds out of rough stems. Wrought iron gates, a formation of flared leaves. Five figures of stone, each foot standing on a stone rose. A lion with a tongue and a tail flashing, and a flag-bearer, stone. Twisted light stands of wrought metal. A black horse and rider of metal, sword raised. A man helmeted. Lions of stone. Faces seeing. A robed figure of stone. Read NO ENTRY. Read METROPOLITAN POLICE. Letters in white. Black-shirted chest of a walking man. Hear a bell among bells. One leaf lying like a lamb on a rock. Golden towers in grey shadows. Round green lights of the green of deep rivers. A cat's face of stone looking over the drop of a wall. Hawk of a face with eyes sunken. Hear a crackle and buzz and a voice. See leaves move silently apart in a section of sky. Policemen in yellow walking over a zone of short grass. The cough of a baby. Feet among feet. Hear, "And so I went to." Short-backed lion of black metal seated beneath a black man of metal. Read OLIVER CROMWELL. 1599 1658. Hear the scuff of a foot. A scarved head. Hear, "Her family." See hanging coats in a lit window. Stars over a gilded pyramid. Hear the revving of engines. Blubbery revving of a passing bike's engine from idle. Cry of a horn. Elephant cry of two car horns at once like tusks of sound. Three

beeps of a small car. Animals of stone, carved,
like parts of a wall climbing out of itself.

See a bronze man higher than milling-about
figures. Hand at a pram. Hear, "See what your
mum got to say, eh." Hear the toll of a bell and
it lingers. A triangle of laughter. Leaf curled
like a ram's horn. Yellow shirts, yellow ties.
Orange braids of a man's hair. Shoulders draped
with a black shawl. And the fractured click of a
camera's shutter. Hear, "You're just." And
heavy men watch. See a moon-grey headphone
hiding an ear. Hear a voice, "But it's worth
coming here just for a few." Hear the toll of a
bell and it lingers; and clatters minutely at the
end of its note. Hear a cough. Hear, "You can
walk as far as." Hear, "There's going to be
about two-hundred p." Hear, "Be when they
come out." See the tuft of a beard in the peg of
two fingers. Air stained with the sharpness of
peppermint scent. Hear, "O his shoulders
Anna, I need to be taller." Hear a man
humming a song to himself. Hear the toll of a
bell and it lingers. And a faint chime falls down.
And you hear, "Because I'm here," Hear, "I
should do this." Hear, "What do you think of."
Hear, "It's great ... the whole outpouring." And
you hear, "Touched a lot." See point-tipped
green leaves. Hear, "Just being here is." See two
eyes narrowed. Hear, "It's not somewhere."

Camera pulled from a bag in the manner of a
hat trick. Stitched backs of shoes standing on
tar, layer upon layer of a heel's plyboard. Hear,
"Through here ... sorry." An empty car moving
on a path through a crowd, figures parting and
mingling like many insects. A black pointed hat
with a silver tip. Hear the toll of a bell and it
lingers. Hear the raw cough of one throat and
other throats cough. Eyes narrowed. Squeezed
cry of music through the click of a camera.
Hands hold cameras on arms above heads. A
two-children noise. And you hear, "Get down."
All rise on tiptoe and music grows up. All
bodies climb down from tiptoe. And hear, "O
there's a breath of fresh air." A word lifted into
the cupboard of an ear. Hear the toll of a bell
and it lingers. A wrist swivels clockwise to show
a watchface. See a tear in the well of an eye like
a mouse in a corner. A window is lowered. The
click of a camera. Pass figures lined up against a
wall and the air is cooler like caves from the
sun. Hear, "Excuse me do you know what
direction it's going." See men in red coats with
black fur. Synchronised march-steps. Parade-
men pass like red-shouldered rhinos. Tall-
hatted men march. A grey, dappled horse trots.
Hear the toll of a bell and it lingers. See bronze
men on plinths like men on tea chests. Hear a
sound like lapping like a water of languages you
do not know. A clock of bells and a bone white
clock face. Hear voices singing and through

trees they come and voices join up with voices
to sing like hands holding hands. And you pass.
Gull swings down a dark corner of the sky. Sun
passes light like a hand over the heads of the
crowd and you pass. Cyclops of a camera. Hear
the wooing yell of a baby. See a coiled fibre of
dust. See the eye of a woman turn to the edge
of its hole in the head with a pointed look from
its pointed corner. See sunlight set light to a
strand of hair. See a black hat moving at the
level of heads. Hear a roughness of coughing
like a sound-shape of scree. Trees shift, from
the crowns of trees spikes stand like an army of
spears in the cooked-fish-eye-grey of the sky.
See a mouth whispering into an ear and the
listening head lifts up at the chin and the
mouth drops open. See faces turn to the middle
of the square among the fixedness of buildings.
For one minute mouths are still. Hear, "Lose
them in giving, by their return." Horseshoe of
fibre floating. Quivery alarm of a small phone.
Hear, "Of souls, what thou gave us ... if we are
thine." The cry of a baby. And a flag buckles
and unbuckles to a shaking straightness of
rectangle fabric. And you hear, "And death is
only horizon and horizon is nothing save the
limit of our sight." Hear amplified coughing
like a kingsize-crystal of the original cough. See
hands holding hands. Hear a voice say,
"Remember now thy." A gull cries and the cry
sighs downwards like a gull flying. And you

[88]

hear, "The light of the moon or the stars be not
darkened." Hear, "Shall tremble and the strong
men shall bow." And you hear, "And the dark
door shall be shut to the streets, and the voice
of the moon shall be brought low, and the
grasshopper shall." Scrape of a foot and you
pass, hearing, "Mourners go about the streets,
or the golden bowl." Voices and feet
murmuring. And hear, "Or the wheel broken,
then shall the dust return to the earth and the
spirit shall return." Hear a murmur of voices
low as sheep noise at the eating of grass. Eyes
turn like the stares of a herd of sheep's eyes to
a place of disturbance. Child in a pink fleece.
See small scabs of dried blood on a woman's
thumb. A man blows his nose. Two women talk
and turn counterwise from each other like two
meshed cogs and walk. Look to see feet
navigate feet like voices among whispers. Hear,
"Thy soul." See eyes fixed on the back of a
head. Two hands unfold a sheet of white paper.
A painted blue circle. Tail of a chestnut brown
horse. And you hear, "Stood before them
there." And hear, "Cried with a loud voice,
saying." See a hand twist open a screwtop bottle
of orange. Hear a hiss from the mouth of the
bottle. And hear, "Unto the land and all the
angels ... and the four living creatures ... on
their faces." And a man sips from the orange.
And you hear, "Of the elders answered ... and
where came them ... there are they which

came." Hear bubbles breaking within the bottle as the man takes the bottle down from his lips. And you hear, "Shall hunger no more ... nor any heat for the land." And hear, "Shall feed them." And hear, "Of waters ... shall wipe away all tears from their eyes." And you pass. Hear voices of many sing and mouths move among the faces of the crowd. See a flag at half mast and the sun breaks from cloud. See a golden hand, and feet on tiptoe. A man turns and walks through the crowd and people part to let him pass through and you hear, "This is extraordinary." And you hear voices rise up in a single note and voices as one. Hear a sigh between two words. And hear, "We gather in this great." And pass, hearing, "How shall we explain the numbers." Hear, "Ability to make all however fleeting vouch for that." See dark eyes turn. And hear, "Cradled in." Hear, "I can hardly believe." And hear, "And the curious thing is we are not." Shadow of a nose and a woman swivels her head, like an owl. Hear a cough and look up to see a flag shake and crack above heads. Hear, "Not on the splendid." And see a bird fly. Hear, "We cannot resolve that it shall be happy." Stone beard tied in a knot of stone. Hear, "And yes, laughter." See the well of an ear spiralling into the side of a head. See arms folded. Hear, "Of course, the laughter of the book of." A round gold earring like a small moon on a man's ear. Hear, "To." See sun on pointed, dark-tipped leaves. Hear, "Faithful." See urns of stone and the mouths of their cavities darken. See the grey span of a pigeon float down to the heads of the crowd and a phone rings. Hear an amplified cough and see two faces look to the sun and four eyes squint and grow far in their creases and you turn from them as a cough alarms like the cracking of deer over twigs and you see the back of a man moving away through the crowd as a bell note cries in the low rings of bells. See dark windows pointed like tips of laurel. Hear the toll of a bell and voices climb from the trembling note of metal struck hard. Hear the toll of a bell and it hangs. Crackle of a stiff plastic bag. See a hand pull a straw from a plastic skin glued to the side of a carton. And plunge it like a sword into the body of the carton. See a mouth close lips tight round the top of a straw. Hear a gurgling of bubbles hammering the wall of a carton. See figures in red at a pace. Small pale straps and grey steel spikes with acute-angled triangle glints of shapes. Maroon-dressed woman. Two horses ridden. A camera held into the air. Voices sing and many heads tilt and fall down. And the murmur of feet and the noise of fabrics moved within. A huff. Dark glasses reflect the long head of a horse and you smell cigarette smoke and the note of an organ dims to a husky breath. Hear an amplified cough. Hear, "Let us pray." And voices in unison, "Our father who art." You walk and you hear, "Who trespass against." Two ladies, white-haired, and see their lips move with the motion of words but hear no words from their mouths as you pass. Hear, "Most humbly and heart." A hand lifts to cover a mouth. Hear, "Because he lives and we shall live also." A black hair flies up. Hear, "Father of all." Smell an oiliness of leather. Hear, "For those who mourn." And the sky grows pale like congealed lamb's fat. Hear, "Amen." And the word is made by many at once and the word ends and a boy's hand touches a girl's neck and you turn to see a red face meshed with grey stubble. Cracked brown boots on the feet of the body bearing the red face. See a clot of plaque between front teeth. See a man in black wearing white gloves. See the body of a red bus moving, a horse, a woman in black cloth riding and the cloth on her legs and arms in a padded fashion. See the outstretch of a pigeon ascending. Hear, "In and through the light of our." Hear, "Praise thee the depth and reality." See dark shadow drop from the chin of a bronze man. See black metal grilles and hear, "A century of violence and of aspiration." And you hear, "The frustrated shall live as neighbours." Hear the word "Amen" separated out into overlappings of soft pronunciations. A big voice says, "Where there shall be no darkness or dazzle, no fears or hopes but one equal." Footstep and footstep. And hear, " No

[92]

ends or beginnings but one equal." An organ
cries up and low voices rise. See a long-haired
man with a black scarf wrapped. See an oily red
lipstick the colour of flowering currants.
Flowers on a woman. A man singing loud. A
gull drops to heads and you turn to see a crown
on a dome of stone and the green cab of a lorry
deep among crowds. Green buds like the small
eyes of insects. An amplified rustling and a
knock like the sound of a tumbler clocked onto
hardwood. A chime of bells wobbly as water
contained. A voice walks over the volume of
crowds and you hear, "I see myself now at the
end." Hear a hum like a fly close to your ear.
And you hear, "I am going now to see." Music
at a man's ear and the face of a woman turns
and her lips ruckle up and her brow grows
knitted and frowns. A big voice says, "And
wherever I have seen the print of his shoe in
the earth, yay, sweeter than all." And the eyes
of a woman grow sharp with a look. And you
hear, "Word I did use to gather for my food,
yay, my steps." See a girl put a finger up into
the air. And you hear, "Followed one another in
at the beautiful." And you hear a murmur of
footsteps and voices. Hear two cries. A voice
above the volume of crowds says, "O heaven."
Sun opens in sky. See the convex of an eye's
lens placed to the eye of a camera. Hear, "Be
upon you and remain with you always." Voices
sing up. Hear, "Almighty God, the late most

[93]

high most mighty." A double cough rasps like a
foot ploughed into gravel. Hear, "Excellent
Lady of the Most Noble Order." And a foot
scrapes. Hear, "Garter of the Most Noble." A
thin cry of horns. Hear, "Thistle of the Royal
Victorian Order, the Royal." Horns in two
notes repeat. Hear, "Chair of the British." A
pale man's face. Hear, "Venerable Order of
Saint John of Jerusalem." Dough white face in a
window of a fifth floor. Hear, "Most Excellent."
Horns cry a brash note. Hear, "Defender of the
Faith of the Most Noble Order." A noise like
breathing. Hear, "Bless with health and all
worldly happiness." Scrape of a foot. And horns
cry in unison like running sheep bleating into
the sky. And a voice above the volume of
crowds says, "Thus it hath pleased." Faces turn
to look up. Hear a rumbling clatter of an
organ's pipes breathing. Hear, "God save our
gracious." And the voices of many sing. Hear,
"God save." The glint of a tear. A piece of
gravel the shape of an anvil. See two dark
horses with riders. See two women turn like
rudders and walk among figures. There is the
clatter and discord of the notes of an organ cast
up like hands and shaken. See a flat hat and
grey stripes of trousers. Murmur of voices like a
low meadow stream. A flap of dry skin on the
ridge of a nose. Faces look up. See a pigeon fly.
Hear, "Sorry, sorry." See three flags of cloth.
See the line of a scar on the cheek of a face. See

[94]

white gloves on hands. A dog barks four times.
See a white tissue put to the holes of a nose.
Hear, "Get a glimpse." See a silver-grey camera
and it sparkles in a flat way. A dog barks two
times. A mouth smiles. Hear voices saying
words you do not know and the voices grow
distant. See a woman stand on a bag on the
ground. Hear the cry of a baby. Mouth of a
baby at wide aperture. Hear the click of a
camera. And you hear, "What I should have
done." A siren wails up to a pitch and falls
down. A sharp snap of a cough. And a wind
rises up and the hairs on many heads move. See
two pigeons flying. Hear the chime of a bell
like a bowl dropped. The face of a clock reads
half past twelve. See a gold circle. See black cars
gathered. See a small girl. A lilac fur hat, and a
girl on the shoulders of a man. See the heels of
small shoes tapping the chest of a man. A
pinstriped jacket. Hear clattery ooze of an
organ's bass notes. Man in a bright yellow
jacket on the top of a stone wall. Wall like a
castle. Scowl of a bronze face, figure of a man.
Hear the voice of a radio say, "Cathedral." Hear
drums and pipes rise and see bodies on tiptoe.
See a camera held to a head. Hear a strained
and lead-soldier cry of a man's voice shout to a
row of men and the slow beat of drums begins
walking. Squawk of a voice like a telling-off,
sharp like a hatchet struck into wood. See a
blood red flag carried. Hear, "Hurry up, my feet

[95]

ache." And see a green metal man among trees studded by leaves like splinters of jade. Leaves like intersecting and bisecting plates of grasshopper green. See grey turrets and barbed horns of stone. And a dark bird flies from turret to turret. Hear the voice of a radio. Bark of a dog. Fingers on a hand curl. Hear the click of a camera and a scream like a mosquito from the body of the camera. Darkening of sky to grubby ash-grey. You turn. See a black turret. See specks of skin on a man's black coat and the turret is above the man's head. See the face of a girl turn down on the neck examining a camera in the grip of her fingers and thumbs. Read Her. Letters in black on a grey-white page and the page rolled into a tube and gripped in a vice of fingers and thumb. Count ten faces reflected on the curve of a lens. See a freckle the colour of oak on a woman's face and the skin is like peaches. Hear the yells of men over crying of pipes and the depth-boom of drums beating. A single bird flies. Hear the cry of a child like a small peacock's howl. Hear falling scales of bell-notes repeat. Coarse grey hairs on a man's face. A voice remarks, "Here we go." And you hear pipe music passing. Arms rise up with the bodies of cameras. Muffled vibration of the thumping of drums. A red parade like a vein through the body of the crowd. The roof of a black car is glossy. Black car and black car. Hear, "Oh my god." See faces crane up and

press out and feet rise on tiptoe. Wreath of
dark roses thrown to the roof of a black car.
Patter of hands in applause and a pack of
whistling mouths and cries follows a black car
through person to person along the banks of
the road through the crowds. Car after car. See
figures seated in the glass panelled case of a
glossy black car. Face of a woman under the rim
of a black hat makes a long smile. Feel the
warmth of a body nearby. Hear, "I can't move."
Hear, "See 'em anyhow." See a rectangular
group of men in red jackets on green grass
holding brass tubes and funnels, with white
gloves. Long guns like beaks backwards over
the shoulders of men and tall hats of fur on the
heads of two rows of men. A triptych of dark
planes like men with arms out. Hear the
throbbing of engines vibrate through your
bones and the crowd is a complex of hands
clapping hands and mouths pointed in whistles
and faces tilted with eyes to the triptych of
dark planes. A vertical sword. A man in red
adorned with gold. And you hear, "You have to
go all." Chime of bells falling. Hear, "Still loads
of soldiers." And hear, "They're not real." Hear,
"Oh yeah." A child lifted to the shoulders of a
man. A child's blue eyes. See a small fly
wandering over the weave of a black cardigan.
Back, necks, heads, riders, manes and reins of
two horses pass. Hear the word, "Bye." People
turn. People push ways between people. Hear,

[97]

"Everybody just." Hear, "Squashes." Flash of a ring in silver. See ostrich feathers worn by a square of men walking. One row of guns move together and men break into rows of three and march like three-headed six-legged men. Hear, "Don't worry, you stand there." A white coach. White gloved hand. A blue van with black windows. A black car with two men. A line of cars. Broad-rimmed hat in a car. Long gold hair in a black car. And guns rise up and the daggered heads of guns are silver like the mouths of fish. Read VYW1. A bird drops. Two cars pass. Feet of a man in red stamp a one-two. See a sword raised. The position of held guns shifts all at once in the arms of men. A hand to an eye and you pass as two fingertips stroke the lid of the eye lowered shut. Toll of a bell. Man in a dark car. Headlamps dazzle in soda-froth sunlight. Blue lights flash on-off. Black feathered hat in a black saloon car. Hand waving. Car after car and bells toll dark sound. A hand wipes beadwork of sweat from a brow. Hear the beep of a phone for attention. Flags of colours mounted on bonnets of cars. A black hat flared with blue feathers. Image of the face of an old woman. Hear, "This is." White streak between the eyes of a horse. The dotted line of a yellow stitch on the shoulder of a blue jacket. Pigeon-grey hair of an old man. Brass instruments carried in hands on foot over grass. A hand raised and lowered. Men in red

clockwork like walking crows. Feet step on the
spot. See figures in yellow. A grey horse moves
forwards. A drum beats. Men in red march with
polished brass horns. One woman riding a horse
at a walk. Drums pass and each beat is a
boulder of sound and the pace of the beat is the
pulse of a heart. See dagger-end guns and hear
feet clap to the ground. A dark-as-blood flag
carried sidewinds like eels sliding through
water. Hear, "They're just marching past us."
The toll of a bell. A grey horse at a saunter. See
a white tasselled mane. Hear the toll of a bell.
A red group of men pass from sight among
heads. See mouths on the mouth-parts of brass
horns but no horn sound passes. See fingery
feathers attached to tall hats. Deep boom of a
drum falls lower in sound. Eyes on an arm
beating a big drum. You walk and you hear,
"See you later okay ... see you later okay, bye."
Pass two red-jacketed men carrying swords
before them. One step of many uniformed men
and one step again. A smell of old clothes and a
body. Wisps of white hair from the neck of an
old man like beard in a hedgerow. The laugh of
a woman like the croak of a jackdaw. Hear, "Is
that good enough." See tree-foliage blurred
through the corner of a lens in a pair of glasses.
Hear, "I think that's about it." Sharp cry of a
phone. See a phone to an ear. A man puts his
thumb to his lips and rubs there. See figures in
black walk two-by-two from a pale stone

building with ribs. See figures in black walk
two-by-two into a building of dark stone. Hear,
"I wasn't there for the main bit ... it all
happened very quickly ... it's hard to take in."
Pass a woman's mouth with a cigarette and the
eye of the cigarette lights to an orange like
wooden embers flaky with ash. Hear, "I'll go
through the floor." Five spots of dirt on the
skin of a white glove. Pass railings with black
claws of iron. Read PEACE ON EARTH.
Three yellow hooves and one black of a passing
horse. A man and woman in black clothes both
quiet. Four white helmets afloat on heads cut
up by black railings in sections between and
you walk. One pair of black glasses. Hear, "Erm
... Natwest at the moment ... oh yes, in
principle." See black-clothed figures moving
among trees and the trees with leaves like green
fires of light. Turn to see figures on balconies
and black horses of bronze yoked to an
unmoving chariot. White gloves folded in half
on a lap and a plane-leaf green shawl on a
woman's sloped shoulders, hair like a white
waterfall.

Two women running on black heels. Traffic
dammed-up by a signal of red lights. Pass long
seed pods. Shadows of trees like cracks over all
surfaces and flat fissures. See eyes watching a
woman's face pass. Man walking and chewing.

Low, red light of a lit cigarette's tip. Woman
and child of stone under twelve figures seated.
A winged bat with a lamb's head in stone.
Buildings carved of wood and see shadows like
shady characters in among corners and under
things. Hear a language you do not know. A
magenta light thrown over a building like a
frock. Read Queen Elizabeth II Conference
Centre. Cobbles stickle-backed like razors of
light and shadow. Haze of light into a fog. A
leaf falls. Stars of light. Figures cut into stone.
Hear, "I've lost my teeth." Hear, "Say you got
up." Read Broadcasting. Hear, "Brass
candelabra." The street littered with figures
ahead. Lion and unicorn face to face. A room
containing many figures. Hear a beating music
from the window of a silver car. Hear the rush
of cars. Sneering face of a man, lips up like a
growl. On two bags passing, read, SIMPLY
FOOD. Read OVAL BOX. Hear, "It's five to
me, so." Swinging back-and-forth arms of a
woman strutting. Read DTI. A door opening
and closing. Hear, "I hate things like this." A
face close to the surface of a wall, a hand out
touching the wall gently and moving along the
wall like a spider creeping. A hand clamped
onto a neck. Hand adjusting a collar. Read
HSBC. Hear, "How do you split fifty billion
between seventy-five people." Read Abbey.
Read Orchard St. Face frowned like an ill dog.
See feet tilted up. See a lady walk straight on.

Two-pitched note as a door opens and closes. A rank of tail lights like red embers of various upright shapes. Two green lights appear like a gateway opened and all cars move. Read Extra Value Meal. Read SELF SERVICE. See a smooth-skinned man pulling up the zip of his jacket. Hear, "Okay, yes." Hear the word 'yes' spoken in unison by more than one voice. Figures side by side. See a woman giving a man a note, and the man is seated behind a sheet of glass. Hear, "To the rest of." A song sung aloud. Man walking carefully. Read VICTIM SUPPORT. The eye of a lit cigarette held at a hip. Hear, "Basically." Yellow and black checked hat. Hear, "We're going to have to go on-line." Three blue flashing lights in succession from the handlebar of a moving bike. See stationary cars. Hear, "Did you listen to Dead Ringers." Hear, "Missed it ... was it funny." See a miniskirt of old wool on old legs passing; wool, mustard yellow. Read Look Right. See an arrow pointing. See a foot kicking a cigarette lighter. Turn to a shadow of dark glass the colour of damp smoke. Long cigarette pegged between the fingers of a strolling woman. Hear, "Going down through the." Read GIANT. Read Therapy. Read DIESEL. A ravenish woman rolls her eyes back and aside. See a shop of suits. See headless mannequins. Crooked-necked man smoking, his eyes narrow to slits, hair slicked oily, lips moving without

words, the cigarette sticks to the skin of a lip,
pulling the skin as the mouth opens a bit. See
the man holds one finger up to the window of a
shop. See a blue shirt moving at the window of
a seventh floor. Turn to see a man at his finger
scanning the list of a shop's opening hours and
he looks down and the fingers of his other hand
bundle stiff sheets of hen-egg brown cardboard
and see the wrinkles of the fingers are dark. A
face in a beard. A man strutting back and forth
mutterishly. Read FRY. Letters in yellow chalk
on wood. Read The Lord Chancellor's Dept.
See green, red and yellow, seats in a white
room. Read Brrrrr. See a shaved head wearing a
cap like a field of stubble in winter wearing the
frost and the birds. Hear, "Like very." Hear,
"Some things should stay wrapped." Hear,
"Hey." See a face worried, eyes flat like a face in
a shock. Read SMOKERS GIFTS. Read
SPECIALISTS IN HANDMADE. See a long
sable-haired girl. Read PASSENGER
CAPACITY 77. Read "I'll do it tomorrow." See
leopard print socks. See eight dark buttons in
two columns of four. Curl of a hair on a man's
head. Lips lipsticked to a dark red and moving
apart and together again, sticking with the wax
of the lipstick. Image of a rhinoceros. Read
WITNESS APPEAL FALSE
IMPRISONMENT ON TUES 20TH NOV 01
AT 3.50PM. AN 11 YEAR OLD
SCHOOLGIRL WAS HELD AT

KNIFEPOINT HERE BY A BLACK MALE.
DID YOU HEAR OR SEE ANYTHING.
CAN YOU HELP. Small siren's melody. See a
heap of pink the shape of a body curled under a
blanket. Feet pass, a foot lands on its shadow.
Two colours of brick. A man seated by a door.
Smell cooking fat. See a hand place a straw into
a mouth. Short-haired man stares ahead, seated
beside a window. Eyes behind glasses. Read
Pension for fatal shooting. Read Act with
courage. Shadow struts into a shadow. Tree
leaves glitter. Hear, "It's a magpie." Hear, "The
whole lot ... fifty pee ... one pound." Hear,
"Halfway mate ... I've been working." See
people walking in one direction only. See a red
light. Read £1.99 WHITE ACE. See a dark
face and a mane of hair, and the face of a man
scanning the print of a newspaper. See white-
soled trainers. Hear, "And they walk quickly
who walk past." See the street and people
reflected on the convex shields of a pair of
sunglasses. A girl putting a bag down. Spike-
haired man smoking. The smell of smoke
moves into the smell of chipfat. Green-centred
white flowers, starred as wild aniseed. Read NO
BIKES PLEASE. Hear warbling music. Hear,
"Yeah, hello I ... sure, at Victoria." See a face
watching things and faces pass. See shutters.
Hear, "It's too fucking white man." Hear, "It's
a friend of mine." A bent woman scoops her
posture to walk. Arms and legs bent like the

[104]

limbs of a flying bee. Hear, "We don't have the strength." Hear a voice from India. A flowerseller gazing for a long time down at his watch. See a sky like blancmange on the watch glass. A girl makes her mouth into a square shape and cries. Hear, "Howl howl howl." Shirt falling out of trousers. See eyes, glasses, beard and a belt. See dark skin, ringlet, nose-jewel and brown leather patch. Hear a cough. See smoke sail out of a mouth like a train from a tunnel. Feet tapping ground. Folded arms pass. A man coughs. See some figures moving faster than others. Eyes in a head, watching a man pass. A woman with naked breasts carved in stone. Skin jerking in creases under the loose chin of a walking woman. Read MELONS 1.80. Hear, "You come back the last bus." Hear, "She ask you." See the mouth of a red-haired woman quizzing a head by the well of its ear. Grey ground stroked with shadows of feet stepping and lifting and stepping on. Two beeps of a car's horn. Deep horn of a red bus. Hear an old woman snap, "Will you please let people get off." See the speaking old woman clutching the arm of another old woman. Dark triangle of trees. See a beard trimmed to a square under a face. Read MAMMA MIA. Read H. STAIN LTD. Hear one crinkle of a creased plastic bag. Click of a wheel. Street glints on the left-hand lens of a pair of sunglasses. Warmth of a perfume and the taste of alcohol. See four silver five-pence pieces dropped by a woman into the cupped palm of a man. See a man on the pavement lying down. Read FLEXIBLE. Read HEALING. A woman places a foamy-filled glass on the ledge of a window and she sits in a room darkly lit like a red maple syrup. See a man brings a glass filled to the brim with clear barley gold liquid to the windowseated woman and sits beside her. Baby in the bucket of a pram. Blue dummy in the baby's mouth. A woman yawns. White teeth flash like a horse's chomp. Read BAG O' NAILS. See a woman in a pink top at the window of a third floor. Steps down into subway and a man is reclined, yawning on a lemon yellow mat. Hear, "Left or right at the end of the subway ... go straight on." See redness to the eyes of the mat-reclining man. Read 41. See black and white tiles. See a woman sitting. Read TEAS. Pale moon face of an illuminated clock. Read Child age 5 smuggles tobacco. See a woman vacuuming. See a man dragging horses by the manes carved in stone. Pass urns. Trees into dark and a ripping cry from a motorbike's engine combusting away. A row of grey lights the colour of calf tongues. Taxi with a thin orange light flashing on one side of its black bodywork. Read HB 005. See smoke rising. Light curled on black iron spikes. Read ADVANCE WARNING. See red lights on a dark tally of railings. Illuminated steam like the breathings of a horse. See green rooms, quiet and lit by their lamps. Smell burnt oil and the complex of petrol. A jogging man. An angel of gold with arms out. Two men walking together without speaking. See children and crows occupying an area. A man alone yawning. Leaves alive with the wind. Massive cage of wrought iron. Spikes and a muscular unicorn of metal and see a lion's face in stone. See long shadows of railings stretched thin. See two policemen, each rubbing hands together at the palms. Dark trees. Read PEDESTRIANS. Leaves picked up by a wind curl into corners. Look up to see black-winged creatures. An angel of metal, golden and still. A shady path crossed by cloppings of footsteps, feet like the shadows of birds. See figures gathered like starlings in different directions. Pollard trees, warty and gnarled stumps of crowns like fingers of leprosy. Cool air is dark and faces like moons. A ring of electric lights like a crown. And you hear heavy feet and breathing also, hoarse and sighing. Leaves lying quietly full of shadows like shadows in shadows. A hum of traffic and one flash of a light. A throaty grunt. A glint three times. Rustle of a bag. Night floating on the convex lens of a pair of glasses. Scrape of a leaf. Light in a glass tweaked into a star with rays. Hear, "A beach out of ... which is going to be this." And you turn to see lights passing over and your head swivels up and

round to the passing of lights and a building
shields the lights opaquely. Three figures ahead
dark as crows. Two ticks of a bike. There is the
step of a man's foot and you see a man by
himself. Tree leaves are shiny and black among
sticks and spikes of tree branches like rib-
xylophones. See a flag composed of an
elongated X with triangle petals of red, white,
and blue. Count six figures. The noise of a shoe
heel scraping the ground. Bins like low cages. A
woman alone and gold light over the face of a
building behind her, and the building lion gold
with the lie of the light. A man's feet cross
through a square of light on the ground. Look
up to see three stars. A black face in the
darkness and the cough of a man like the bleat
of a goat and there are leaves black against the
sky orange in its dark. A light grows into a light
from the dark and fades. Hear the reed of a
saxophone and the smell of the heat of engines.
Hear, "I'm only ten minutes." Hear, "You don't
know what." See the glow of a cigarette break
and sparks of glow fall as crumbs into dark.
Read The Ritz. A group of figures wearing long
coats. Hear one squeal of brakes and see eyes
turn in a head to their left. Read Make your
dream true. Read CAGED HUMILIATION
with no parole. Read PRESS AFTER EACH
COIN. Read Strict Mistress 8374 2530. Read
Unhurried Services 7407 1430. Read 3 Dial
number. See the gloss of box leaves wink leaf by

leaf and many leaves at once and you walk over
the asphalt of road passing a skip containing
cardboard. Hear, "But anyway it's a first." And a
woman strides with arms swinging. Read
Telephone. See a girl pushing her tongue up
into the space behind her top lip. Black shiny
hair, a woman leans back on her walk with
hood down, flatly between the blades of her
shoulders. See fish in blue water behind glass.
See a long beard and a coloured wool jacket like
a rag rug with arms and a collar. See a man with
the eyes of a dog. Read G84. See black eyes
involved in something to their right. Hear,
"Hey, yo." See red light reflected on glass. Read
Flu. Read The Palm Beach. See a man talking
to a phone. An old woman bearing a stoop. See
blue light reflected on windows and you pass a
limping man and enter into a square containing
low-crowned trees. Hear, "The Best." See a
room with eight grand pianos. Read DANGER
MEN WORKING. See sparkling light. A huge
polished car. Read B. Read Bank of Ireland.
Iron black as yew leaves. Read FIRE. Read
Keep. See cigarette butts lying on the ground.
Read DRY RISER. See an open-plan office
with many desks lit, with no men or women.
Read Telephone. Read WATER. The smell of
paraffin. Four chrome-skinned bench legs. A
room with tables set for eating. Read COACH
& HORSES. See two woman step from a
shadow. See groups of figures carved in wood.

See cardboard masks the size of men. Read 1
Bruton Street. Lights and a face frowned to
wrinkles. A face with patterns of joy. See a
portrait of a dog. See two stars of light. See four
cars slowing. Hear, "Cut hair." A band of light
reflected along the edge of a bonnet. Read
CAN 1. Letters on a black car. Read 133. See
the burn-glare of car lights and a violet flash in
one. See a long-maned wooden rocking horse
and the nostrils grotesque and flared. See light
passing between needles of foliage. Read TO
LET 8750 sq ft approx. See a man pushing a
pram. A woman and two men pass. Hear, "That
will be the Friday, Saturday and Sunday, and
then I'm going home." Hear, "Just for dinner."
See eyes in a rectangle slot cut in black cloth.
Hear, "I met her before ... a couple of times
I've been in there and she's been behind the
bar." Hear, "I must introduce you to her ... she
speaks so many languages." Read The Tanning.
One man in a taxi. One head in a turban. Hear
a shriek. And you turn right to see lights the
colours of a peacock. See a man and woman
alone with each other. A cloth cap worn. Boots
in pairs. See a coach turn and pass behind
buildings. See a man alongside the reflection of
a man on a black window. A girl holding her
nose between finger and thumb. A camera held
up in an alley. See lights turn green from pink.
Two girls in black giving smiles to men held in
their arms. A man's mouth speaking, you

cannot hear the words. See a photograph of a
woman alone. See the face of a woman looking
up. Hear, "Excuse me." Hear, "I don't know ...
the stone." Hear, "Went to a birthday party."
Pass a girl smoking a cigarette and she drags in
deeply and the light grows bright and her chest
expands. See globes of light. High boots and a
face with a frown buckling-up between the
eyebrows. Hear, "Ha ha ha ha ha ha." Read No
Dirty Footwear or Site Clothing. See a red lit
room and there are faces and glasses of beer. A
red car appears and passes and disappears. See a
room, see a circle of figures eating. Hear, "I just
said." Hear, "So what is it? Spell it." Smell of
raw meatfat and lemon detergent. See dinner-
eating figures at tables of candles and gleaming
knives and forks and spoons and white dishes
with parcels and small piles and pools of food.
See wineglasses with bowed reflections. Pass a
white taxi. Pass an armchair drawn in white
chalk on a brick wall. Hear, "A friend of mine
works for classic fm." Read NO BUMMING.
Read EXODUST. See windows of upstairs
rooms lit dimly. Read NO PARKING. A man
in glasses talking alone. A woman bearing a
mop and bucket. Read Chilled Lagers. And
beside the sign for lagers a man is talking. Hear,
"Nick, hi." See a woman alone walking towards
you. See two eyes of a bird, one by one. In blue
light read BT. Eyes of a bird. Mouths of
shadow. Man with a beard and a man with no

beard. The dark skin of a face, eyes look from the head, see the clothed body of the man below his face seated at a desk in a lobby alone. See a group of stones on the pavement. See legs walking away from you. See figures seated, talking and leaning back on their chairs. Read Champagne Available. See a stretched car with black windows. See two circular brushes turning together. A man buttoning his coat. See a hand cupped over a chin. A man in step with the beat of music nearby and he leans and then backs-up several times like a confident dancer. See a window and behind glass, painted tins and images wrapped up in dust. Read ENJOY. See a man eating at a small square table alone. Hear the engine of a bike clacking at tickover. Cry of two horns. One rev-up of an engine and there is a sharp slapping noise repeated faster and faster. Boxes of empty green bottles. Count fourteen bikes chained to posts. Black binbags full and tied at the mouths. Three girls in a line walking fast like a team. There is a soapy, sharp smell of beer. Grey cap on a passing head. A window space hung with braids. Hear a cheering and clapping and high voices pitched up over each other. Read 24 hr. See two garden gloves. See light in a glass of white wine is pale like sap. The body of a blue bike chained to black railings. Read NEWMAN PASSAGE. On iron read Ductile Stanton Plc H Thames Water. A woman passes. See bodies of moving fish in illuminated water. See yellow and orange fish scales. Read EXPOSURE. See a movement but do not see what it is that moves. See black paint split and bubbled on cement. Look down to dark basement windows. Pass a man reading, sitting on a bench at the foot of a tree. A dark window containing figures of golden-haired children. A thin, stooped man lighting a cigarette, his head cocked to one side and the flame of the lighter like a yellow canary perched on a small brass box in the man's hand. A wreckage of plastic rolling on pavement. Hear the footsteps of a woman. Read Mrs Tin Carries On. Read Presidential Spiderplants. See semi-spheres of condensation on a pane of glass. A man steps from a car and stands and turns and walks away. See windows of light. Read ALL DAY INDIAN. Read Mon-Fri 8.30 am - 6.30 pm. See a small boy running. Read CARJACK WARNING TO WOMEN. Stiff bristled brush swept over paving by a woman. See three pigeons stabbing the flat, blistered body of a yellow, triangular crisp. And the crisp rotates once. Hear, "Got shitloads to talk about ... it's probably me that never shuts up, and you have to listen." Car. Car. Flashing tail light of a passing bike. A group of cigarette butts at a drain's grate. See slots between the grate's metal bars into the ground. Noise of ventilation fans. Car. Read Up to 2 hours £8.00. Read King & Queen. Read Blood Tests. A head in an upper floor window. See arms moving and an alarm sings and stops. See pieces of stone flaking from stone like a map of political boundaries. Read Night Bill. See the face of a man, serious, and the man cycling. See steam rising up from the ground. A dark tower like the muzzle of a dog. Read EXCEPT FOR ACCESS TO PREMISES. Hear the scream of an electric motor. Hear the humming of thousands of parts in the passing of cars. See leaves trapped in metal grates. Hear the swishing of fabric over moving bodies. See a man pushing a toy rabbit into a woman's hands. Brown cigar in a man's mouth, see wrinkled tobacco leaves rolled together. In a yellow-walled room a man sewing two parts of a jacket together. See a hand rising up and down with the motion of piercing fabric, feeding the needle, pulling the needle to thread-tightness, piercing back to the other side of the joined fabric. Hear the cry of a boy on a bike, "Yeah." See the boy chased by a boy on a bike. 'Squill-squill' sound of an engine running. See two eaters scratching their heads, chewing and the jaws clenching and unclenching at the muscles in the side of the head. A shaking shrub. A laughing child. And hear, "Work is work, it's an illusion, it doesn't have to be your whole life." Read OPEN. A woman steps from a door and steps forwards three paces and unlocks a car door with a keyturn. Man in a shop holding a

shoe. Leaves on a tree. Read Greek. Hear an
alarm crying. A man turning aside from
company to talk into a small phone. Hear, "We
have to arrange the full size." See a stone lamb.
See many dark windows. See a stuffed rabbit in
a dark window. See people at tables. See four
mouths drinking. Hear, "For fucking years."
And the word 'years' is extended along the 'ear'.
See a group of pieces of rubbish shepherded by
the wind into a corner. Hear the voice of a
woman speak into a phone, "D'you know that
I've drunk at least four pints." Turn to see the
four-pint woman bumping into acquaintances
in the dark street. A shop of cars parked in a
glass and metal building. Man with long crinkly
hair like wool, the head balding. Girls pass the
crinkle-haired man with faces marked out in
happiness. You turn to your right, see a dark
tower like a sitting dog and semi-dark dishes of
metal attached to its flank. A woman turns and
you see her face smile at something behind you
and her eyes as she walks enter shadow. Blue-
green aquarium-coloured light of a building you
pass. Hear shrill music bleating. A girl walks
with eyes fixed ahead unflinching like two
boulders on a hill. Dark eyes look straight onto
your eyes and turn and you pass. See a pale
froth on two paving slabs. Brisk-whiskered
wind brushing through the space of the street.
A skate of wind passing up-street. Hear the
growl of a bus saying the one long word of its

journey. A brown bottle lying on its side, an illuminated shadow of red-brown like a lozenge of dry liquid over the paving beside the bottle, like a blanket of dried blood under the body of a sleeping man's head. Read Happy. See a campervan passing and see inside the room of the van the faces of two. See a plastic cup, a crumpled can. A figure driving. See a freshly discarded apple core, green-fleshed, one crest of apple flesh oxidised yellowish brown like a sulphurous mountain. See a pink ticket lying on the ground. Cry of a siren and a moon of saliva lying on a stone. A sharp air moves like a scalpel through and like a comb through the hair of heads. Cars move together. Read VIOLATING MANY. Hear an echoing voice like a man in a cave crying aloud. Hear, "No, not that, I was thinking of you being." A blonde head passes. A man drags a red blanket up in his arms and throws it to hang over a railing and cries in the air a word like a crow. A man like a bear walks voices out of his mouth with two fingers twitching at his face. A woman drops two keys and turns fast and bends down like a tornado to retrieve them and twists up and hurries. A blonde woman walking fast in a direction South. Lights diffused into dark air like moon in a mist. Tooth upon tooth of sharply cold air as a shark of wind swims up the street. Cars in streams of car traffic. See chairs lined in a row. See red tail lights moving away.

A limousine reverses into a side street. See a
man watching the limousine reverse over tar
ground. See a man from Asia. See a plastic milk
crate in a doorway. A small dark house set
alone like a hen in a yard. See black plastic bags
outside a door, tightened at their openings to
small O-shaped throats. A repeating sound like
a 'peep'. A girl runs. See the shadow of a man
and look up to see eleven sets of tail lamps.
Hear a 'peep' sound repeating. A triangle of
shadow. A leaf shaking. Man on a bike. Pass
thin weeping branches of willow, like the tails
of greyhounds. Three traffic lights gleam red
and cars move from a sideroad into a main
road. See long canoe-shaped willow leaves. Read
SEAL. Letters in iron. Hear music travelling
fast in a car, nodding the heads of four in the
car. Glitter of light on a spangled ribbon and
see many colours on the eel of its movement.
Read NO STOPPING. Leaves are green gold
and a shadow walks up from behind and passes
through the shadows of green gold leaves.
Tooth by tooth the wind eats into the bone of
its air and the bony air moves across skin like a
cold front coming in as it falls down into the
mouth of the wind and you see the arm of a
woman goose-pimpled and the fine hairs of the
arm raised up like the masts of yachts. See
towers with lights like a row of smashed teeth.
See a woman looking out of her eyes and see
the eyes are black. Girl wiping her nose with

the cloth of her cuff, she walks with a swing at
the hips, ever so slightly. A man in yellow
passes on a bike with a squeak. Tooth-white
cliff of teeth appears in the dark face of a man
smiling. Mouth opens, mouth closes, and you
walk over gritty-faced slabs and see a car
stationary at a red traffic light. In letters of iron
read OPEN. Pass a ripped white envelope.
Yellow globes like planets flashing. A South
American face. See a man ahead with his face
lowered and wiping his mouth he sneers like a
dog lifting its lip to bare teeth. Clak-a-growl of
a diesel engine starting. See a man in a white
diesel van. Star in a tree. A scrag of plastic leaps
like a cat. Man on a step. Pass green metal
panthers tall as men. Pass a printed image of a
woman. Face of a girl. See a gaunt face wrapped
up in linen. Hear, "I told her, I said to her." A
grey beard. See the eyes of a crab on a plate.
Read Mornington Crescent Station. The moon
of a baby's face. A seated woman, a pink glass
between legs. See eyes that stare. A plastic lid
on the ground. Pass the narrow gap of an alley,
dark between buildings, is a slot, like a goat's
pupil. Read Storm at Be British. Pass three
men, a crazed pane of glass. Sheen of wet
pavement. Meat on a hot metal plate smoking
and the smoke is a grey. A nose trimmed by
shadow to a curled hook. Read HD 16369.
Small coloured lights ahead. A woman in
denim, jeans and jacket turns left and walks on

between buildings in a chasm of her own.
Rattle of a bus and you feel heat pass over your
face as it passes. Fur of an animal exhibited in a
shop's window. One piece of orange peel on the
pavement like a pithy coracle. See the flat palm
of a woman's hand pressing a glass door. A
whistle nearby. Squeak of a brake. Small beard
and eyes reflecting black light like moon behind
cloud. Count fifteen red lights and possibly
more. Hear, "Right, I'll tell." Ragged white hair.
Man sitting, polystyrene beaker in hands. A
smile sloping up to one side. Two doors open
and close by themselves. A woman passes
dressed in creased denim and her lips are curled
in a pinched look. Hear, "Not yet, not yet." See
a jeer of mouth flashed. Peach light in a top
floor window. Twitching walk of a figure in a
long coat with marks of grease smooth like
satin and a torn hem and see the figure leans to
one side. Green cap. Blue plastic bag. Eyes lean
over half-moon glasses. Beating drum music. A
man stops and see his mouth intimate words
into a small silver box held to his face. Hear,
"Hello there George." A man stoops and
coughs. See wet road disturbed by cars
crawling. A man shrugs his mouth and
shoulders and his head pivots side to side like a
weighing-scales balance. Plastic bag strewn with
tyre marks. Hear, "Excuse me, do you know if
there is a picture house somewhere down
there." Hear one slam of a door. Man gripping

a counter with two hands clamps a tin can between the chest of his body and the rim of the counter. A tree glitters with lights like boiled sweets. Dark glasses on a woman's face, her hair silver-grey and her mouth opens to speak. Hear, "Well, let's ask how she is." See a man holding chopsticks pause and the chopsticks rest above a small bowl. See a waiter nodding. See a woman, a man hugging who steps back and smiles flatly and hugs her again. Hear a gasping breath of tears, feel gasping damp and hot breath like a flush through skin as you pass, feel hot air from the mouth of the woman hugged and hugged again. Look up to many small stars like holes in a badger's corpse, stars twitching like the heads of maggots. Red and blue lights of a distant tower. Old face in a window. See a man's hand fishing the sack of his pocket, the man on a blue-seated bus. Read P531 CWL. Leaf like a skate's wing. Woman at a kerb's edge tilts to run forwards. Legs crossed in a basement room. See a red light flashing, on, off and on. Glint of pavement like a quartz crystal's wink. Pass an opened door, see a long darkly lit hallway. A finger in a nose. See a carton of milk lifted up to a mouth and the diamond hole of the carton's funnel placed to lips and tilted back to drink. Songbird hops close to a man at work eating. Man at a bar drains the foamy dregs of his glass and turns from the bar. One splash of water from a car's tyre passing. Old man coughs with one finger straight before his mouth and walks on with a wooden walking stick. Skin of running water over the road's asphalt. Legs of a woman walking uphill. Hear a song begin. A tired face. A face with a beard talking to a beard with a face. See eyes like boys' eyes for sweets and a mouth mutters words. A cloud moves over a star. An ambulance passes. Read London Ambulance. Letters in red. There are green lights. Black-framed glasses. A pair of blue eyes. Fake sheepskin over thighs of a woman. Lights like eyes. See a hand selecting buttons and pressing each one in turn. Woman leaning on a wooden stick. Legs running. Hear, "Take." See a boot pass over a boot, both boots of brown leather. Sweet smoke pouring into your eyes and throat and there is stinging. A narrow-eyed face with a near smile. A smell of diesel like boiled eggs. Hear, "Hello." Read Smile. Hands into pockets. Two figures kissing, smiling at the mouths and the kisses part and the mouths grow straight with a serious quiet. Heap of clothes hangers. A mannequin. Pass fragments of green glitter. Read TASTY CO. A painted crocodile. Fraction of a second stare and eyes turn. A woman crosses the road with no name. On a ticket read 10. Hear, "On time and we don't even want." A woman with dark skin speaking. A shadow moves in a direction Southwest. Double beat of a bass drum.

Wrinkles of ribbed, beating water. See red and
clear lights. There is a smell of sandalwood
burning, hot-sweet and oily and a red smell.
Clunk-clunk and the rumble of a train passing
over a bridge of wide metal girders. Two notes
of a siren. Three women walking ahead. Pink
unsteady face of a man. Stagger of a man's
shadow. A mirror mirrors a man. See a wooden
dragon. Car-filled road. Arms together. Seated
woman on a passing bus. A seated man swung
back at the head as the whole bus jolts. Four
figures sit down. Read HARTLAND. A car
moves off. Cheeks ruddy with heat and you
smell alcohol. Blonde hair is long. Pin-heels
stab paving like crowbeaks as two women walk.
Hear, "Make some money." Stars and candles.
Read Africa Waist Curtain Wool Hat. Read
The Monarch. Pass one flat crisp packet and it
is blue with creased rivers of reflected shine.
Read est 1974. Hear, "You know what yeah, I
got the tickets." Look up to a white plane. See
the faces of two men at a window. Hear, "O
man." Read PAY HERE. Letters of yellow.
Read CAUTION SITE ENTRANCE. Pass a
man smoking a white cigarette. Dark voices like
shadows. Read SERIOUS ASSAULT. See
brake lights light up within plastic caverns. See
clear drinks carried. Blue light afloat on water.
Read VANILLA COCONUT. Glossy tiles like
square teeth and then like the eyes of sheep.
Read MINICAB. Hear, "Everybody, no matter

[122]

who it was." Slight quail-cry of a man calling and walking fast. Read TO LET. Leaves tightrope walking on a rope of air fall one by one to the road. Four walking figures. Read NW1. Hear, "That's what people I spoke to said." Excrement of a dog. A suitcase-carrying man. See a railway track gleaming under streetlight. Read GABRIEL. Dark red lettering. Hear the 'der-dring' of a bike's bell rung. Rustle of a white plastic bag. Slam of a door. Hear, "And it was now six o'clock and I'd been working since five." See triangles peppered with white lights. Hear, "Of today but." Stain of vomit over paving. Hear church bells. Hear voice echoings. See quiet lights ahead. Read Manna. There is a pattern of footsteps walking in time and it breaks and breaks apart to a scatter like brown rabbits fast across hillside. Hear voices in rooms, you pass windows. A broad-backed laugh like the cry of a beast bearing a great weight uphill. Rollicking laugh of a woman rolling and kicking her laugh. Broken joy of a laugh like a piece of crockery dropped to the ground. Pass two women. Pass a cat. Pass a man with sideburns like the wool of sheep. Read PRIMROSE DENTAL. Read PEAS. Headlamps ahead. Read Telephone. See taxis pull up and stop, each with a squeal and sharp end to the squeal like a ruler snapped. And two doors slam. And taxis exit together. Carlight swings across leaves like light across

dunes at sundown and the road is like sea at
night also. A figure walking ahead, uphill. The
hill climbs. And you see stars pinched into
small cold places like pins of death. One figure
stands ahead and breaks apart into two figures
that walk in directions away from each other.
And two figures jump once together in half-
darkness. Leaves silver-backed as sardines,
serrated as swordfish. See a glob of foamy saliva
full of little eyes like frogspawn. Figures turn
and walk away, downhill. See dragons of breath
rise and the dragons breathe grey-white fires of
breath into the scantily starred sky. Hear,
"That's so exciting ... I thought of flying over
for two nights." A voice pours from its blonde
head. And you turn to see two jets moving
through the night sky and a small dome below
you beyond many buildings merged in the city
of their group and only lit windows visible
among many. Dark patch of space. Crane-arm.
Turn to see a crow's nest. Shadow of twigs like
stitches. Shadow of a stone. Wicker crowns of
trees. And watery roar of far-away traffic below.
A taxi drones motoring uphill. A siren making
an arc of sound below, and it passes. See tail
lights beyond trees and railings and you turn
and walk over black tar paving to where earth is
scraped open without tar or grass. Streetlight
hooks two eyes out of a dark head passing
nearby, and eyes glint once with orange and are
put back into the head's shadow. Walk and feel

grass underfoot and there is a triangle of black with towers rising behind and one flashing light on a dull orange-grey pyramid set on a tower marginally above neighbouring towers. See a figure walking alone. One star above blood-black earthline. Two figures walking up through low trees without leaves and there is a groggy dampness to the sunless air. Read and the views. Hear, "Go nice." See a man on a boat emerging from a bridge over dark water, and the man quietly holding the boat's rudder ahead. Music from the direction of the man. See big leaves in the window of a lit room. See fire in a grate. Car. Car. Doorbell button lit from behind like an eclipsed sun. One slam of a door. Five black bags in a row. Car. Variegated leaves, glossy, are like certain fish. Purr of a bus passing yellow bollards. See Persian rugs. Read TOW AWAY ZONE. Read LOOK RIGHT. Choked bark of a buckled diesel van. Car. Car. Car. Glug of an exhaust. Read CONTROLLED ZONE. Read R837 KJT. Read G858 UPN. See fur worn on a head and hair on a hand. Hear, "He was so unprepared, it was wonderful." An accent on the 'o' of 'wonderful'. See a man and woman at a window containing details of flats and houses to buy. Read SPREADEAGLE. A man dragging plastic sheeting and running. See a bicycle parked. Hear the clack of a door. See a dribbled liquid on paving. See a leaking black binliner, full and knotted shut squatting on pavement. Turn to see tarmac wet with running water on the far side of the road. Read SANDWICHES & TEA PARISH CENTRE. Read EUSTON ROAD. Letters in circular iron plate. See car doors and the air passes gaunt with cold. A car starts and hisses to a purr. Pass black railings and flowers of iron set within the railings at intervals. See a bed in a basement room. Read GIVE WAY. A man with a snooker cue under his right arm, walking, looks into a bag he carries and there is a sparkle once. Pass men kissing in a room. Over the window of the room in blue letters read TAVERNA. Hear, "God some of the blokes can't hold the beer ... and language I can't understand." Car. Hear the steps of a woman. Crying horn of a siren. And hear, "I've never seen you smile so much."

Read Dog Nuisance. See a section of rotted wood about five inches long. See cracks at one end of the wood like a cliff of shale and there is a paler uncovering of softer fibres like roots in a landslide. Read WATER 16 VALVE. See one bough of a sycamore. Hear, "No, no, no, no." Repetition of a voice like the croon of pigeons. Eyes under the colourpools of blue sunglasses. One scrape of sandpaper. See pages scattered across a pine table and the grain of the varnished table like bands of colour on a

spinning top. Paper cup raised to a mouth.
Three seeds connected falling as one. Square
shoulders of a man, boulder of a man and you
turn to see a child's drawing of something, and
a cigarette in a woman's mouth glows a bit and
a woman leaves a shop by a door and walks in
flip-flops holding a plastic bottle and a small
box. Pass ivy over bricks and two women walk
towards you. See broad holes among leaves. See
bright sycamore keys. Hear, "But you know."
See a tall-capped toadstool, pale brown and
quiet among the roots of a tree. See a diamond
pattern of tree bark cracked and hear voices
and the wind drives a hustle obliterating the
shape of voices into a dimness like men seen
through a blizzard. Cut trees with forms like
tortured bodies, branches like the feelers of
snails half-retracted. A leaf scrapes over road's
tar, high brittle noise of a leaf and you pass.
Black plastic fork discarded. Leaves shake like a
rattle. Round lip of a smashed milk bottle
fragment, the neck, like a ring, like a throat.
One cadmium red flower and a blackbird runs
crouching low, strutting two feet, stamping to
hop and comes to a halt. Read Resident Permit
Holders Only. Sharp long-note, watery cry of a
bird and you turn. Walk the scent of a flower
and walk from the scent of the flower. Read 44.
Look up to cracked rendering, dark sooty-black
brick of a building. Shrub sprouted from
guttering. Form of a star in cast iron. Noise of a

train in a gully, the resound emanating like a
roar upwards. Leaf runs like a blackbird, falls,
scrapes like a child's knee over pavement and
its sound is a graze. Turn to an open space
between buildings and wind comes out of it and
you turn to see a mouth chewing behind lips
and the lips are pink with a sheen. Cast eyes on
black brick and turn again to walk seeing two
figures behind a window adjusted by the
motion of your walk so they move within the
frame of the window and you see the crowns of
their heads and then don't. Read TRADE
WASTE. See tables and chairs set together,
empty. Read ZOO. Crushed packet of wet
cigarettes, cigarettes like a bunch of sinews.
Hear, "Doesn't seem to be the right move."
Read ideas above our station. See a green fly
with spotted wings. See flowers you cannot
name and the lime green interior of a room and
turn right to see clipped trees standing before
terraced three-storey houses. A lady in black.
Black car alone, parked and quiet. Green grass
and elderflowers half-flowering. Three feathers
of a pigeon laid over each other. Red flowers
exude a heavy odour almost human, like sweat,
and see small white centres to each of them.
Black trunk of a chestnut, twisted like a giant
rope. Bike drives to a halt. A biker dismounts
and removes his helmet. Hair rough as a
donkey's. Crushed can. Read OKE. Metal can
spiked onto railings. Read Pepsi. Five cars pass.

[128]

Three-leafed clover plant. See ribbed plantain leaves and small red transparent leaves laid over each other as chainmail, as the scales of a fish. A woman cycling, large leaves tied into a plastic bag in a wicker basket attached to the bike. Cracked segment of tree bark. Read 10. Read 11. Serrated edges of leaves and you turn to see a clump like a fist of polystyrene and a flushed woman pushing a child-bearing pram and the child you see is a sleeping baby and you hear the cries of birds high-pitched, but soft, very soft cries and you pass hearing more general cries of traffic pass in other places. One leaf falls to pavement which is an undulating tar strip and grasses breaking through like triumphs and you pass the face of a man with stubble like a field harvested and scorched to a bald soapy greyness. Read JASON'S TRIP. A large woman steps and turns away and leans against a wall looking over into the tangled garden of a church. Turn to see rusticated grey stone walls of the church and dark windows black like the black of dilated eyes. Furrow of a man's brow and a clatter of chains on the bed of a passing lorry and you pass over water and see a fragmented dish of reflected sun and it breaks and gathers and breaks like a breathing thing of parts, like a flotsam of mercury but piercingly bright. Hear, "You don't tell people that you are trying to hide it." Scrape of a foot. See a man and thin dog walking through long

water with wet steps, the dog delicately. Seeds
floating over water like meniscal dust. Car
passes. Small leaves and a bird flies. Turquoise
T-shirt embodies the chest of a man running
and you hear the pants of hard breath and a
wheeze once like a cough dividing a breath in
two like an axe splitting wood. Cry of a bird
and you look up to the sun though oak leaves.
Dark broad leaves also. Read CARAVAN
PARK & MARINA ELECTRICAL
SPECIALISTS. Three women crouched. Hear,
"Shall I phone them and tell them we are on
our way back." Read WARNING. See four
eyes turn towards your own and pass by and
walk on. Read GREEN GLASS ONLY. Family
of four figures ahead and the high voice of a
boy. Hear, "You get used to saying it, and then
you find you're on the floor ... how many guns
there are on sight ... few of them who might be
carrying guns." Hear, "You're embarrassing."
Hear, "Two extra large children." Woman on a
phone. A small booth containing a man. Read
TICKETS. Pass and descend to a tunnel of
concrete the colour of camels and the quietness
is cold, like going in from the sun. Air through
leaves and hissing and sirens of small birds
make a meshed chatter among leaves and you
read Hoofed Mammal. See a blonde girl in a
woman's arms. Hear, "With shoots of leaves ...
to rely on its good sense of smell." Read Danger
Deep Water. Hear a language you do not know.

See a long-snouted creature with white tips to
the ears, the bulk of its body grey-white. Hear,
"Reading, I didn't get the whole head." Hear,
"No, I said that would be someone else." A
man's yellow mouth. A man's yellow teeth. A
man's cigar hanging from lips, sticking to the
lower lip as the mouth talks. Hear, "It's quite
lovely ... in Spanish or Portuguese it's ... in just
that one language, settled by reasonably
educated people." See thin horizontal nostrils
and a small black eye like a button moves. See
muscular teeth like rock chisels and the ridge of
a nose humped and ears rounded upright, tilted
back with white tips like small upturned
crescent moons, softly. Turn to see bramble
thorns, red, and read Staff Only. Three birds
flying. See a woman with a long-lens, a camera
at her eye, her face hidden behind. Hear water
hitting a surface. Man and woman eating nuts
from a packet. See a tall-necked creature, the
body coated in cracked-apart platelets of tan,
with centres of caramel colour. The body of a
duck passes, violet rhomboid of plumage and
see the paddle of orange webbed feet
submerged, the grey tongue of the tail. Grey
mouth of a tall-necked creature and see a tail
like a whip descending and breaking into a
tassel of coarse black hair like a charm or
talisman, a nose up to a steel cage containing
two green melons. See a creature in the
shadows of an interior with a long dark face

[131]

like a donkey's and see horizontal stripes across the legs. Ten pigeons among grasses and see the speckled feathers of a duck. Read Okapi. Read first described and named at a meeting of the Zoological Society of London in 1901. Crackle of leaves like fire as a creature walks. See roots of ripped-up trees out of red earth like a Medusa and turn away to see a black-horned red-brown creature, and a whole group of similar creatures like a herd bearing thin vertical stripes over their bodies and walking on black hooves. Read also reported to eat burnt wood after lightning storms. See the mouth of a calf at a teat, the calf drinking. See long bristled noses lowered looking forwards with eyes, front legs pushed out. See a creature lie itself down. See backs spined with bristles. Leaves clatter and you look up to grey sky. A woman in a red top smiles. Cry of a bird. Blue flowers you pass. Read are part of the co-operative breeding programme. A yellow leaf. Hear the word 'mummy' cried. A man and dog seated on a black bench, the pink tongue of the dog visible. See two children standing in a puddle and the foot of one child stamping a splash up out of the water. See a white, sharply-tusked creature at great length chewing a brown stick, the tusks curved like rounded sabres. Hear, "I have asked you not to get too wet because I have no spare clothes for you ... come on now, you're getting soaked." See a woman from above, her left hand on her right breast. See back legs of a white creature touching at the bony knees. White hooves with black spats. Short white hair, directional, like iron filings near a magnet, hair like a goat's. Withered husk of a chestnut. Black speckle under moon-pale hairs of a creature. Hear the swish of a tail flicked. See grey lips and black beads of excrement scattered. Read Bearded. Read stay with their mother for up to a year. On your right, read Baby Nappy Changer Unit. See the green speckled dark back of a starling. See four creatures of bristle, long heads with rough bristles spraying out. And one lies down. See the flat flange of a pink nose, mouth opened clamps the tail of another and it chews. Eyes of the reclined creature close. Bristly cheek scrapes across the back and flank of another. See the long nose of each creature projecting far beyond the small eyes of the head. Mute growl of an opened mouth. Black hooves, a creature trots and furrows up earth with its nose like the blade of a plough and grunts into the ground below. See tusked teeth and the diamonds of the ears back flat against the neck and one creature whips round bearing a long twig clamped in its mouth and another lies down like giving up and another examines by snuffles the body of the lying-down creature. Hear many birds chatter and you turn to read Red River. Read Order: Even-toed Ungulates.

Triangular head with broad and pointed ears,
black triangle of dark hair, black-snouted and a
white spine. The creature shakes. See tusks.
Turn to see the pink legs of a pregnant woman.
Read Small Mammals and Moonlight. Read
Meerkat. Read help each other. See the tongue
of a bee enter the trumpet of a white flower.
See a long small creature and two more appear
with black eyes and long fingers and one gets
up on its hind legs. See a thin stripe of black
hair under a belly and black lips seem to smile
and several creatures at once crawl into a tangle
of plants and you see only parts of faces
containing the eyes. Read Shh. Room
containing small monkeys among trees. See fast
movements, quivering. Read Goeldi. In a red
light see small black monkeys crouched like
men on the smooth branches of a dead tree. A
leap and landing and you hear a muffled noise
like a cushion hit. Black hand on a black head.
Read Golden Lion Tamarin. Read Threatened
Species. Read and older offspring help by
carrying the babies on their backs. Cry of a
child like an owl's hoot and it makes a shiver
out of echoes murmuring mmmm's around like
a whisper. In red light. Soft grey face. Hear the
thump and heavy drone of a single bee against
glass. Glossy black eye of a long-nosed creature.
Read Two-toed. Read almost their entire lives
upside. See a creature of fur but no face. Beard
and long wisp of a moustache like a thin cloud

across the moon. Pink nose trembling bisected
by a vertical groove between the nostrils. Ears.
See ropes and rats and wood ship-lapped.
Ringed tails like slowworms. Black bulge of a
glossy eye. Nose within the smashed body of a
hen's egg. Claws the white colour of roots. Feet
balled into fists rubbing two cheeks. Read
Striped Grass Mouse. A white-faced monkey
with long hair and long-fingered, shaking. Black
fingernails and tail. Hair of a face yellowed
around the protrusion of the black mouth. And
its two hands onto each side of its face. Turn to
see the body of a rat. Figure of a woman
reflected before the rat like a shadow lying
across the air and turn to see a man with a
cigar. Read Beware Pickpockets. And enter a
dark space. Read HUNTED FOR FOOD.
Creature in the shadow of a tree. Read Giant
Jumping. Read Rat. Ears with light like the sails
of a boat. A leap and a run and eyes turn into
dark. Read Short-eared Elephant Shrew. Read
This enclosure is being refurbished. See two
creatures together and hanging from one limb
by a small hand curled over the peg of a branch.
Clack of a camera's lens-cap dropped. One
creature unfurls from another and climbs like a
viscous motion through trees very slowly. Read
The slightest sound or movement causes. See
two figures walk from darkness and walk
connected by the hand. Click of a footstep and
faintly, an echo. Turn to a thick-limbed

creature, silverish with a dark stripe, scratching, eyes red. And bats with elbow claws hooking the entire bat up through trees and bats with wings and claws and feet moving by a multitude of directions at once. Curved head of a mouse and mice crawling mice. Ear of one mouse broken. Tail of a mouse up like a mast and the base of the tail sniffed by the nose of another. Read Spiny. Read prickly to eat. Read Harvest. Read Jersey Bank. Read Voles, like many rodents, don't live for very. Long proboscis of a creature, hair rutted with grooves as if combed. A whole creature suddenly runs. And you turn and walk through dark doors into daylight and see flies. Water green with copper-headed ducks. Space of red light in a dark space. Read DO NOT CROSS. Frond of a fir. A blackbird flies. Cream flowers in tight, hexagonal groups on a bush. Read PRIVATE NO ENTRY. Enter a tunnel, grey in cold air as you walk and a stripe of gloss green paint. Birds scattering out. Man with a map, head in a position concentrated, the map held in both hands. Read Health Notice. Hear "May we have your attention." Fox-red creatures with black faces and you pass seeing yellow eyes in fox heads. A head turns, fixed on your passing. And see a soft-haired, long-haired gibbonish creature and see in the hand of the gibbon remnants of red pepper. Read Dangerous Animals. Bronze girl holding a bird of bronze. A human ticking noise. See a lean-bodied tiger. Read ribs are carried as a good luck talisman. Read is eaten to protect. Hear, "That is weird, she loves." White whiskers of a pacing cat. Mouth ajar, shuttered breathings of tiger face to tiger face. One of two striped tigers leaps. Hear, "This is a bird and he is called." Thick-haired ruff of a tiger's neck. Pink tongue of a tiger's lick. Lips and legs standing very still. Pink V of a tiger's nose, gold-green eyes like a polished stone and ears curved. See a pinhead of water on the edge of one nostril. See long bills of birds and a feather nibbled of its point. One dusty pink cheek behind a beak. Pointed-eared cat in a quiet position, eyes half-closing, opened and closed. Hear the bark of a dog like a rough cry of tyres in a road accident. See a squirrel run and there is a thin spotted tail attached to a spotted cat. Man in a white T-shirt with the index finger of his left hand in the room of a nostril, turning slowly. A lump of sweating carcass. Orange testes of a lying cat, between pale buttocks. See a lion sitting. Lion pacing. Read This is the lion of the Bible and of the Roman arenas where. Two women turn and walk. Read THE LIONS HOUSE cut in soft stone and perishing. See concrete steps. Sky is a grey. Cluck of a bird. White eye in its frame of black lids. Black bead of an eye. Read PENGUIN. And hear, "If you like." Hear the croon of a bird and turn to see roses unopened. Fronds about the length of two men from a tree to the green flatness of grass and a woman smiling and leaning against the body of a man and sunlight in sections in parts of a tree's crown and a man with a broom without a handle. Turn left to see beyond railings a man head down hands in front urinating against a tree and turn right to see a large red-eyed owl the size of a spaniel and the head of the owl swivels to face your eyes and its black ears curl with the wind, and turn left to see a woman's hands ruffling rough the hair of the man urinating. See white birds flocking and unflocking and a squirrel runs beneath a shrub and you pass into a place with rockfaces together about the size of three small houses. Hear, "Sometimes displays a strange rocking behaviour." Hear, "You'll feel better, you will." And you hear one bright gentle noise like a kiss. Hear, "The zoo is now closing." Pale seed floating. A black door opened. Read PRIVATE. Cabbage leaves strewn over a wooden board. See four faces looking to a grey sky flat as their faces. Pink bottom of a black chimpanzee and see streaks and dots of pink within the cream petals of a rose and the chimpanzee stands hunched in a green room on a shelf with one finger curled scratching an ear. And you pass beyond a green wall and see into the next box of another room, a gorilla sitting with its mouth open quietly and its nostrils a shiny black, belly slumped onto the legs and the room green and the creature sits on a shelf with arms by its sides. See the hands of the gorilla and it walks with its face to one side and you hear, "It's scared," from the mouth of a small boy and hear, "Bye-bye gorilla." Girl in grey clothes strides and a pale bird flies and a crumb of food falls from the mouth of a monkey. Hear the small sound of a monkey moving and see two pink nipples in the black hair of a monkey's chest. Hear a soft squeak from the throat of a monkey and the squeak-making monkey scratches the coppery reds of its back and the hairs glint freckled and the mouth is like a cut in a cloth. See a stream of urine fall from a monkey and one bead of urine hangs like a star glinting from a hair. Cry of a gull. A grey-haired gorilla eating alone with celery sticks in the hands, see celery fed into the mouth of the creature by hands pushing and the teeth chewing like the hydraulic jaw of a bin-cart's mouth. Black mouth, black ears, red eyes and the long pupil of the gorilla and the gorilla turns like the shrug of a sulk and you pass to see copper-haired creatures with faces and the curled ironwork of a fence and a woman locking a shutter and brown leaves with blisters and each leaf moving on its stem like a hand on a wrist. Hear, "Don't wear any tight clothing." A woman and child eating crisps and a long puddle ahead reflecting a colour like the sky. And you see a broad road with two cars moving along its length and hear footsteps and a creak. Leaves blown. See the letter G embossed into the surface of yellow plastic. A passing bike and the pitch of an engine rising and falling. One crow flies to a roofline. Clouds the colour of tin and see dock leaves crinkled like lizards and see the speckled gloss of laurel leaves like glass. Turn to a white beard. Two men together carrying a long bag. Man jogging. Hear, "I'm not being funny." Sound of footsteps fading and you turn to the belly of a man shaking under the cloth of a blue shirt and the man walks over grass blades among cherry trees at the end of their blossom. Light in the sky like a bruise. Trees rise in blackened green clumps and a far tower stands like a box of dark green and a mob of aerials like a tribe with spears on its roof. Two figures lean, their dark clothes moving like sheets in the wind. Hear the dry noise of leaves together and a sinewy streak of sun breaks low to the horizon and the sky is dark like a slate and a single drop of rain falls onto the upper part of your left cheek. A white ball bounces and the wind grows into a crammed air like a scrum of men and runs apart. See men standing on green grass, right, and a group of figures, left, walking and you pass between. Leaf curled on the grey path rocked by wind and a copper-gold dome is among trees like a planetarium, like a sunset, like a mosque. Man running after a white round

ball and you hear shouted, "The ball you cunt."
And a tickle of laughter among ball-kicking
men. Hear, "You mo." Turn to see a black spire
like a spine piercing to the sky. Hear the crying
of a small boy and, softly, his mother saying,
"Shh." Turn right to see a black crescent moon
of metal. Hear the creak of a woman's shoes.
Hear, "Come on, that's barely moving." Thump
of a ball and you turn left to see a couple
walking and a man with a black beard still as a
bronze but he moves on and a voice grows
larger as you walk. Hear many cars far like the
view of a din. Red shawl over a woman's
clothed body. Green bottle in the hand of a
woman. Hear, "Pretty early on." A red ball
kicked between a triangle of three men. Hear,
"I'm getting there, I don't know what I." Black
body of a crow beak-stabbing the earth, plucks
and swallows. Globe of dandelion seeds. And
you kneel to see the quivering pale stars of
seeds, parasol wings flexed out from pin-points,
each attached on a whitish stem to a brown
urchin-shaped hub, the major stem below of a
fleshy green with colours red descending from
its crown towards the earth, and from there
green descending down among grasses and you
rise to stand and walk on seeing one man in
green tweeds and hear the hob-nailed clock of
his bootsteps, grey hair brushed to the left and
the cuffs of the shirt pink. Look up and you
feel drops of rain like temperature without

[141]

weight on your skin. Blackbird's wings opened
and you see ribs of feathers, its yellow beak stab
ground and drag up a red worm and swallow the
whole twist of the worm. Turn to a man like a
blackbird walking with a lean-forwards to his
body and head craned forwards further in a
hurry. See a fountain of water beyond the man
and smell rain on the dry earth. See a coot dive
and the tail flip up and the surface of the water
close like a mouth around the tail of the coot
and the mouth swallow itself to a ring of ripples
and you walk. Copper-headed duck lands. A
passing cyclist and you turn to see two boys
wearing blue hoods over their heads and there
is a shake through the footbridge as they walk
across. And the blue-hooded boys lean halfway
on the rail of the bridge and smoke cigarettes.
Duck mounting duck. Long grass beyond mown
grass and the length of it like a wall. Balustrade
of a painted cream building. Clang of a metal
bell. Two clangs of a bell. Blast of exhaust and
an engine drones in a warble. Figure in a long,
pale coat, a small pale dog running behind.
Note of a pigeon's song in rain. Four women
walk as a group. Hear, "She's going to eat with
us." Hear reply, "Yes?" Hear another, "O, I
didn't realise that." Man and woman sprawled
across the back seat of a car, man mounted on
woman, like a creature with four arms. See an
umbrella unfolded. A voice changing its subject
says, "It goes in my handbag." Hear repeating,

"It goes in my handbag." Hear, "When we went
to Guildford one day." Hear, "Yes, very heavy."
Clang of a bell. Hear, "I like the automatic ones
you can press a button." Hear reply, "I nearly
had somebody's eye." Hear, "At least we got to
the end of rehearsal." Hear another, "You
recognised him." And you pass the four women.
Figures under a cowling in from the rain and
you walk seeing the sky's dark over the folded
and unfolded forms of pink roses like old men
and women. Old man leaning forwards with a
stick, hear the tap of the stick once only. A
pigeon flies up and you read INNER CIRCLE.
Quarter-crescent area of buttercup flowers like
a haze. Cigarette at a mouth sucked to a bright
eye. Read COURT 2. Clip of shoes. Man
reading in a car alone. Read R31 X00. Leaves of
a tree broad and dark and downward pointing,
spires of yellow flowers rising. Girl in a pink
top. Figures leaping and running low and
leaping to the side. See figures playing tennis
and the rain falls. A girl and boy in a car's rear
seat and the car doors and windows are closed.
Read THE IRONWORKS. Leaves vined over
black iron. Livid green of light with a pure,
watery red in the green reflected from windows,
tall building against dull, violet-blue in the grey
sky. Small and pale bird flits up with only the
dim noise of a flutter and drops down and lifts
up again. Two dark women and a small child
and gold paint over wrought ironwork. Hoarse

cry of a small bird and a yellow stain to the grey
of the sky as you look up to a brightness and
turn to see four chimney pots. The wooden
door of a small house closed. House among
trees. Bank of nettles, serrations of leaf-edge
and alive-green deep creases of the leaves' veins
and the ash-coloured bristles of the nettles.
Raindrops fallen cling to leaves. See the
thorned serrations of thistle leaves and stars of
cow parsley and no petals, see green cases like
the bodies of grasshoppers with pale lids and
each with two prongs like a set of horns. Five-
petalled white flowers trembling with small red
anthers. Red curled and shrivelled leaves. See
holes among coppery leaves. Sharp raw
dustiness of straw as a scent. Smell bedding of
animals and animal excrement. See pale backs
of leaves lifted up like skirts in the wind. Two
white lights on a car reversing. Swing and see
raindrops on the curved body of a silver car.
And a small boy is whispering yells, kicking a
bramble stem. Legs of a woman in blue shorts
jogging. Fine-haired haze of grasses falling over
with seeds and water drops. Leaves of
dandelions and daisies. Reflection from the
glosspaint of a green bench. Colour of sky
intimated within the green of the bench by
reflection. Throaty call of a duck. Fluff of seeds
afloat and hear, "Yeah, bits of." Water black
with late light and at the shallow edges of water
see a yellow lurking within the black like a

submerged bloom. Shaking tail of a copper-red
duck. Crinkled and dark leaves of beech.
Cracked bark of a tree like a giant bituminous
rope. Diamond lattice of willow bark. Powdery
white line across mown grass which turns an
abrupt right angle to your left and you step over
the line and walk. Shimmer of railings and a
clump of grey feathers in a heap. Sharp cry of a
bird like a pain among trees. Flat echo of the
same cry from the direction of water. Pale seed
sinking through air to earth. See a figure
standing, arms folded. A clot of small black flies
overhead like smoke, and each fly winding
through the mass of the cloud. A cloud of small
flies like a trouble. See a band of cigarette
smoke curl a grey disembodied vein like a dry
vapour. Hear, "Be on the basis that you need to
stay on the." A red hood pulled back from a
head to give dull golden hair to a hand. Thump
of a kicked ball. Figures in white costumes,
arms folded behind backs, see arms at sides.
Blood-red stain of a daisy petal. Hiss of a metal
can opened with escaping gas. Hear words in a
language. The two ears of a black dog
backwards with running, rolls over and looks up
and leaps up on all fours and runs in a wide arc
like a joy. Conference of low blackbirds
strutting in glides across grassland. See the cast-
iron arm and legs of a bench, its side profile
like the shape of a chicken running. A
monument. White, tall, capped with a pyramid-

like structure and like a small steeple, ahead and there is the sharp 'creel' sound of rubber dragging on tarmac. See the worn-smooth head of a stone cow in relief, the face obliterated and on the adjoining face of the stone the body of a lion with the head obliterated, and the stone milky, and on the third face of the stone you see many words and you read THIS FOUNTAIN ERECTED. Hear, "I don't think we're that bad, no." Click of a bicycle mechanism. And you read BY THE METROPOLITAN DRINKING FOUNTAIN AND CATTLE TROUGH ASSOCIATION WAS THE GIFT OF SIR COWASJEE JEHANGIR (COMPANION OF THE STAR OF INDIA) A WEALTHY PARSEE GENTLEMAN OF BOMBAY AS A. Woman passing on wheels. Darkening of the sky. Read TOKEN OF GRATITUDE TO THE PEOPLE OF ENGLAND FOR THE PROTECTION ENJOYED BY HIM AND HIS PARSEE FELLOW COUNTRYMEN UNDER THE BRITISH RULE IN INDIA. And rain falls and you hear, "Came off him." Heavy rain and dark sky. See leaves pounded and pounced on by falling rain. And small water drops leap up and down on the tar like cats pouncing. Dark chestnut flowers in conical towers among the crowns of dark trees. Thrumming of a helicopter overhead almost dark. And figures walk between dark trees and stand out of rain in the very dark shade and you look to see crows standing about in rain, clockwork on the rained grass strutting. And the shade under trees darkens. See a brown dog turn from the sound of traffic and you pass a wet, white paper bag punctured. Two women sitting on swings in the rain. Hear, "I would have turned round and shut the door." Walk on. Hear. "I'll break both your necks." Hear, "Stay doggy, stay." A tree full of the shadows of itself. See the image of a red man made of red light within a black circle. A cherry-red car and a girl of bronze with her hand held to her eye looking far. Read SAINT PANCRAS. Read MATHILDA. See T-shapes of iron like the heads and ears of lambs. See a bronze triangle of leaves and flowers. Read T435 RCE. A silver car. A woman's face in the upper-deck window of a passing bus and you see her eating the last triangle corner of a sandwich. Man in a sarong and cracked leather sandals. Flash of a light in the dark grey and you read Progressive. See many lights of cars in two streams of traffic moving fast in a westerly direction. Hear, "Er, well, you know." Hear, "I'll give you a shout." A big rumble. See a boy and see a cigarette packet in the hand of a running woman. And a car's horn cries twice. See two girls walking as a couple, arm in arm with a smile under their eyes from face to face. See yellow wires leading to silver discs at the ears of a passing man. One choke of a car's horn. See a woman's legs split like a clothes peg over the nipped-together legs of a sitting man dark on the bench of a bus shelter. See wet pavement ahead like a sheen and you look down into the well of a basement and see a window without lights. And the rain falls against your cheek like a change of temperature at pin point.

Wail of a siren dies. See a man feeding a table top into the crunching jaws of a dustbin lorry. And a long mirror and a wooden wardrobe. Hear revvings of an engine and see a blue and white plastic bag bloated with air, banging the roots of a tree. Scrape of a man's foot. Reflection of sky on the glossy page of a magazine. Cast iron lamp post ornamented like the trunk of a palm tree. Tense surface of a dark puddle disturbed to a scowl of reflections. A window. Arrowheads of railings. Static crackling of a pigeon grappling a thin and brittle sheet of plastic. Hear, "My birthday, I'm sixty-five in three months." Hear reply, "Three months." Hear, "You alright." Man speaks to a man under blankets. See stars. And you hear, "It is cold." And you pass seeing a man in a room, sitting alone, his head in his hands. See vomit, dried on a kerbstone. Man at a window talking. Shadow of a walking man. See the unlit room of a cafe. Man scratching his stubble. A

IX

man's face with blood on its nose and lines
rooting the smooths of its cheeks, eyes rough as
quarries, hair like a tuft of wire wool. Face like
a thistle. Hear, "It's a sad business, you know."
Hear, "I've got rules in my head as well and I'm
not taking." Hear, "I know it's out of order
about how thing's done." Hear, "If that's his
natural dad." Hear, "Couldn't get any for you
mate, he's not in." Leaves drag across the road,
scrape. Hear, "I sees you all tomorrow, yeah."
Read If this is what's happening outside, what's
going on inside. Turn to the moon, like a bright
goat's bladder in a sky black as a burnt
grassland. Hear, "I eat my ass off man, I tell
you Lee." Hear, "When I imported the twenty
foot container in I had to type up every single
item." Two girls, voices, no words. Amber
flashing. Read All Worthy Bros. Money
advanced on pictures, bronzes, violins, safes and
fireproof room. Hear, "I did three men in three
days." Hear, "I was just thinking about you, do
everything, and ever as normal." Smell the
sourness of air by a road. Reflection of tree
within a puddle. Hear the cough of a man like a
goat's bleat in mist. Read ROOM WANTED.
Read PRIZE ALES. Black nailheads over a
black door. Woman leaning from a window.
Pinnacle of a dark fir. House without curtains
and see through the body of the house by its
windows to a scene of trees. Read WORKING
MEN'S COLLEGE. Lettering gold. Yellow

tractor. Read PLEASE PRESS BUTTON.
Read A MEAL IN 2 mins. Flat brown paper
bag. Leaves hanging in darker and lighter
shadow making an effect of light like the x-ray
of a man's ribs. See scratched edges of leaves
with brown scores where the flesh of the leaf
has died. Read DENTAL SURGERY. Clipped
scrape of a woman's walk by the sound of the
shoe. Hiss of bristles dragged over the face of
paving. Scour of a man sweeping. Motion of
sunlight into a downward slant of the throw of
light-beams and you look up to grey clouds and
see the passing of clouds in a Southwest
direction. Rolled-up newspaper in the curl of a
clenched hand. Four pigeons standing along the
rim of a long trough. Spasm of trees and you
turn to see the heads of flowering tulips and the
whole body of tulips moving like the flank of a
lying-down creature breathing. Bench without
people. Read LITTER. Man walking towards
you in an orange jacket, who yawns once with
his mouth wide which shuts as you pass, see
black spaces between teeth. A leaf dives to the
ground from the body of a tree. Woman
pushing a red trolley and a man pulling a black
suitcase. Rose window of a church like a steel
rotary saw. Clock face without numerals. Read
NO BALL GAMES. Strand of a white hair.
Read BAR ICAN METAL CO LTD 01 389
8477. Read J B POTTERY SPECIALIST.
Read TAILOR LADIES & GENTS SUITS.

Letters on a brown door. Read ROCKING
HORSES £49.95. Huge form of a naked
woman, flesh painted pink leaning out part of a
wall. Read CRASH REPAIRS. Read SIAN +
MICHAEL LOVE. Letters scrawled over the
dust and brick of a wall. Apple core on paving,
flesh of the apple brown on ridges, core on the
shore of a black puddle like a mangled beached
object, like a whale decayed on its side, skinned
and bitten. Turrets of a brick building ahead
and you see black windows and figures walking.
Read WINGS MOTORS. Read BIG EAT.
Read TRANSIT WORKSHOP. Three birds
flying over an arched structure and you see the
structure is glass and steel like a station canopy
and you look up into the canopy through an
opening to see yellow light emanating down
through the pieces of the glazing. Puddle
shaped like a diamond, roughly. Read PANEL
BEATING. Puddle with straight sides like a
lozenge. Body of a pink taxi passes out of a
dark lane. Within the body of the taxi see a
pale woman dressed in pink. Smashed frosty
glazing of octagonal shape. Hand adjusting
spectacles on a face. Man slumped against the
door window within a car asleep. Two cars.
Crack of sound and you look down to see a
page knocked by the wind and each time blown
it makes a sharp noise, flatly. See window panes
collected with dust. Pair of muddy boots.
Blackened brickwork. Man with white hair and

you see two skulls of brass, one on each lapel of his jacket and the jacket is black leather. Stone steps, a black grille before them. Belly of a pregnant woman. Man seriously writing on papers attached to a clipboard. Black frames of windows and see a man's face wincing like the muscle of an oyster. Orange light and you see a windmill-shaped building ahead. Skeletal cross on the roof of a building. Clock face which reads ten past seven. Steps leading into the ground. You pass and there is warm air rising from beneath ground and figures walking up through the air from the ground. Oval eyes of a cyclist and hair blown across the panel of a face. Rubble in a heap and see mottled teeth of an open-mouthed standing woman. Read M. Greyness. Read BRAVINGTONS. Letters of brass. Read ULTRA BLUE PLANET EALING. Two gold rings on a golden chain on a woman's neck. Footprints in hard grey cement. Clap of a shoe's heel striking down and read TWISTED. Letters scratched into glass. Road rises and you read THE POOR SCHOOL. Leaves wrinkled dry with the wind scraping together, a sound like a hoarse wheeze. Black windows over dark rooms reflecting dark morning sky and read ALL ENQUIRIES. Read BUSES LOOK LEFT. Fine hairs over a small tree's stems and leaves. A figure ahead with a child clasped to its chest, arms of the figure holding the child from underneath. See a red collar. A man in the sun and his hair glows like a toaster's filament. Hand holding two silver coins. Turn to see turrets, turn to walk, passing red berries among green leaves and a hand with a half-smoked cigarette put to a mouth. Circle of traffic cones and a wall leant against by gravestones. Sunlight like a cut into curved metal to a gleam and a flash brighter which dies as you pass. Read £3695. Read £4995. Read £5495. See numbers on boards within cars. Roar of an uphill engine. Read FOAM CUT TO SIZE. And sun glances over paving like a torch searching and passes away and you see figures ahead grow dark and the hair of a woman gold like a fire. Red hair lit like a fox's tail. Chromed grille of a car makes a flash and you pass hearing rumbles of large vehicles. Man and a woman clasped together. Man and a woman entering a taxi, man after the woman, a red hand, hand of the man with the mark of a bite, see pale flesh. A stack of cartons of milk like a bale. Read EXIT. Read CARETAKER AT NO 42. Splayed wings of a pigeon flying, a yellow twig clasped in the steeple of its beak. Woman carrying objects at speed. Two women pass and one with eyes nearly black. Pink rectangular container. See a building half demolished. Hand at a woman's hip. Broad pavement without figures. Read IN-DEPTH SECURITY. Breath of a passing woman's voice. Haze of a sunlight and see more sunlight over cloud behind

chimney pots and more over higher clouds in a
distant view of watery yellow. Man in a bone
grey jacket, unzipped, walks to a door and
opens it. Hear, "Oi, mate, have a bit of spare
cash please." See a girl with two plaits carrying
the case of an instrument. Woman standing
alone at a corner of two buildings with hands
throwing bread to pigeons. Strutting birds stab
with grey heads like short bradawls. Foamy
crumbs of pale bread beak-driven about. A man
sweeping. Mottled back of a pigeon. Man
starting to cross a road draws back from the
road to its edge and pivots on heels at the kerb.
See a woman's cheek and chin give a shake as
she walks. A woman leaving the door of a house
with wet hair and the black door slams behind
her. Man with a large stomach within a pink
shirt bowed out between the buttons. He
yawns with a small mouth. A woman carrying
two children. Drift of sand on a window ledge.
Sprouts of new grass shaking. Wooden reels
with long red plastic cables wound on them. A
man pulling over his head a bright yellow
garment. Cloud like a waistcoat over the sun.
Squeak of a bike's brakes. Read R633 DKP.
Rear of a blue car. Read G452 VME. Rear of a
white car. Long-haired woman staring ahead,
holding in both hands a sugar-crystalled pastry,
square and flat. Legs of a woman running over
seed-strewn paving and you turn seeing many
seeds for birds pecked in frenzy. Read Genuine

Wild. Black letters on the side panel of a passing white van. Read We're bringing the music to the party. Hear a laugh soft like the sound of a flute's deepest note and read SHEPHERDESS WALK. A green cafe and black-haired man quickly eating the contents of a plate without a breath of pause. Shoes of suede and see wooden shoe horns. Read & BRITISH EMPIRE PIPE CO. See cameras and the heads of figures at the viewfinders of cameras. A street of cobbles like a stone shore. Figures at cameras watching a man and woman in tidy conversation. A grey jacket slumped in a heap on cobbles like a beached jelly fish. Red cheeked face of a shrew-like man, lean, and walking. Read OPHTHALMIC HOSPITAL. A thin woman whose tongue licks her lips. Crack at the side of a building. Silver-rimmed glasses. A green man of light becomes unlit and you run over road passing before the lined-up bulls of cars' noses. And hear engines behind you. Tall man in black with crumpled trousers walks with a cigarette. See a structure of blue arches. A ramp sloped into ground. Raised-up head of white hair and the line of a cut on a man's chin, tongue protruding between red lips. Building into sky reflected on a puddle's skin and the face of a woman passing, she makes a shake to the water. Hard wax on the side of an empty wine bottle. A metal arm scraping with the bucket of its hand, four claws to the

bucket. The arm reaching down to a hole.
Clatter of metal. Hear music. Read SOLID
CONFIGURATION FORMED BY
CHANGED EVENTS. Woman walks slowly.
Read CENTRAL CALCULATORS ONLY.
Sun burns from a window's face reflected. Dark
panels of a wooden door. Read IF I JUST
TURN AND RUN PUNKS JUMP UP. Blue
spots on a red tie. A man signals with a hand
cupped, his hand upright before his face,
fingers curled like a sail fat with wind, the
shape of a pasty, moving backwards, and the
face of a lorry towing towards him its huge
mass. Read SCANNING AND LITHO
PLATEMAKERS. Read PRESS THE
BOTTOM BUZZER ONCE. And you walk
between two high red buses in the narrow
ravine, a corridor in the road. Read SALOON
BAR. Traffic at large moving from five roads in
five directions. Violet flash of light on the slate
of a puddle. Pass soft, small, fleshy leaves of a
plant. Read ESTABLISHED 1865. Read DAN
THE AUTOMATOR, BLINDS MADE TO
MEASURE. Read ELECTRA MARITIME.
Thin woman in black. Thin face of a woman. A
copper pink pigeon's head stabbing white
bread. Pale grey dome the colour of wet ash.
Columns of grey. Man standing alone on the
long shore of a puddle. Blister under the glued
surface of a billboard poster. Fronds of a string.
Read CENTRIC HOUSE. Plant growing from

mortar like two green wings. A man steps from
the back of a red bus and you see his foot
touching the tarmac. Look into a dark space
inside the gape of an arch and a dusty sweet
smell is there. An empty packet for razor blades
on the pavement. Arms folded at the chest of a
woman. Water running over cobbles and
finding ways through the tiny shallow gorges
between. Two men at the back of a van. Hear,
"This morning." Blonde-haired and creased face
of a woman. Hear, "This morning." A white car
crawls slowly through water. Blue grey granite
cobbles and some are pink grey. Read HAVE
YOU SEEN THIS CAT. Read NO
INNOCENT BYSTANDERS. See two white
mannequins. Black metal mesh like a veil over
smashed glass. Look to see brushes and tin cups
and many small wooden structures. Face of a
painted woman. Door knocker like an
elephant's face. A woman in black squeaking
past and a black bag is carried, see high black
boots almost to her knees. Read DAY OR
NIGHT ENTRANCE. See a black leather
binocular case and see a black car in a room
containing many white bales. Read
SECONDHAND WORKWEAR. Cream
roses in a tarmac garden. Read PLEASE DO
NOT. A man walks with a brown envelope. A
blackbird flies up. See water and rubbish. Shake
of a woman's thigh walking. See a man's cheeks
inflate and hear the exhaust of his breath. Parts

of a fridge-body and see two waterlogged books
and see they are novels. Read POST
CAPTAIN. Read NINE ENEMY. You pass a
dark and long tunnel, a small opening at its far
end. Figure wearing a headscarf composed of
black threads. Woman with ochre-red hair.
Wings flap in a tunnel. Shadow of a bird over
pavement and it runs over you, a whole shadow
crosses your face like a change of light without
sound and you turn and you walk. Hear, "Every
morning during the quarter final round." See a
man sweeping a body of water into the mouth
of a drain. Open space of grass bounded by a
line of black railings. Cloud clotted in sky. Read
THREE COLTS. And you hear the shrill,
repeated song of a bird three times and a
complication of perfume is several scents
merging together as two women pass in
opposed directions along the same pavement.
Smell diesel. Smell burnt oil. Read
DIFFICULT TO DEFINE IMPOSSIBLE.
Hear, "Why, you give money on credit?" See a
man in the door of a cafe. And a boy walks in a
white blaze of sunlight. Hear the pedalling of a
pigeon's wings and a small whistle-sound in the
wings. Read LONDON INTERNATIONAL
LINGERIE CENTRE. A mouth shut, mouth
of a woman. Two trees encased in mailcoats of
ivy. A woman pulling blue tights up over the
skin of her legs. A man shaking a hand out from
a black cuff. A building of more than four sides

of yellow. A man and woman smiling together. A girl wipes a damp eye with the stump of a knuckle. A man's mouth engaged in rapid chewing. A dome rising among leaves of trees and the leaves dark and you walk down into the ground to a room containing wall-mounted machines with red numbers, grey buttons, black fascias and men in blue uniforms and a row of grey gates and the air has a dusty vapour. Bang of a gate opening and a figure walks through. Bang of a gate closing. See many eyes passing like the beads on an abacus.

Hear, "Been trying to keep." A woman passes to climb onto steps. Hear, "Tomorrow night." White curly hair of a man. A woman alone. Hear, "Fuck off." Moon like a moon over marshland falls through a black roof. See a man crouched over the mouth of an unopened bag. A black and white picture of a grey creature. Pronged shadows of railings tapering to blonde points. White eyebrows on a dark face. Tick of an engine. See dock leaves and tall-stemmed thistles. A loudspeaker behind a woman's head in a car and a brow creased with frowning. Green plait from a square of hair on a man's shaved head. A pale blue shirt, a man with keys opening a red, curved box of painted metal. Read BESSY STREET. Sunlight on bricks. Read LONDON BUDDHIST. Scratched portion of a car door. Long primrose-yellow car parked with each wheel submerged in a long black puddle. Low shady houses and music radiating from the warm rat's body of a car. See a man seated half-concealed by reflections over his head on glass. Hear, "Padlocked." Black and red dress of a passing woman. Sun on the rim of a pair of glasses. Read NO ENTR. Scrape of a car. A single bee and you look up to a moon pale in the blue sky, and grey as a rabbit's tail. Moss scab on a damp brick. Three thin oxidised slices of melon. Three boys playing at ball. A dark face, below is a blue shirt. See a beer can filling the space of a breast pocket. Leaves black-red, dark as blood pudding. A man's face passes. Read FAIR RENT IS BENT. See cracked surfaces of paint. Hear, "So many different ways." Stud of a man's earring gleams. Shadow of a woman dressed in black floats over a brick wall. Read EAS KEEP HIS SITE TID. Sharp wind blows in from the west sky and the spears of railing shadows are over pavement. Hear, "Yeah, you better before I go anywhere ... I hope he's got dinner at home." Read XX SURGERY THIS WAY. Man on a wall and one foot lifted from ground. Two hands about the nose of a man. A pair of crutches. Three figures at a wooden table with glasses containing peat brown drinks. Read Perfect Rooster. See red bucket seats. Hear, "I said you're like ... well, that's you to your." And hear, "What was the irony of." Read Concretensteel. Four men as a group in another language. See a finger drawn across a throat and hear, "Should be like this." Read LA VALE E SOCIAL C UB. A long-haired man eating a chip screws chip paper into a tight ball. And the chip-eating man stands as you pass and throws the ball of his chip paper into a corner. Hear, "Barbecue must be lovely, huh?" Pale light on cylindrical concrete. Read COCONUT STARS. And two eyes pass, watching from a rectangular slit in a cloth. Pass a man with a balding cranium. Wind blows and shadows are flung down and up over buildings and grasses among ceramic tiles strewn are cast down and shake. A bright wooden stick in a man's hand is lifted and the face of the man shielded by the other hand. Read MDCCCXC. Moon behind wires and see many names scratched into soft brickwork. Read OPEN. Letters on the ground. Read DUCTILE C SLIDE. See the image of an arrow pointing to your right. See a woman running in black clothes. Hear an attempt to start a car and a harsh cry like a jackdaw of a voice responds. Sunlight fading on clothes out to dry and the smell of spice frying in bright yellow oil. Read AZOV HOUSE. Bright body of a plane overhead and a girl in the square of a small garden dressed in a pale pink skirt. Man with three children, black glossy hair of a girl. Hear, "Sorry." See a green space with shadows and sunlight and a warm earthy brick, a dome, grey construction of metal girders, a cage, a girl running and women gathered at a van's opened doors and see boxes of vegetables within the van's box and the moon-like heads of cauliflowers and hear, "I know that you have a tough time getting a." Look up to see the moon among the open framework of fourteen-sided metal gasworks. A woman and child. Hear, "Shall we cross the road." See one side of the moon faded off and see steamy whites of clouds to your right and hear, "The man who bites straight away." Body of a hawthorn and see a trimmed beard and a tractor stationary. See the dark, broad form of a plane climbing sky. Flat umbels of elderflowers and the creeping hiss of leaves bullied by the wind. 'Tak-tak' sound of leaves hitting leaves. Shadow sharp as a needle. Hear, "Six seven six seven eight." Voice of a girl. Woman walking alone in green like a parrot's green back and long, pointed shoes like the beaks of egrets. Turn to a cracked toffee of rubble, colour of salmon flesh mixed with the silver-grey flecks of scales, like oats. Hear a clash of hit metal. See a porridge of rubble. A head of hair like a shock of darkness and shadows move and you turn to a glowing red diamond of a tree. Read HE WHO SAILS ON THE WIDE SEA IS. Grille to the dark room of a basement. Steps leading down onto pavement ahead and see a face crouched like a

[162]

bird in the cube of a small room watching you
pass. Read NO DOG. Read Deep Excavations.
Sunlight blind-bright on chrome parts of cars.
Turn left into shade and the wind is acute. See
red light over grey cement is pink as sliced ham
and children are gathered as a mob and see
others running in groups. See a hand tensed,
thumb out like a lobster's claw. Two women in
long black dresses. Read G. DAVIS IS
INNOCENT. Pink face of a painted man.
Trees against arches. Emerald green of a
pigeon's neck shivers. Two men laugh and
shake hands. Hear, "You going to your sister's
house." Hear reply, "Yeah." See two crows
flying, turn and read JACK IN THE BOX IN.
Painted pink letters over the face of a wall. A
tube the width of a man. See the rigging and
flags of nettles and a thick clamp of shade
among green dock leaves and see reddish brown
stems, thin like the legs of pilgrims. A plastic
bag containing a brown substance the wind
grips and drags a few inches rustling around its
unliftable substance. See drooping chains of
nettle seeds. Three gold packets of cigarettes
crumpled, like three broken kings. A white line
to a red line. Letters scratched into paint. Read
SENIOR SERVICE. Turn to see sunlight
range a dark building without floors and see a
cocoa-brown tower and set into an alcove one
face of a white figure dressed in blue paint. See
a red figure proud of the roofline behind the

figure in blue, it is bearded, and the sun pouring light over it makes the back like a red rock. A black man of bronze holding a deck of black pages in one hand. Blocks of a stone hit with a drillhead. Shadow of a man passes like a rook and see scrolls of carved stone and a black chain and anchor set into concrete. Read THE MISSION. Green man of light. See a plant growing from a wall with leaves milky in shade. A cloud-shape of paint. Cry of a cat. See red thorns of a rose without flowers. Turn left to see a sunny gold set on a white stone building like a church and a clock face beneath, read half-past seven. See unclothed children in the space of a room. Empty room, through the next window. A blue door. See cobbles under worn tar, like a stone sea under the road. Steel cry of a passing train. Red cross on a white rectangle. Hear, "I'll see you later." Read BROWN BOTTLES & JARS ONLY. Hear the high, muffled voices of children. Read CHANGED PRIORITIES AHEAD. White words on red. Sounds of children clear and bright like monkeys of flame. Two men quietly together through the noises of leaves. Five-petalled white flowers immersed in sunlight and a rust-speckled chrome wheel hub, and a man in a grey jacket and a child with golden wings and lips holding onto an indigo pyramid. Hear the voice of a television and five leaves scrape over road. Black speckle of brickwork and a man

[164]

jogging and the noise of his footsteps passes
like dry leaves blown by the wind. Three figures
walking. See water ahead and a long boat
quietly rocked port to starboard by wind on the
water. Turn to a man's face framed by a black
hood. Wave lapping and see the algae-green
body of a plastic machine on the shore, flint,
fronds of green weed and red fins of sunlight on
cupped parts of waters. A far shore and pale,
low hills beyond. Scabs of a froth afloat and
green rocks below. A woman jogging, soft flesh
moving over her bones. See the single arms and
legs of cranes and figures moving about ahead,
in groups and a figure alone on a boat, shadow
of a leaf shrinks. Pass the eyes of a man, a
mouth closed, sun on the ridge of a nose and
see pairs of figures ahead making couples. Sun
reflecting square rocket-shape of a tower with
many tall windows and a hand swinging a black
bottle by the neck and a man with blonde hair
and red places on his cheeks. Man and woman
pushing a pram containing a child. Noise of a
baby crying and a word in the body of the cry
like 'ma'. Sun of many colours reflected and see
lilacs in the greys and silvers of tall buildings. A
woman's hand at her throat. Woman alone with
long, curly red hair. Body of a man in a blue
jacket. Hear, "She's absolutely ruined." Steps of
tightly crystallised granite. See the far shore and
leaves and birds. Two men running. Shadows of
grasses interwoven. Hear, "She said, can you do

that for me." Leaves of wrought iron. Octagon
of clipped grass. An ant passing over a lake of
polished pink granite. See the dim reflection of
the ant like a shadow beneath the ant. Hear,
"My lord." And words among words you cannot
make clear. Hear, "Like we met everyday." See
a man in a yellow jacket holding a clipboard
between the underneath of his left forearm and
the base of his diaphragm. Brushed steel panels
of a wall's facade. Man at a desk. A man's hand
placed on the chest of his jacket and the other
hand pressed to the stomach. A plastic bag
leaping and dragged on a square floor of stone.
Figure of bronze. Two eyes and a mouth, an
image of scars on a young birch tree's bark. A
tower ahead, rising far into sky and a gate, a
boat. Rivers of silver over birch bark. The
moon between two buildings like a head
between hands. Two figures of bronze seated
with triangular heads and no facial parts. Green
circle of water. A blonde woman eating. A
black-haired woman with red skin. Hear, "It's
obviously not something." Read THE MAN
WORTH £500,000 A DAY. Hear, "Standard."
Man with blue eyes closing a bag by drawing its
zip-pull. Cold light the length of the long room
of a precinct. Echoing and many feet walking a
warble of cries and the mutters of steps. A
staircase rising. A train door ahead. Read FIRE.
Succession of piercing beeps and train doors
shut to a sound like a 'clack'. Pyramid of

[166]

flowers. Hear, "The next train on platform
five." A blonde-haired woman blowing her nose.
Tightly rolled interiors of yellow roses. Yellow
arm and leg of a metal crane into blue sky.
Dark, a flashing on water ahead. A woman's
dark eyes meet yours and turn and pass on.
Vertical wall-face of grey marble. Hand of a
man raised. A woman's head crouched on the
neck. She lights a cigarette. Hear, "A bit of a
time, just move back up again." Look up to dull
silvers of a tower. Hear, "So close." Grey beard
of a man with a hand holding three magazines.
Hear, "Issue." Stairways descend into a long
dark cavernous whale of a hall of grey pillars in
a line centrally like a spine with its ribs.
Woman with a black portfolio. Three
escalators. Grooved metal steps. Black white-
veined stone polished, flecks of green and red
like the flickering of stars. Hear, "Shall we go
somewhere." And see yellow and brown parts to
a stone. See a man seated alone and hear a hiss
like the breath-husk of blown notes of a flute
played to a slow tune, and long empty corridors
like streets inside buildings. The rubble of the
noise of running water. Hear, "It's very
unlikely." A white-shirted man walking slow,
meandering left to right to left. Plastic figures
without faces. Look up to a glass and metal
tower rising. Hundreds of low, yellow flowers
like mouths into the earth and shaking. Sniff of
a man's nose. Green of grass. See black pipes

running among flowers. Hear, "I doubt you'll cross there." And hear, "See a glass bridge and go across the glass bridge." Flowers in areas of triangular and quadrangular form. A man stooped. Hear, "Yes it is, yep, yep." Black form of a bird flying. Read NO REVERSING WITHOUT ASSISTANCE. Black rockiness of water below and see the stilt-bodies of three black cranes standing upright. A black hat like the body of a mole. Hear, "So it's a good case to just put-up and shut-up." Grey cushion-like dome of a plastic material with yellow struts like the prongs of a crown. Sunlight over concrete is pink, like boiled quince. Ticking music from a car. A black metal barge, a heap of earth and spuds of smashed concrete. Sheen like honey over pitted iron on the black barge. Thin spire of a stone. Two figures ahead and you walk. See the pale bone moon. Blinding face of the sun like the skin of a crucible of molten metal. Four parked lorries. Turn to see yellow sky in a haze and the black shape of a fish over a weathercock and the four compass points indicated. Grey plastic building with opened entrances and see a cylinder of grey steel. Terracotta wall to your right. Man at the wheel of a long white bus. Read 3kW. Matted ivy, sunlit leaves like black triangular cups full of gold-red light. A covered area of bricks. Clattery burble of a stretched motorbike. Read P555 ONY. Black helmet on a man's head.

[168]

Muffled clatter of a car. Leaf folded, like a hand. Read PART NO. 013 300 041 H. Turn to read HSBC. Rim of a green and grey tower. Man in white trousers. Black dome like a bonnet of mourning. Tattoo of a red-haired, naked woman of green lines on a man's bicep. Read W NES SP R. A blue car driven at speed. A white bath tub like a shoe for water. Stone thrown by a small boy. See a milkbottle perched on the palm of a hand and chips nestled in a cone of newsprint in the grip of a hand. Hear, "Oh-oh, bloody Indian." See a smooth pale stone building within a green parkland and two children crouched behind a headstone and hear giggles. Trunk of a cherry circled with bands of silver. Hear, "See you later ... alligator." Look up to a stone spire, clock face with golden numerals alive with the sun. See children at the doors of a pale and giant building. Sunlight on the back of a gravestone. See cherry leaves with small holes and glowing like green fish with sunlight and the edges toothed slightly. Two holly plants like entirely bearded faces. Figure rocking within a car seat. See fluted columns and scrolls of stone and volutes. A single balustrade. Turn to hear the hiss of a car and a man with a beard like a sheep dog passes with two long-haired sheep dogs in tow, with the first dog holding a blue can of beer in its mouth. Turned-up nose of a red-haired and milk-skinned boy. Hear, "Run."

A man of green bronze. Hear, "Bastard." Hand of a woman pulling a black thin scarf to her body. See wet bricks. See grasses knee-high. A yellow van reversing. Two dark cars parked and the wind is a hard wind. See a group of white bags filled by the wind and they fly puffed-up together. Read CANS AND TINS ONLY. Scrape and you see a purple sweet-wrapper move. Plane wrapped in sunlight. A dark face smiling, enters a building. Glasses projecting from a hooded face, only the eyes visible. Throat's song of a dark green and speckled bird, neck of the bird like a green foil. Turn to see two grey sides of a pyramid built on a tall grey tower and walk on. Turn, see a wolf-like tower, turn and walk on. Read BOYS CLUB Tel: 07 1- 987 2270. Low building with half-roman tiles. Pink-haired poodle led by a man. See small cube-pieces of broken glass over long paving slabs and the 'hoooo' of a siren. And the siren passes away among buildings behind. Read CONCRETE UTILITIES. See red roses, dark as congealed blood. See small white flowers and a drift of plastic. See holes eaten in printed invites. Read THE LORD STANLEY. Letters in gold and red-veined leaves at the end of a stem glow and you see the brown shrivelled plug of a smoked cigar. Count eight rose bushes. Crushed can, split on one side and the can is blue over silver. A figure towards you and see one hand pull a stiff yellow tape from a

[170]

small box and watch it reel back. See five tyres
lying among tall grasses and a whole acute-
angled triangle of seeded grasses brown with
the sun, flash of a cobweb, hair of grasses pale
and milky as sap. White-haired thistles and you
see broad-leaved trees and the trees flap a dry
noise in leaves like a fire and sun passes through
them to a caramel in greens and the trunks like
the legs of elephants stand very still and you see
two men standing at a pair of gates, the gates
locked shut with a heavy chain of oval links.
Read FOUNDRY. First man with eyes to the
ground and a second man with eyes on the first
man. Cry of a siren. See in iron relief a door,
and a figure holding a string of beads and a
painted red shepherd's crook on a red bridge.
And turn. See a woman and man on a balcony
still in red sunlight and two clouds pass very
high.

Turn and see blossom in goose-grey sky behind
buildings. And one drip of water. Read GAS.
Read BLESSINGS CLEANING SERVICES.
Wind blowing scraps of pink blossom. Broken
plant stems pushed by the wind and the sky is
lighter low in the North. See an orange light
flashing. One squeak of a brake. A car horn
cries twice. A car wheel rides up over a kerb.
Two headlamps of a red bus. Read LET BY.
Read FIRE HYDRANT. Canal water

stretching a straight line. Swan preening
feathers, white on black water sieved by wind
to a gravel of boiling. Barbed wire coiled. Read
E.W. Hoe. A pigeon's eye, orange, round with a
black spot. And a scrap of polythene like a
squirrel turning makes a hiss. Pass a man and
woman, a plastic bag at the end of each of their
four arms. See a face wince at the eyes and
mouth into little lines like lines of cracked
glass. Pass a blue hat. Read AHERN. Pass two
bikes. Sheen of a headlamp passing on the road.
Brick-shapes regular and powdery red. Read
TO. Pendant earring at the ear of a man with a
stomach, one glint of a small light there and the
man's body, arms, legs, managing a forklift. See
a red van parked. Slats of sunlight over ground.
Rough blocks of a building. Bead of green glass
embedded in tar like the eye of a fish. Five
notes of one song and you hear the marching
song of a school party and see many children
together in blue with the blotched and yellow
face of a woman among them, hair pale and
smooth thinly drawn back on her head, hair
dashed into a small clip and the children
making a loudness of their march and scattering
steps. Turn and one drip of water bangs down
and breaks apart into many smashed beads of
one drop. See grass blades out of tar. Flash of
light and rising pitch of a siren cut by a brick
wall to a quiet siren. Hear, "Oh, I've dropped
me tea." Hear, "Oh Shel." See the long strand

of an egg's albumen drop from a cracked egg
onto a hotplate, eggshell in two emptied halves
in two hands. There is a fine rain and fast-
moving hay-coloured clouds. See sky-blue
wooden shutters heaped as wreckage. Rusted
black bulkhead of a car. Read PEDESTRIAN.
Hear music of cables played by the wind. Read
ALL VISITORS & DRIVERS. Moan of an
engine's labouring. Read G. See spots of paint
on tar like blemishes on leaves. Tree branches
pronged into sky. Pass a column of bricks rising
smoothly. Read HOUSEHOLD WASTE.
Bollards of black and you hear a sound of metal
tapped. A puddle ripped to a splash. Blebs and
glints of rain in flour-paste light. Hear a phone
ringing and a crackle of plastic pram wheels
over wet gritty ground. See a woman talking to
the mouthpiece of a phone. Walk between two
diesel vehicles at tickover and see a cigarette
lying on tarmac. Read FULL SUSPENDED.
Plastic litter floating and a clod of blunt cloud
moving like a singed hat floating on a stream.
Paler lights in dark and massive moving cloud.
Shape like a child's drawing of a sheep
swimming among swimming dogs of cloud.
Body of a plane passing through the body of
cloud. Dark colliding with the dark of two
clouds and yellows emerging on the upper parts
of each, full of light like confusion rummaging
across the calm of water at moonrise on a lake.
And the hull of each cloud is like a bruise. Two

men crossing a road. White stripes over road and a girl clapping her hands together. Hear, "Huge diversity." Hear, "Destiny." And the word 'destiny' lingers like the harmonic of a plucked guitar string. A woman in a car, see she is chewing. White teeth of a woman driving a car through the cry of a man shouting. Hear, "There's that man down there." Voice of a child. Winding of an engine starting and a clattery climb of a mill of tappets clacking. Plume of black smoke like a cough and you hear blackbirds singing at once. A scar on a man's half-smiling lip like the mark left by a ship for hours after its passing on the wide skirt of the sea. Hear the noise of trees rises up like a wind's rattle and see clothes on a washing line out to dry with flapping arms and legs. Two red vehicles pass like painted fires with the sound of sirens and the sunlight dusty after them. Cab containing the helmeted faces of men and the helmets are yellow. Silver pipes pass. Turn back to see a building with a turret locked into a casing of ivy, leaves like heart-shaped scales of green and green-black. Eye of a dog flashing and filled with sunlight like a murky pool, like sunlight in black tea. Three yellow teeth in the opening of a smile. Man with a stick. Cry of a voice. Hear, "Da la ley." A man's tongue moves onto his face crookedly, moves across the lower lip by small staggers of movement like the movement of a hen's neck. See a red bird-

shaped tongue that flattens to a shovel-shape
and moves cleaning the surface of the lip and a
crumb picked up onto the wet surface of the
tongue as it passes. See the man-with-tongue
pushes a road sweeper's cart and he swings it to
face fully the other way dragging it up over the
ridge of a kerb. See half a banana skin striped
black and with flecks of black where the skin
remains yellow. A wobbling-handed and gently
passing man. And a woman with shaved grey
hair in the lit space of a room you see in the
face of a window has wrinkled baggy skin and
arms loose on the bone. Blue oval of a cloud's
reflected cloud. And the body of a woman
wearing grey underwear and her back turned to
the window is hunched and begins to bend
down, see the beads of her chainy spine, and
you pass. Hear a pocket of metal pieces shaken.
Mist like a goat's milk. Old man leans on a
knotted stick. Steam climbs out from mouths.
Read HOUSING DEPAR Area Carta. Boy
with grey eyes. See the torso of a man in a
white T-shirt with hands on a balcony and the
mouth shouting, "The state of it." And a voice
calling, "Dad, just come back in." And you see
the face of a long-haired girl and the girl's hair
dark and pulled behind the back of her head
tightly like the wings of a walking crow. A rain
caught in the twisted air falls like a cloud of
midges and you see lenses of small water mist
the glasses of the shouting man, you pass. Man

[175]

in a window to your left banging a table once
with the wooden handle of a knife and his eyes
flash out to a figure passing in the street. Core
of a pear with one black fruit-fly standing on its
oxidised pale fibrous bitten flesh, the stem a
mass of dark fibres twisted to a curled point
like a scraggy horn or scrutty hawthorn in
winter. To your right a curtain drawn back
from a window slowly, a face looks out. See a
woman pulling the curtain with a tug of hand
and see the woman wears a flowered nightdress
with a lace collar and her hair is curled on
curlers and she grips the edge of curtain in the
entering light with one hand resting on the
window like a lamb and looks into the state of
the sky. Sound of a silver car. Dead leaf moves
backwards, crouched low like a dog frightened
to be hit. Pass a sheet of clear polythene with
beads of water. Acute, sharp-ended woodwind
cry of a bird. Deep red flowers the colour of
dark lips. Voice in the space of a doorway. A
door closes to a dull click. A white petal falls
from a small magnolia tree. Cry of a songbird
and a sound like sandpaper over stone and the
thin creak of a dry metal hinge. Low sound of a
woman singing under her breath. Two girls
playing and a giggle running about like a mouse
under the breath and behind hands. Two
blackbirds, first drags a worm, second sits
watching from a metal bollard, first stares at
the worm on the short grass coiling its body

[176]

into a circle-shape with ends, and clamps the
worm in its yellow beak, one worm-half flat and
grey falls to grass, the second blackbird flies to
the flat grey half-worm dropped and snatches
it, the first flies up crying like a shrill chatter.
Black bark of a tree and branches like a skewed
wattle over sky. Man in a blue sleeping bag on
dew-littered grasses with a face pale as a peeled
potato with a mouth gaping, three policemen
around him, one crouched, touching his hand.
The eyes closed. See two white buds in the
process of opening. Six bubbles in a ring afloat
on a black and wind-troubled puddle, like parts
of an armada in assemblage. Felty mats of cut
grass strewn over the pavement. A rectangular
page pinned to a post. Read MISSING CAT. A
car passes. And read Have you seen Poppy
She's very shy and has a red collar. Car. Car.
And you read If you can help please phone. A
light swings over wet bricks like a sickle and
the bricks are like closed eyes in their shadows.
Walk. A crisp packet flipped over by wind,
blown between a woman's legs and on. Crimson
through leaves like a syrup. A boy in grey
clothes hanging from a black branch in the
complex baldness of the crown of a tree, a boy
below bearing a black stick beating down
nettles. Smell the sweet bruised bitterness of
broken nettle and pass yellow flowers gaping.
Girl in a room upstairs. A tube poked from a
window. Read NA 4 ?? Read HE WAR. See

down-pointing daffodils. A crisp packet turns over. Read WALKERS. See a red lamp lit behind net curtains. Corpse of a cat on its side stretched stiff with fur clumped and wetly ruffled. Mouse with a punctured face. Read HOOPS. And a sour smell like a gas leak but stronger. And a grey train moving into sun grows blackened. Read LAND. Muffled voice of a car radio stops. Car. Car. See one black figure ahead. Five people exit a car and four doors slam at intervals. Hear a jangle of keys knocking a bright steel sound. Read NO DOGS EXCEPT GUIDE DOGS. Two cars pass. A heckle of hot fumes and one engine clatters. A leaf down-pointing. Three towers. Man in a white cap. Hear dripping water. Car. Read SKOL. A darkness in the tunnel of a bridge's arch and see two men ahead. See a small car without wheels on four milk crates. Read HAND CAR WASH. Read HOLYHEAD. Read Ambulance. A white van passes at speed and the speed moves it to be gone quickly. A flying-up plastic bag. Buds on a black tree opening to red and green leaves like small black beaks with green-red tongues like tiny flames. Flashing round shape of amber. Read crossing ahead. Curly-haired woman, painted green fingernails, black boot heels like hooves, keys on a ring swing from the claw of a hand by the side of a hip. See rusted iron the colour of brown horses and see small yellow

[178]

flowers in the shade of tree saplings behind
sheets of corrugated iron. A woman with
perfume passes and there is a heavy clop to her
step. Sun on concrete like a dry, filmy
substance. Blind-light squares of glass reflecting
sunlight. Bruise-blue sky. Read LITTLE MAN
WAZ ERE. Man rubbing his hands like a fly
rubs its legs. See coloured rags tied to a string
and see black text printed on each of the rags.
A clatter of sheet iron. Figure in a dark room to
your left. And a woman ahead to the right
wearing a maroon coat with flaps like maple
leaves in the wind at dusk. Seat folded down
forwards in a car like a crouched chimpanzee.
See pale spring flowers of a yellow familiar to
you and read R891 DGY. Read 22A. A grey van
passes and metal shutters fling about rattling
and then whisper a sound of clatters growing
smaller. Body of a grey mouse streaked with
wetness, small black eye punctured, its pink
claws curled at each foot. See a blonde girl and
you turn, and on your right read RAG. A gold
wrapper. And there are pink flowers, each petal
an extended tongue, the cone-centred flowers
shady like soft caves the size of a bee each and
the walls of the caverns cool like shades of
damp stone in a river's gorge in summer. Two
stone lions lie quiet. Bright bark of a dog in a
chamber of echoes repeating back less-bright
barks of a dog. A bark five times. One bark of a
dog like a choke. See dark faces within the

opening of an arch of bricks. Note of a tenor
whistle. A boy's eyes meet your own and deflect
and you walk hearing a high, strung noise of
wind through cables and the hiss of leaves like a
rising sickness in trees red with the falling sun
and the wind drops, flamed flash of sun from a
sheet of glass, pale gob flung from a man's
mouth, and you hear, "Have yuh?" And you
hear, "What you like?" Read GUM. White
stems of sycamore and a woman carrying a blue
bag, one finger out of the handle, curved like
the hook of a shepherd's crook. Two men in a
doorway. A man steps. Orange leaves pointed,
orange as heated hot-knives. Pigeon eating the
cooked leg of a chicken and the knuckle of the
bone burnt black. A small boy with both hands
down inside his trousers at the front. Read
WARNING. Hear voices. Read STOP. Clatter
of engines raise a drone like a swarm and walk
and you read I VICKIE & XERIE on brick
wall. And you turn to blazing cloud like the
mirror of the sunset curdled and the light
fanned and shot like arrows into shafts fanned
as broadening tapes of water glisten over rock
by falling down, pink violet yellow in the
sodium-flare of white you face. Scrambled cloud
glowing like a child's cheek from running or
crying; it is bright and red like a sore eye. Look
down to a line of stalled traffic and figures in
each of the cars and pink blossom like sea mist
at sunset engaged in monster forms of

movement. Hear a cough. Read FERODO.
And two men talk and see them listen and talk.
Man picks up a plane leaf and wipes a black
dipstick in sunlight with oil glinting like fish
scales. Scar on a woman's face. Flash of gum in
a mouth. Dark sky of yellow, cloud made by the
darkness of sunken sun to a stronger colour like
deep cadmium to butchered beef red. Eyes
dark. Headlamps and you read TRAFFIC
CHAOS AFTER FACTORY BLAZE. Read
'CHAOS AND BLAZE' in red letters. Read
NINI CHANGES CAFE. See lips of a woman
rolling lips. Screech of a car. See a woman, her
shoes placed before her feet on the pavement,
she stands, still, straight, her toenails long and
pink tigered with white as shrimpshells. She
looks down. She looks up. Cars pass and many
tyres hiss. Spots of flat gum on pavement and
you look to amber lozenges of light like burning
fires seen from the dark sky and on craned
necks see faces in traffic. Skewed light on a
page a man reads with short hair black as a
mole. And a woman walks with her skirt held
up at the hem, pinched between finger and
thumb and she trips. Hear, "Fucking shit," from
the mouth of the hem-lifting woman. Golden
petticoat of light over the barrel of a plane.
Turn to see a man urinating and the stream of
his urine smashed through by sunlight and
there is a green yellow like falling fire from a
fire-eater's mouth. See a white rough-haired

dog sitting on a man's lap in the front seat of a
car. Beard in headscarf with gold circles
embroidered like small grilles in portholes.
Hear, "What do you have to say for her?" Pass a
turmeric skirt enclosing two legs walking fast
short steps in burgundy shoes. Polished stones
with markings, almost scenes depicting
leopards in brown grassland, black trees and
torrents running through the stone. Two
figures in a bus shelter and you hear a sigh of
breath in and out through a nose. Approaching
feet from behind and two women pass. Read
RUSHED TO HOSPITAL. See shaded eyes
and a mouth in shadow moving. Hear, "No,
you'll be fine, don't worry." And the voice
passes. See a man behind the counter of a kiosk
clipping nails. A man's foot touching ground
and a bright beer can of blue and silver in his
right hand and blue bag swinging from his left,
his face turns, beard and lank strings of thin
hair and he has one finger tapping the lid of the
can tilting his head slowly he walks. Rustle of a
paper bag and you turn to see a man reading
words in the valley of an opened newspaper.
Read TELEPHONE. Two men in black
jackets, each with a chain to the pocket. Man
reading a wet crumpled page and see lips
curled, the chisel-edge of a tooth bared.
Woman eating a green apple and the face
puckered. See the up and down of her jaw and
the clench of her bite. A grey bird flying. Leaf

moves. Read Life's Too Short. Green leaves
hang down like the wings of birds. See nipples
under a man's T-shirt. Read IT IS ILLEGAL.
Read LITTER. Pass a flower stall. Car.
Cigarette smoke. Read Low Cost Fares from.
See a black leaf nipped by a footfall. The image
of a scorpion. A leaf rushes and staggers up into
air and falls and scrapes over bare concrete the
length of two man-strides. A musty smell from
the ground. Read TEXACO. Twig lying like a
direction on a concrete slab. See a plane in
bright cloud with darker quarters of cloud to
the right of the plane. Blossom breaking over
your head, you pass. Read 020 8709 8000. Blue
brick building. Read Meal deal. Woman in a
shop staring out towards you and see red lights
to your right and a man with a red tie. Curled-
up face of a man from India and a dark space of
windows behind the head and look up to a sky
bloody with streams of dark cloud in the gold
wreckage of the sunset. A man hooded. Read
BRITISH. Black dog with a studded collar.
Black-haired woman and see blonde hair out in
a wind of running. Read Moderating your
health. Smell hot dry rubber and you walk and
hear, "Just lie on the." Fast bike quietly with a
small tinker of a rattle. Hear, "Yeah, I'll." See
men in buildings and noises build up. A red car
starts. Read STOCKING UP? See a hand move
hair to behind an ear. Man jogs in a black long
coat. Shrill beep of a horn. Light reflected in a

puddle and the spire of a church like an upturned cone, a cone hat, like a megaphone turned to its wide end down. Apricot sky scowls over a black puddle as you pass. Turn to see a black puddle. Dark forms of a church in deep terracotta. Read BUTTERMERE HOUSE. Read MATTER OF TIME. See a man locking a bike with a bike chain. Man's head in the cave of a hood. Turn left to see a decayed end-of-terrace house and a woman running to a taxi. Hear, "Please, outside my." Hear, "Sensible enough." See a shutter dropping down over windows. A woman's eyes stare down at shoes. Hear, "You fucking cheeky shit." See wires of black and orange routed into the ground. Hear, "Me?" See a girl yawning awake. See three pairs of green men of light flashing. People pass who talk and they pass with a chatter like starlings. Read MEAD. See a green man of light. Voices pass talking and holding hands. Read TWAT. Read GOLDEN FRYER. Read Venus in the Park. See the thin arms of a white fountain of water. Trees hatched into leaf and leaves move like blackness with a red and green colour within their black. Read CHRIS. Read Gents. Read HAIRDRESSERS. See a man sweeping a floor. Read ALL LEADING BATTERIES. Read NEW GLOBE. A man walks alone. See tyre-ruts in mud. Tarred tow path. See green lights. Dark sky with five towers like the ribs of a

skeleton laid out. See a train moving the eel of
its length. Scuffle of feet tripping. Coiled cloud.
Read FACULTY OF LAWS. A single brake
light like a red coal carried about. Grey lead
dome. A covered stairway leading up into the
side of a building. Read LION USED CARS.
Read LY81 WWT. Brown leaf. Black bag
circling fast like a merry-go-round and then like
a leaf on a wind and then like a child swung out
on a father's arms and you pass. Man in a bus
shelter. A woman smoking and she is quiet to
herself. Heap of rubbish in a doorway. A
smashed mirror with fractures reflecting and an
umbrella carried. Read ET PLUI
SUPERUNAM CIVITANEM. Read Arsenal
V Chelsea. See a lantern swinging. A
weathercock signals to the Northeast. Read
OCEAN ESTATE. Hear a cough from an open
van window and read PARTY ON ST. See a V
of white hanging from a neck and there are two
rows of traffic side by side arriving at a stop.
Read FORMOSA HOUSE. Two cars. Read
QUEEN MARY COLLEGE Except
Emergency. Hand in a pocket. Three amber
lights dim, three red lights glow. Man without
moving stands in the room of a phonebox.
Read Save Even More. Read 360 degrees. See
one blue crisp packet and it moves to the right.
A hiss of brakes. See warped railings and
daffodils bowed and a gruff smell of smoke. A
man walks reading a paper. See three men

[185]

talking beside a car and a streak of reflected sky like the rind of bacon on the chromed mudguard of a passing scooter. See a blue-mantled tower ahead and turn right to read BISCAY HOUSE. Read GANDHI CASH & CARRY. See the figure of a woman in a high window and you look up and the building appears to tilt and see the hand of the woman in the window has a mug lifted to her face. Turn to see a man spitting. Read PRIDE OF ASIA. Read WHITE HORSE WINE. Read this is not. Read THE OLD GLOBE. Read STEPNEY. Hear, "How are you." See the hands of two men clasped and shaking. Hear the long note of a siren and read CAUTION. Smell spice of a red-brown nature. Read TOILETS ARE. An ambulance passing. A girl with a stare stands. Smell paint and spice from the darkness of shadow. A web of a smashed window and a sticker stuck onto the pane of glass reading HEAR. See a man on a telephone. See three plates lying on a table spotted with food. And on black railings read NO PARKING IN FRONT. See two eagles before a dark house. See a blue room containing glass faces of washing machines. Read CHEAP CALLS. Woman laughing and the squeak of a pedal and a man locking shutters across a window. Pass a building with windows boarded. Read One Zone. See jeans tight over legs walking, creased and uncreased. Read

[186]

Chocolate Value. Hear one rattle and look left
into gloom and a bicycle passes. There is a blue
light on a green car to your right and two birds
rise to your left and to your right a couple in
arms and crossing to your left a man looking
sideways to a woman on his left and to your
right read X us KANE and a man walks out of
a house and drops a white bag into the barrel of
a bin to his left and turns right. A man leaves a
building and turns left and walks in a curve. A
grey light of neon. See cherries displayed. Man
in a jacket of yellow. Read DIY in black letters.
Yellow light in a room and the walls glow with
light. Read CAPTAIN JAMES. Read Sing Lee.
Read OPEN. Read LOCAL SHOPPING. See
four storeys of windows like a ladder of glass
with unlit rooms behind. Read THE THREE.
Rustle of plastic and you pass the sculpture of a
man with a hand to his mouth like a man eating
bread. Hear three notes of a car. Hear the
chatter of a blackbird and three cars pass.
Gravel at the foot of a tree and a man walks
fast with a striped hat and see dandelion leaves
appear to move to your left as you walk and the
earth is black and wet at the feet of their stems.
Read NE PAIN IN E BUM. Two traffic lights
red. Hear voices turn into laughter and look up
to a woman standing on a balcony. Strip of
expanded polystyrene, rags of plastic in trees
and see a bronze head on a stone plinth. Squeal
of bird music above a hum of car tyres, engines,

and the horns of cars beep abruptly. Man kicks
a blue crate and talks to the crate. Read THE
BLIND BEGGAR. See a woman's face and
shelves of grey manila folders and the mouth of
the face speaking to a phone, body of the
phone is pink and yellow. Read ROYAL
MAIL. See figures on a bus. See an upstairs
window light up and a spark of light on the skin
of an earring. Read Urban Bar. See an orange
and black painted tiger. Clatter and one sharp
clang of a metal pole describing it's pole-shape
by the travel of the clang-sound into a long
hollow tube-sound. Black-leaved tree. Read
LONDON HOSPITAL. See a man with a
phone in a yellow-lit room. Read ABU USHAD
& CO. A woman in a broad, diamond-
patterned skirt. Sheets of a green stone
cladding. Orange eye of a cigarette. Read
JALALABAD LAW ASSO. Two men with
dark skin step from a red bus to a man with
light skin. See a nurse moving among curtains
and beds. Striped black and white bollards.
Read WALK-IN CENTRE. Read raja. Read
TELEPHONE. See a tall brown brick conical
tower. Red light and pinkish orange-grey to
many clouds like the swollen bodies of antelope
or pregnant mares. See saris worn in upper
windows. A shop of mannequins. See a foot
pressing the lip of a shop shutter to the ground.
See a man thumping the body of a phone in a
phonebox. Read The Davenant Centre. See fish

[188]

and bubbles within water. Read BITTU. Two
beeps of a car alarm. And see a man pulling a
metal shutter down to the ground over the
windows of a shop. Look up to see a crescent
moon and see below the crescent moon the
tower of a mosque. See a picture of a man with
lumps on his skin. Read Quality Fuels. Read
DENIM WORLD. See boxes. See a man place
a pink sheet of paper into a box. Read MAIN
ENTRANCE FOR MEN. Read MAIN
ENTRANCE FOR WOMEN. Read Zero. See
street light reflected on a black puddle. See
yellow bollards. A bearded man in long
garments making a low wailing sound. Hear,
"That's why." A wind gets up and see hair
moved by the wind. Read WHITECHAPEL
BELL FOUNDRY. Read FIELDGATE ST.
Read AD 1870. A pointed-down earring on the
earlobe of a passing woman, her skin dark. Four
parked cars. Man in a black turban. A drawing
in black crayon on stone and read Vienna waits
for you. A man in a high voice talks to a phone
and the small sweet smell of a flower you
cannot name. Open area of green grass between
high towers at sunset like a picnic rug beneath
adult legs. Read SHELDON ENTERPRISE.
Read littlepenny. Man in a dark doorway. Read
EUROPEAN COLLEGE WISHING. Read
PUSH. Hatted man and a man singing on a
black bicycle and a head bobbing up. See traffic
moving to your right like blown sands. Read

FREEDOM PRESS. Hands of a man zipping the zip of a shoe. Hear, "I, I, I used to be so bad, did you check." See black-framed windows together like the wires of a cage. A man running. Read BAISU BARA. Hear, "Oi," shouted and see blue sky like a hole and hear, "If you need help." A smell of frying onions and the face of a white-bearded man and see a wet-floored alley to his left. Hear, "Fucking you." See offices without figures and a room with a bar containing many figures drinking alone and some together. Hear, "Where, are we going the right way?" Hear reply, "I wouldn't know." See a man without legs on a square board mounted on casters rolling at ankle-height staring ahead and he passes like the noise of a train at great distance through a still night. The left eye of a face agitated. Read DANGER KEEP OUT. Read PETTICOAT LANE. Read Stonehenge 2001. There is a dark smell of water. Short-haired man glides on a moving escalator. Car. Read SUPER. Face of a man and face of a woman in a car and the lips of the two meet and kiss. READ 15 EAST HAM. Read Head Room 1.98m. Man on a bench. Read ST BOTORP. Black windowed, brown brick building. Read HOUNDITCH. A sheen of lights on green tiles. A black-haired woman walks and you see orange indicator lights flashing. Pass arcade screens with bright flashings and see the backs of heads. See the

faces of men and women at monitor screens
and their faces illuminated dully by light
emanating. Hear a voice but no words. See a
white arrow on a blue background. Bright stud
of a cigarette end like a flat planet of fire
without flame in the dark. The cold end of a
cigarette in a man's mouth. Read 1701. Read All
Closed. See a closed shop and the street grows
dark as you walk. Cars move and see plants
with variegated leaves. Small orange battery.
See yellow lamps. A phone's cry. Hear, "Hello,
who?" And hear running. Read SUNGARD.
Man and woman kiss. See a shower of welding
sparks fall from the dark. See a small church
with lights and you turn. Cry of a bell. And you
turn to see lights. Read TAX. Cry of a bell
hangs. Blue-rimmed towers stand high. Gold
bosses you see behind mullion windows. Read
Lloyds TSB. Read MONTE DEI PASCHI
SIENA. A scrape of footsteps. Hear the word
'yes' spoken slowly. Read DRY FALLING
INLET. Warm air is blowing and you read
LEADENHALL. And you read PRIVATE. See
iron gates locked and you turn. Read THIS
STONE WAS LAID BY HIS MAJESTY
KING GEORGE V ON THE TWENTY
THIRD DAY OF MAY MDCCCC XXV
THE SIXTEENTH. Car. Car. Someone
walking. Car. And you read YEAR OF HIS
MAJESTY'S REIGN HER MAJESTY THE
QUEEN MARY BEING PRESENT. See

leaves of stone. Read RARIDAIN. Black
rubbish bag. Man stops on a street corner to
light a white cigarette with a struck match and
he walks. See cobbles like skulls in the earth
and some chipped like teeth. Two griffins of
stone and see stars of gold painted. Hear many
cars roar like the roaring of a great water
vibrating in the earth at your feet up into your
legs entering your breathing. Read Quality
English Lamb. See flowers bunched and two
men talking and bins full to the brim.

See blinding light around the silhouetted forms
of lifting cranes. Black gates of iron. Read St
MILDRED'S CHURCH DEMOLISHED
1872. See a blue filmy light over the surface of a
dark window. A wind passes and rolls the butt
of a cigarette. Read THOMAS HOOD WAS
BORN. Hear the flinty clip of a woman's shoes.
A film of sunlight passes over grey tar bringing
the grey to a greenness like the colour of
cooked broccoli. A man's mouth carries an
upturned smile and the man talks. See a
woman's smile which extends to deep lines. See
a woman seated alone in a corner. Her hair
long, black, wavy, her torso bent into the L of
the corner. See a man talking crouched next to
her. See three individuals walking, talking to
invisible companions. Read PRICE SAVE.
Read CHEAPSIDE. Pass a woman in white,

[192]

smiling, pass rows of tiny grey elephants. See a
pink and white shirt of stripes and movement
within. Golden hair in a tail swinging. Read
SILVER PENCIL 50p. Five winged faces with
ovals of sun across cheeks and two bodies of
stone leaning back. See an abundance of stone
flowers wreathed and vined over the face of a
building. A click of metal. See glasses balanced
on the slide of a nose. The pavement of tar
polished. See two hands of a woman pushing
her red hair, in locks like smoked herring. See a
brown top, tight over a woman. And pale blue
eyes and two women in black strolling slowly.
See crinkled leaves of oak, leaves flecked with
crimson spots, one with twelve, one with seven,
one with five red spots and dull light through
the courses of its veins. Hear voices in a
language you do not understand. See the glass
faces of two watches glint. See the bowl of a
black pipe containing a whitish plug of
smouldering tobacco. Pass the reflection of a
man's legs and see the pavement is flat with
sunlight and the tin-bright sun sears the edge of
a building shrunken. Shadows like spiders from
a woman's legs. See groups of figures sitting
among walls crested with pink tulips like
mohicans. See a glass lifted up to a mouth is
exhausted of contents with one dazzle's glint on
its rim. Light over smooth skin, skin and hair
glow like smouldering. Look up to see the road
curving. See a giant grey dome like an asteroid

on a building like a plinth of many wings made
of stone among trees. Hear, "Where's the
underground." A woman walks, with eyes
pierced by pins of light, she passes watching
you. Turn. Read SVCH . SCENES . OF .
GOOD . AND . EVIL . AS . MAKE . VP .
HVMAN . AFFAIRS . THE . CONSCIENCE.
Turn. See freckled cheeks and turn to read OF .
CHVRCH . AND . NATIONS . THROVGH
. FIVE . CENTVRIES . FOVND . PVBLIC .
VTTERANCE . THE . FIRST. Turn. Look up
to the figure of a golden man bearing a cross
and a halo. And turn to read RECORD . OF .
IT . IS . IN . 1191 AD . IT . WAS . BVILT.
And turn to see smooth brown hair like a
horse's coat, and coarser hair, long, like a
horse's mane. And turn to read BY . BISHOP .
KEMP . IN . 1449 . AND . WAS . FINALLY .
REMOVED . BY . ORDER . OF . THE .
LONG . PARLIAMENT . IN . 1643 . THIS.
Savoury, creamy smell of damp cement curing.
Read IN . 1643 . THIS . CROSS . WAS . RE-
ERECTED . IN . ITS . PRESENT . FORM .
VNDER . THE . WILL . OF . H.C.
RICHARDS . TO . RECALL . AND. Turn,
and walk seeing bollards of red granite, see
crystals the pink of raw salmon. Look up to
faces with winged hair and the sun glances a
blinding fire over panes of glass. There is a
plateau of paving. Hear echoings of footsteps
like muttering. Read ROAD SAFETY. Hear,

"If you don't hear from us, alright then." Look up to see red skeletons of construction structures, cranes and the zigzag of metal bars bolted in sections into giant legs and arms. See closed doors lit with sunlight, huge and wooden, and two figures sitting side by side on one of many steps of grey, crisp, cut stone. There is a hiss of air through many leaves and hear, "Hee hee hee hee." Read THIS HOARDING. A bus slows. Read AVE MARIA. And hear the slow toll of bells float on the roaring traffic. There is the hum of blowing fans. See grey rubber casters on the legs of chairs, grey cobbles set like tumblers on a tray a car passes making a lumpy noise like flappings of rubber. Read AMEN CORNER. Look up to see white and grey struts of cranes. Read AMEN LODGE. Read EUROTECH. Pass a man in a bright yellow jacket. A woman alone. See bricks of bright red oxide and a terracotta frieze of stone masons. See a road descending into the earth. A head of red hair below ground level. Read SITE OF CHRIST'S HOSPITAL. See a carved balustrade of grey granite. See carved and polished stone. A man smoking. The back of a man against a wall. The hair of the smoking man's head short and corrugated with the draw-marks of a comb. See a small plot of grass. Read THIS WREN CHURCH WAS DESTROYED BY FIRE BOMBS IN DECEMBER 1940. UNDER

THE PASTORAL AND
REORGANISATION MEASURE OF 1949,
THE PARISH OF CHRISTCHURCH WAS
UNITED WITH ST. SEPULCHRE
WITHOUT NEWGATE HOLBORN
VIADUCT EC1. Read COUNCILMEN. Read
Sacred to those virtues that adorn a Christian
and Tradesman. this Marble perpetuates the
memory of IOHN MALCOTT. citizen and
Mason of LONDON. who was 35 Years an
inhabitant of this Parish. and died on the 21st
of January 1766. in the 49th Year of his Age.
Hear small feet run and there is laughing
behind a wall. Look up to stones set together as
a high wall and see beds planted with roses. See
manure folded into the earth like scabs of
fibrous, dry substance. See pale grey thorns on
wooden, red-brown rose stems. A woman walks
quietly and a yellow bag swings. Read Near this
spot stood. The head of a man nods to a car,
smiles, crosses the road. See a blackened man of
bronze. Hear, "To get a contrast." Purple
smears across charcoal-grey bark of a tree. See
the bony grain of varnished oak. See a small
garden among trees. Look up to the fishbone of
a television aerial. See a black and white crest
on a man's jacket. Hear, "No he gets very
funny." Hear the quavery voice of an old lady.
Pink and red tulips. Trembling spear of a leaf.
Read PATIENTS CROSSING. Hear, "So I'm
not." See two hands buttoning two halves of a

[196]

jacket. Read NURSES GATE. See scratches
over wooden panels of a door. Read
STUDENTS AND PATIENTS ARE NOT.
Read BLOOD TRANSFUSIONS. Read 45
LITTLE BRITAIN. See the backs of two men
walking ahead. Hear, "There's somebody
waiting over." Pass shrivelled cups of purple and
decayed tulips. Read MENS LAVATORIES.
See two bars missing from a car's grille. Hear,
"On Friday we head off." Hear, "Yes, three
hours on the train." Sunlight brings fox-orange
to a redness of bricks. See a red band around
the diameter of a black cap. Read CL 516
Supervisor. In silver letters on a man's shoulder.
A woman's mouth opens, she coughs. See green
and purple metalwork. Look up to see a small
flag of red, white and blue triangles, a cross
meeting at the centre of the flag diagonally.
Read CORPO. Read RATION OF
LONDON. Smell meat far away, a fatty, wet
smell. See a cast iron star like a thistle. There
are yellow lights shedding a dim, gristle glow.
See a pale blue scooter with white tyres. Read
Your loan can be for anything. Pass black
spikes of railings. Hear, "Not quite sure yet."
See dark red glossy lips. Pass a varnished
entrance to a bar. See a man holding a brown
bottle of beer in one hand. There is a smell of
fish. Green cast iron gates. Hear, "Hold on,
hold on." Hear, "Many years ago I came up
here with Ian and Sans, and I thought, what's

going on, right." Pass a group of figures knotted in conversation. Hear, "And she married him." Hear voices murmuring out of music. All hands visible holding bottles and cigarettes. Hear, "Isn't this where." See a woman in white with a red tie binding her waist with a crooked angle. See white ripped threads dangling at knees. See a man walking like a blackbird runs. A man in a car with a nose small for his big face. Read facade international. Read ST JOHN. Read BINARY VISION. A hand runs wavishly through thin hair and traffic passes. See dark bottles standing on cobbles, long-necked like a glass flock of craning geese. See green bamboo stems and chrome-silver light-fittings in a room without people. See black heels stride from the door of a room and they are like tall hooves. And a golden lock of brittle hair and a green glass candlestick. Hear, "Fish." Hear three voices like low moaning winds over moorstones. There is a red face. Hear languages spoken you do not know. Hear, "Yeah, he's, yeah." See shoes and jackets. There is a red light alone like a moon, redder, and then another, like a setting sun dilutely. Pass a heap of tarry gravel, hard-core rocks and sand. A man with grey hair opens a van door. A man with grey hair under the open bonnet of a white van. See a substance sprayed into the snout of an engine's air intake. See a glass of wine with light passing through. There is the growling clatter of an engine

[198]

starting like sheets of metal hit with hard sticks, it clocks into combustion and splutters to a standstill with a chuff of smoke from the tail of an exhaust you see. Read YOGNA NEWS. Turn to see a white van lurch a growl of engine revving. Pass through an arch. Pass a white door, dust in a crack of its paint. Read 1. Blue door. Read 2. Green door. Read 3. Black door with a red and white rosette. Read 4. Blood-pudding red door with a blister. Read 5. Pinewood-coloured door with a vertical crack. Read 6. Pass a woman in an emerald green jacket. Pass alongside a strip of black railings. One siren of a bird chattering. Hear a woman walking alone by the click-tap of the tack-hammers of her heels. A brick church among trees standing squat. See the hand of a figure holding up wine. Hear, "We had a lovely lovedream." A dog among bushes, fox red along the spine, and it curls, and gets in among leaves like dog's ears. A small bird sings up and down and up. A man and woman seated, settled on a bench with bags beside them at their seated hips and three claps strike the air like wood blocks slapped together dryly. Tumblish flight of a transparent fly caught on a quiff of updraft tumbles like tumbleweed, its legs in its wings. A blackbird sings among echoes. Shrill caramel blackbird note returns to the beginning of a song and sings again the same. See flints protruding through earth like the upturned teeth of hogs and the bark oozy with gleamy globs of red-honeyed resin. There is a cracked, black bark like the plated skin of a crocodile, and the diamond pattern of an adder's skin behind the head and down the spine of the tree bark. Turn to see golden numerals flash like teeth and a bicycle passes with a repetitive squeak like chicks in a nest or the panic-button-cry of a mouse in a cat's mouth. Read ROSEMARY SCHOOL. Read The Worshipful Company of Mercers. Pass big, round, dolorous leaves and look closely to see veins like spines and ribs of sprats. Three trees in an alley like old men and women, bent into hunches, twisted up to the slot of sky between houses. Read FURNITURE DEPT. See flowers of chestnuts like chandeliers. Muffled cry of an alarm like a broken squeak-pip of sound. A man walking, white-jacketed, a blue can of beer in one hand, see the cuffs of the white jacket greyly grubby to an accumulated sheen. Read GIRLS & INFANTS. Letters cut into pale stone, Roman script. Up and down of a bird's cry. A tower of walls and windows like a stern seriously intended face. See brown leaves like small leather jackets, oak and sycamore dead on the floor. See chairs and planks strewn through a discarded playground, beard of grass like pin-mould. One polystyrene cup speared on a railing's spike like the head of a man without features. Tree-flesh oozed between railing-bars,

[200]

bulged like a wooden cellulite under bark. A woman passes with white pages clamped in four fingers folded over one edge of them against the palm. Pages curl and flap like children turning back in the rear window of a car. Hear the cry of a car's siren. See the sugar-dusted look, grey, of mildewed nettle leaves, the jagged edges like rip-saws, bristled hairy. Two men seated on a bench, talking, you walk seeing the tentacles of a long plant flowed from a wall. Belly of a woman protruding like a peeled egg, colour of skin through a gap between trousers and shirt. Pass a car containing policemen, and blue lights revolving and flashing. See the eyes of a blonde-haired woman watching things from the corner of two streets, her backside seated on a low wall, the wall pushing a V-shape of wall-edge into her buttocks. See a car containing policemen slow down and begin to turn. See the arm of a boy pointing in a direction. And the car turns and drives that way. Pass a man with a green phone. Pass a curled fleck floating. Read TYSOE STREET. Sirens congregate. See young girls gathered and excited chattering like starlings over crumbs. Giggles in heads down softened to pigeonish noises, the hands over mouths of two girls. Hear, "Mike, Mike." See a bird rising. Pass blackened acorns of iron, about the size of a man's fist. Read BOU 176K. See a wooden steering wheel within the saloon of a carbody.

[201]

The flat plain of a puddle's skin flashes gold once and grows black as you pass. Trill of a bird's note ending. Pass a flat cap on the crown of a man's head. Pass an iron grille, rusty to a brown fur like suede. Pass a bicycle leaning and a boy crouched on a step. Hear, "I will tell my mum tonight, I will tell her that I was bonked I swear." See the colour of foxes on bricks of a wall and the shadow of a figure passes the lumps and bumps of the wall and ripples in the cracks like the undulations of a fish moving through water. There is a sharp stain of fishsmell on the air. Hear the bright peal of running water splash from a tap. Pass a crushed brown paper bag like the body of a wren lying on its side. See a net curtain pulled astray. Hear the gurgle of a running car's exhaust. The echo of the clunk of a hollow steel pole dropped onto concrete within the four walls of a courtyard. Pass two boys seated on a kerbstone, and the stone grey with small ruts from the stone-saw visible. Pass a long stone trough. See yellow roses and a green door the colour of rose leaves, and paint flaking. See yellow ragwort flowers like the wings of small moths. Hear, "Right, yeah." Hear, "What's the best thing." Read DR. DAVID DAVIES DR. KEVIN DEWHIRST DR. SONIA MUNNELLY DR. KARINA UPTON. See a Bulldog on a short leash, heavy-jowled. See oranges and apples behind glass. See three cardboard tubes held together by strips of sellotape. See a woman climbing from a car and closing the door with a slam-shut briskness. See a brass lion's head small as a hand. Read FILTHY MACNASTY'S. See a group of five women seated and look up to blue sky and see pale lines scratched across the blue. Read GEORGE CRUIKSHANK 1792-1878 ENGRAVER, AND ILLUSTRATOR LIVED HERE. Throat of a woman clearing itself. Denim trousers and a jacket. See black iron railings. A woman in a purple dress thin at the arms and legs holds by her hip a black can of beer, see her face set with creases beside a raised bank of grasses and white umbels of cow parsley, blades of annual meadow grass and mists of Gloucester Fog. A wooden man with straw hair. See a woman alone in a room. A darkening of gold light across a window pane. The pale tower of a church. One flower in deep shadow and shadows within the throat of the flower. Read FENNER BROCKWAY. Pass a yellow door with a brass fish knocker. And read SAINT MARK'S CHURCH THE LONDON CENTRE FOR CHRISTIAN. Stroke of a breeze. Hear a door slam. See stone slabs and you walk over slabs. There is the face of a woman, half-shadowed, her eyes glint once and blink shut-open. See a stone head and walk. Hear out of the breaking of glass a sharp brutal high pitch like a flame and, "Don't you

[203]

fucking." And the sound of glass like a violence
of fractures into a tinkle like a splash of
clatters. See a small boy of about ten years
wielding a heavy hammer. And he slides the
hammer in under the cloth of his red T-shirt
like the body of a wounded sparrow to be
nestled at the heart, and with his hidden
hammer starts to chase an older girl with
threatening noises beginning to yell uphill.
Turn to walk and see a slow-walking man ahead
with his head involved in the pages of an
opened black book. A pigeon flies up. A
songbird sings. Read SADLER'S. See a man and
woman indoors eating together, on opposite
sides of a small table and one candle shines the
tongue of its flame uprightly between. See a
fork touch a mouth. Flash of silver. See pale
yellow roses in a small garden. Read FOR
SALE. Hear a woman's cry of joy. Hear, "We've
got a sold sign." Hear voices. See the painted
head of a man on a wooden board. Hear, "I'd
be out at twenty past seven." Hear, "If you
write hello." See a fast-moving bike and the
rider in black leather, look up to lights perched
in trees and the leaves deeply-glowing a
greenness of halo about each lightbulb. See
black electric cables. The bassoon of a car horn
pitch-falls as it passes. Light rows over water
like a boat. Read ALL SOLD. A cyclist cycling.
A man walks slowly and his head is lowered. A
face with meeting eyebrows pulls up its

shadows. One car parked is curved like a dung beetle's aubergine-black instrument-case of a body. Hear a quickening of the tap of footsteps and look up to see a hanging basket like half a dark moon. Hear, "Yeah, I know, he's very." Read METROPOLITAN WATER BOARD ON THE SITE OF THE NEW RIVER HEAD 1613 1920. See grit among conger-thick roots of a bulging tree, the roots like eels descending into earth. A woman standing alone in the shade of trees is clothed in the pointed ellipses of lights between shadows of leaves, like the eyes of Argo. See the hair of a woman whisked through the passing of air like a squall of movements in a walk. There is a heavy sharp smell of tar like black bitter toffee. A woman with a smile, a flash of white teeth like the crescent of a moon on its back. The laugh of a woman. See the tapping of a woman's foot. A passing bus containing many faces, the red body of the bus accelerates to overtake a struggling cyclist, the turning-out of the bus causes the double-decked height to lean. Two cries of a car's horn. A man with a shaved head passes, see the field of its grey stubble, a serious expression in eyes squinting uphill by bike. Turn to see blue lights flashing at the upper end of a long dark street. See a group of boys like crows strutting and turning sharply to each other and looking further afield with pointed looks on a dark street corner. Hear, "We love

you Kay." See a room with many shelves of
large folios, black and cracked leather spines.
See round tables surrounded by four grey chairs
each, like tables with their table-pups craning
heads to reach the source of milk. See a
mahogany-brown floor, polished. A man
carrying two black bags. A black face with a
white cigarette. Hear the click of a light
switching on and off. A breeze lights up. See
the bars of railings reflected on a dark window.
A smashed glass. Boarded-up windows of a large
building. Read DY HYPE. Body of a man
slouched. Read THE BULL. See a clock set in
the wall of a tower. A group of figures in stone
relief and you hear the crying-up of laughter.
You turn right, walls of a black building cliff-
high and you hear a siren crying in a changing
pitch of two tones up and down. A man walks
engrossed in a strip of white card held in his
left hand. See a blue light ahead and two
helmeted men in white shirts and black, padded
waistcoats. Hear many figures bubbling from
their voices in an opened doorway. There are
shouts. See a froth of creamy foam above a
blackness in a straight tall-sided glass. See the
two horns of the crescent moon. A silver
pendant bumping against skin like an aircraft
landing at the throat of a trotting woman. An
empty lobby of polished stone. A passing black
beard. A chalk drawing of a child's lion. A
descending staircase. See figures at tables. See a

pink napkin over a leg and knees. Racing
ambulance. A man chewing a thumbnail,
twisting the hand to achieve the curve of the
nail as teeth rip-pull. A grey dome against blue
sky. Hear, "What we do is like what it enables
us to do." Hear, "I fucking, nah." A gaggle of
laughs encompasses you like the wings of
pigeons and you walk out of it. A man with
gold earrings knocks at a door, rattles the letter
box and you hear a clack. Laugh of a woman.
See the laughing woman wears cloth crimson as
blood. Toothy rattle of keys. Read
PERMANENT GUESTS ARRANGED FOR
SIDE DOOR. A man's face with glasses about
his neck. The shadow of a bicycle. Dark
spiderish spokes in distortions of shadow over
slabs and hooked between in the contours of
mortar troughs and paving cracks. A rampage
of banters. A charcoal grey tie at a man's collar.
Cigarette raised in the hand of a man to a dull
dark blue sky without stars. Turn to a group of
men among the wink of beerglass-rims lifted
and lowered like phrases in a melody. Woman
in an office wearing a brightly coloured dress of
coarse cotton, patterns like parrots. She
ascends stairs, her skin dark, she holds up a tall,
red feather duster. Pass wooden slabs formed as
a fence, the wood brown as spaniels, the grain
rough as a donkey's hair. Sky fanned out to a
pale horizon and you see green bottles in the
hands of three running men. Hear, "When we

[207]

get back." A man in a taxi eating a burger hugged by a bap. Man's skin pale like uncooked sausages. A man with a chin hanging low before his throat, his arm raised to hail a taxi. Taxi stops. Hear the metallic click of a car door. Black-cab window contains the head of a man. See a flower-adorned gold watch chain spangle in shadow. A window with glowing lamps of red and blue and green. See a window opaque with blackness. Read LONDON BOY 11 ON MURDER CHARGE. Man perched on a barstool, hand between legs. Read GOLDEN LANE. Read METHODIST RECORDER. Read Environmental area No Through Route. Dark tower ahead, dark tower by the dark tower. See a light fade in one window like an ember dying. Rough image of a monkey painted. Read WARNING HAZCHEM. Flared-out shadow of a lamp post. Hear the fluttering notes of a scooter downhill. Twin-headed shadows of parking meters. Buzzing of a transformer. There is the sound of water hitting a surface and glushing. Read FORTUNE. Two men together walking towards you. Hear, "You can't even." Hear a voice above you calling a word. Quiet plants in a sunken zone, darkly pointed slender leaves. Read CRIPPLEGATE FREE LIBRARY. Hear the glugging muttering of pigeons at low level. Two leaves trembling. Descend into covered walkway. A dusty, oily smell like bus stations.

White hair of a head, legs walk purposefully. An arm swinging at the side of a body, a golden brooch of leaves fastened to a coat's lapel. Read SHAKESPEARE TOWER DEFOE HOUSE RESIDENTS CAR PARK. Flints set into concrete like teeth of a shark. Pillars of concrete. White case held by a black handle in the curled hand of a man, fingers like the legs of a hermit crab. A finger within the grotto of a nostril, the hand twists up turning the first finger within the nose. A mouth still, teeth pull the lower lip thin. Eyes of a woman looking out from behind glass like the eyes of a hawk. Pink ear rim of a man. A man involved in the process of eating. A woman from a window. The eye of a woman. Thin horns of a crescent moon. Shadows of scaffolding criss-crossed. Red stars of paint on a white-headed bollard. Read ARREST DEFENCE SERVICE We regret to inform. Read YE OLDE RED COW. Three dragons of stone. See a fried egg and two oil-glazed sausages on butter-yellow toast. See deeply recessed wooden doors. Two men smoking on a doorstep quietly in the gorge of an alley. A woman folding brown sugar into coffee by spoon. See the pointed nose of a woman. Orange light of streetlamps on the enamel of teeth. Hear, "See you tomorrow." A thin-eyed woman's head rocking like a wooden-horse rocked by a child. Hear, "Nobody ... Delks has gone, and you've gone." See an interior of tables, a white figure in a dark corner. Hear two women laughing. Hear, "She didn't, she had less than us ... she had a water." See the heads of violet tulips raised. Read H. See a woman walking alone, smoking in a striped top of thin bands of colour horizontally around her torso, wrinkled in folds at the waist. Read THIS MINIBUS IS. Pale pinlight of a single star shrinks. You hear a clicking repeated of hobnailed soles. Gleam of light like a shark's smile on the black leather cap of a man's boot. Man walks away. Read THIS IS A NO SMOKING BUILDING. Short-haired woman whispering to a man's ear. Black iron bars, silent. Glint of leaves like the eyes of sheep on dark hills reflecting the light of the moon. Stone face leaning out of the keystone of an archway, lips together and turned down a little, smooth and serious as a deathmask. See a grey and ribbed dome like a pigeon-grey breast of lead in near-black indigo sky. Hear, "Yes yes yes, I want to withdraw every statement." Read FROM THIS SITE GUGLIELMO MADE THE FIRST PUBLIC TRANSMISSION OF WIRELESS SIGNALS ON. Read St Botolph. See a golden sphere rested on a grey dome. A red light falling over black painted metal. Read St Vedast alias Foster. Look up to see the needle of a golden spike rising into dark sky. See triangular glasses. Pass a plastic body dressed in denim shorts and a white blouse like

the symbol of a woman in summer. See the
blouse embroidered with stitched white flowers
like daisies. A blast of wind. Read BREAD
STREET. Pass two women perched on kerb
stones leaning to cross. A man wiping his
mouth with the edge of his hand below the
thumb. You look back to see two women
crossing the road at a run. A flag of red, blue,
white, a diagonal cross and various triangle
parts of the colours, and the fabric of the flag
folding itself hard in the passing wind. Look up
to a black clock's body and turn to see a
photograph behind glass of a seated cheetah.
Hear the pants of a jogging man's breath. Soft,
mute bellow of a car's horn like the low of a
cow in evening. Flashing lights in the dark sky,
red to green twinkle. And see a man rubbing
the closed ball of his eye, face of a man within
the red box of a passing bus, a man in the front
seat upstairs stands, turns into the aisle. See a
relief of figures and hear the chuffing of a
passing bike's engine and see cooling fins
streaked on the side of the chuffing bike's
engine. Read Subway. See a white arrow of
direction. Hear, "I'm looking at the vendors in
the market."

Read CAUTION SITE ENTRANCE. A drip   XIII
of water and a drip of water follows a drip of
water and you look up to see possibly hundreds

of unlit windows like precisely rectangular and
similar caves in the cliff of a building. Read
WHITE LION. Hear, "The next few weeks
that's what I'm basically ... I've sat down and
worked it out." See roses, the folded petals of
iron. See a green room in a tall window. Read
SORRY NO SOILED OR SITE WEAR. A
tyre scuffs its rubber on a sharp kerbstone with
a scrape and a squeak. See a sword carved in
stone and bodies dying in stone and heads
trapped with arms of stone pushing up from the
mass of stone and a winged angel or soldier
with a snake about his sword of bronze and big
cats eating big cats' ears and children huddled
together in bronze. Look up to see a broad
square tower still against dark sky shielded with
unmoving cloud of pigeon greyness and hear a
rustle of clothing over legs passing and the
voices of strollers you cannot make out into
words. Read SERVICES & EVENTS. See
stains of rust over stone. See four lions and a
naked woman of lead. A stone bearded head of
stone. See green and red umbrellas. Rattle of
bike wheels over a manhole cover, see figures of
bronze standing on stone. Cold sound of a
chimed bell. See jackets without men and the
flowers of grey hydrangeas in the dark like the
heads of children playing sardines crouched
away among their corners. See the word
WELLINGTON. See a strongman cut out of
stone. See a man picks up a bottle and unscrews

[212]

the cap. Hear a fizz escaping. Round gold earring, flash like the two horns of an ellipsing sun. Man all in black like a crow's feather of a man. See a flag flying black across a small part of the night's sky like a door of cloth. See chewing gum flattened to spots over dark paving like a blemish of lichens. Read HEAD TEACHER SHOT IN FACE. High hiss of breath in the laugh of a man. Cigarette hanging sloped down from the lips of a man's face. Wind beating a flag from left to right and the noise of the flag beats the air back with its thump-flap cracking of cloth. Turn to see a dome of grey and three women pass. Clump of tree leaves. And a man's eye glances sideways seeing a parked car. See illuminated squares of glass set into pavement below your feet. Body of a man climbs into the body of a car, the one conceals part of the other and the other contains the one as the car door is closed. A man coughs aloud to himself. Read WEIGHT LIMIT. A woman exhales one eel of smoke which frays into three rising eels. Green fronds of a plant in a window. Cars stream the dark road. A boat's bow carved into stone. Light footsteps of a man. One plastic round carton rolls hurriedly over tarmac. Walk two parallel yellow lines. See the arch of a bridge like a back in a ballet. Dark space of a river and the river's smell like a cold, dark, brown green. See twists and currents of water viperishly swim-wrestle and boxers of water smack fists in a shadow and clap to the walls of the river. Four turrets of a church to your left. A jogging man. See dark buildings and a bridge supporting thirteen figures across the span of the river. Fast wind. Two towers on a bridge like two men in a duel. A ship in the dark. Hear the grunt of a lorry's engine and you turn to see a dome of grey and cranes standing above things with their single arms straight as guns at a shoulder. Turn right to a snake of two moving trains with lit, rectangular windows going in opposite directions. Read FT in pink letters. Read BT in blue light. A red bus containing yellow lights and the bus passes. See a river-shore grey like the skin of a trout, like the length of a dead cat, like the slump of an old coat. Hear the 'tink' of keys jangle. Hear the noise of keys pass. Hear water falling on a stone below. Pass a painted hand rail and hold it the length of two steps. Hear the cry of a phone like a lamb's bleat. See granite steps step into the river. Hear, "D'you know David Reece?" Two claps of a bell. Hear, "Yeah, that's." And two men pass over dark water, walking. See small reflected lights dropping plumblines of light. Read The Thames Flows Down. Hear, "All away." Hear a hiss of music at the ears of a passing man and the hiss grows faint and the man passes. A puddle of water like a flat body. A nearby engine chuntering unevenly nearly stalls. Five

flowers of stone. A clatter of metal. And hear
the wash-away of water slapped from a shore.
And hear laughter and words in a language you
do not know. Read All the World's. See a man
with a glass and a jug of water. Sharp perfume
containing tea tree oil behind a cigarette smoke
veil. Read STORM CLIPPER. Slap of foamy
water, wash of curdled hissings and the crack of
water butchered by the shore. Rustle of plastic
and a whine of wind by increments up to a
sound which collapses to a buffeting noise in
the craters of the ears. See a row of faces in a
dark building like monkeys of silence. Hear the
grinding screel of a train's wheels. Hear,
"Upstairs, on." Hear, "Can we go on the?"
Wind running downriver like a shoal of flying
cars cutting up the water up into flying and
curl-fallen peelings from a grater and the river's
underwater like a bituminous treacle creeps. A
man crying. Bridge-strings played by the wind,
aeolian harp of a suspension cable. Hear, "I
suspect the design of this is quite formidable,
so there's just." Hear a sound like a fanbelt of
traffic continuously and the wind makes a
moan. Trains and a bridge of two towers like a
forked tongue. See steam rising into an
elephant's head of steam from a trunk of steam
and its body breaks up into darkness. Water
strummed by wind to a frown of ripples hitting
a stone and the wind skates like a foot on a
skate and the wind straddles each shore of the

river with lapping splashes and sound ploughed
out of motion like an excess. Dark grey of a flat
stone. See buildings like strewn cut rocks in a
quarry. Square chimney and air fluttery at your
head, turn left at the neck to see water's shivery
fever of streams crossing stream, wind-streaked
serrations of panicky river, flat, black, smooth
surface like oil and you pass. Hear a metronome
of a walk. Two policemen together and see one
helmeted face looking down onto pavement
and one helmeted face with its eyes caught in
the sky. Read CITY OF LONDON. Pale
potato chips on paving. Hear voices grow and
hear voices fade. Read OXO. Letters of red
light. Squeak of brakes twice. Read 020 7248
2916. Flutter of a palm's fronds like black,
flexible knives lashing about. A single red light
like a live volcano seen from the air. Silverish
trees on the far shore. A ring's shine like a
crescent moon on the finger of a man. A coiled
fish of iron. Hear traffic prowling. Read toilet.
See an iron fish twisted in the body and coiled
around the foot of a lamp post. Man in dark
clothes rising from a wooden bench to walk and
he walks with feet not leaving the ground. Hear
noises of traffic and see two arches of a bridge
and read SEA CONTAINERS HOUSE. Hear
voices gathered together. See roses apart and
shiny leaves below flesh-pink flowers, the leaves
like small black canoes stranded within the
tree. See a mouth grinning, and pass, and hear

traffic make its crossings each way across the
flowing water and screels of the metal wheels of
a train moving also. See iron columns rising
from water like legs. A sphere of light. Damp
spots on a step. A girl islanded in traffic. See
scaffolding poles. See a chain of lights strung
and the wind moves the whole chain slightly to
bow inland from the river's stream. See black-
branched trees and you look up to stone figures
lit by lights and one shadow like an obelisk is
cast up over the stone cheek of a face. See a girl
with black eyes carrying full bags and see a
stone horse climbing out from one wall of a
building. A hall of words written on stone. An
iron grate and the wind beats. See lights in
windows and a room dull by lightbulb. A
jogging man pauses. See three people ahead and
look to the scrawl of trees black against sky.
Hear, "I'm still okay." Voice of a girl in a red
top. Black hull of a metal boat, there are rivets
visible and you see rust leaked from paint. Man
with a single dreadlock pushed into his lefthand
trouser pocket. Read HMS PRESIDENT.
Look to the lit portholes of a passing plane. See
benches with cast iron legs like the legs of
camels and see golden parts to the arms of each
bench. See two slices of lemon lying shrunken
under one bench. Read DELAYS POSSIBLE.
See opening buds of a tree and a dark space of
shrubs and grasses. Hexagons of concrete. Read
POLICE. See lit windows uninhabited. An old

man walking at speed. See an iron plaque with crystals of rust. Blindfolded woman of bronze. See an anchor and two cars slow to a halt and move. Read DEWER London 1849. See a winged dragon of metal. Read FIFTH ANNIVERSARY OF HIS MAJESTY. And the air turns up and you read OF THE RIVER BETWEEN LONDON BRIDGE. There is a wind darkly and you smell the river, reading AND WESTMINSTER BRIDGE WAS, WITH HIS MAJESTY'S GRACIOUS PERMISSION NAMED BY THE PORT OF LONDON AUTHORITY KING'S REACH. See a child of bronze and a grotesquely faced man and some lions' heads. Read WELLINGTON. See green water moving. And a golden ship. Plane trees' tendrils in grey sky, twigs curled at ends like greyhounds' tails. Hear a rustle of plastic from beneath a tree. Face of a man. Read W.T. STEAD 1849-1912 THIS MEMORIAL TO A JOURNALIST OF WIDE RENOWN WAS ERECTED NEAR THE SPOT WHERE HE WORKED FOR MORE THAN 30 YEARS. Hear a dog sniff. Count eighteen black portholes on a boat and nine portholes containing light. A chain entering the body of water. Read NOT THE SAME. See a fish of gold. Read Look Right. See benches on the bodies of sphinxes with wings. Read TEMPLE. See yellow cart wheels. Read STATION OPENING TIMES MON-

SAT 0530. Hear, "Working my socks off." Read shoeless joes. Smell diesel fumes. Man in a parked car in the dark with a face under the reflections of trees on a windscreen like a coat of arms. Start of an engine. Face into shadows as the face of the body reclines back into the bucket of the car seat without a word. Grey interior of a car's cabin with small lights on the dashboard. Read FEEDING PIGEONS IS NOT PERMITTED. And a smell of flowers and you turn to see many flowers. Stone rusticated by chiselling. See empty, lit rooms. Columns of stone. A single pigeon. Read one of a kind! Air like a dust. A motorcycle screams a driven note passing away and grows small. Hear water dripping. A man holding two ends of a chain. Two girls pass. Read City of Westminster No. See a bed's mattress in the shadow of an arch, see a brown suitcase standing, a book and a clock in the shadow of an arch and see a neat stack of flat cardboard boxes. Walk and see nine boys wearing top hats of red, white and blue. The boys in top hats make a roar of themselves. Lights like stars and see faces in cars and the cars pass and there is one car stationary. Read R151 YCH. A woman passes quickly. See yellow spikes of flowers and see one glint of an eye from two faces kissing. Read ROYAL. And your hand brushes leaves which are cold. Interior of a marble-white flower and a smell of oats in milk. The open

hands of fig leaves. Read JUSTICE HONOUR.
Long-necked woman leaning over children.
Glints among drops of water hanging. Read
BREAKFAST & HOT MEALS. Read NO
PARKING. Red roses painted on iron. Two
cigarette butts. Red, white, blue of a flag flying.
A giant wheel in the sky with thin spokes.
Heavy chain to your left and read
PARANOID. Read PUBLIC
CONVENIENCE. Green bottle and a can
with a dent half in the earth at angles. Woman
eating crisps pale as the ears of children. Read
TUBE MAP. Man in a blue jacket standing. A
man hunched, ripping with teeth from one of
six white baguettes held under arm with eyes at
a screen. Read my mystery solved.

Hear the noise of water kneeling and rising. XIV
Hear, "Straight as a pole." Hear reply, "Straight
as a shark." And hear two laughs. Black towers
lurking in the roof of your eyes, like four
wolves. Hear, "I'm really sick of things here."
Look down to white shoes passing through
orange shadows. See red and brown haloes to
orange shadows. Hear, "Two hours." Turn to
see lights on wires strung between posts. Hear,
"It's ridiculous." Shake of a plastic wrapper. See
two green lamps attached to a black pole and a
man runs. Two women whisper. Hear, "Can be
controlled by drugs." Hear reply, "Well, yes."

Hear the toll of bells. Scrape of two feet. A black hatted and brisk man. Hear, "Although actually, today I had a." Man on phone. A gritty laugh. Hear, "No, no I went to ... erm." Man with hair. A black glove clenched. Paintspots on tar ground. A man slouch-walking. A man breathes fast. A girl stamps through a puddle. Light concentrated onto an eye through a lens. Hear a petrol motor. Bright light at base of a partition like a skirting. Clack-a-clack of a motor. Spray-out in rays of a dark puddle on tar. A square beard. A moustached man waddles. One, two, and three scrapes of a foot. Read Japanese Hair. Hear, "I can get to school quicker on my bike." School party follows a talking man. Hear, "My God, where are we going?" Rumble akin to the sound of thunder moving through the iron girders of a bridge. All shakes. Orange steam rising. And hear, "As a human being." Man, grey-haired, clutching a paper. Bright footsteps. Look down to the jellied flow-away of water. Hear, "Hey." Bodies pass in slow groups. Squeal of crying-out metal. Black headphones adorn a head like two dark moons. A woman bites an apple. She is gold-haired. A shaved head in tweeds. A man in a blanket, sitting, holding a cup. Read COFFEE REPUBLIC. Look down to people climbing. Hear, "Are you in England?" Hear, "It's the first lager I've had." Hear, "Big Issue." See water dimpled. Tassels of blue flying. Raindrops on

ground like water grit. See pale flat beard. Two
men wearing ties. Read JOSEPH
BAZALGETTE. A man walking. See a chain of
light bulbs glowing blind bright. See a moon-
faced clock. The clock face reads ten past
seven. See leaves of iron among leaves of laurel.
Read SW1. See three figures ahead. A dark
bronze man towering into glow-grey sky,
bronze the colour of bletted medlars, the man
on a plinth. See shields and spears set about
plinth. A gold wristwatch flashes like a Midas
smile, glints like a small bird. See palm fronds
like spearheads, dusty red and alligator green-
black. Voices exchanging words. A girl
complaining to older people. Black taxi stops.
See dark windows. Read Highway
Improvements. See hessian cloth wrapped
around the base of trees in a zone of
roadworks. Read 6 tonne. See trees against
buildings. Smell rubber. Child cries, "For
another hour ... thirty minutes." A man looks.
See polished granite. A padlock. Raindrops on a
car windscreen. Read 26 27. A car reversing. See
two women in an office with tight black tops
clinging to their toned figures, like two human
jackdaws in a caged light. Read CRAVEN
PASSAGE. Read DAILY. Read INLETS. A
smashed glass. See a man through a window
talking alone to a plastic box bathing his face in
greenish-grey light. A woman walks under a
black umbrella held over her head. Single cry of

[222]

a car's alarm. A second cry fills up the air. Read
KIDD RAPINETT. A woman facing a man
and a woman over a desk. See cardboard on the
road, flattened. Read EXTREMELY
CHOCOLATEY MINIBITES. Read
REFLEX. Hear a pat of rain. Hear, "It's alive."
Read Exhibition. See two red buses. Read
PINT. A woman walks biting her nails, over
wet pavements. A man shrugs, his tie half
undone. See a tall fluted column of pale stone.
Hear, "It was like, O." Two women walk from a
darker place. Eight bricks supporting one
corner of a black kiosk. An openness among
buildings. An open square with fountains in the
dim light. Read LOOK RIGHT. Traffic
passing. Clack clack of metal. Girl in a
turquoise skirt, her calf muscles tensed under
skin. Hear, "And so." A woman walking. See
four bronze lions sitting. Sheen of light on dark
pavements. Hear, "Go over." See a giraffe's and
an elephant's head, and the head of an ibex in
pale stone. See other animals.

Hear, "I have a feeling." See a bronze horse on   xv
a stone plinth. See a dome with leaves cut over
its surface into it. A bronze head and bronze
hair. A girl, pale, wearing a cap, spinning round.
See benches with figures seated and a scattered
crowd of pigeons strutting and there are lions
of bronze. Hear, "He did a bust of Soane." See

red-gold light of the sun on the ribs of a fluted column. A man passes holding the butt of a burning brown cigar in the seat of his mouth. Hear a general hum of traffic lying down and getting up again like an animal of noise. There is the bitter sugariness of tar smoke curling. See pigeons flying up as a crowd and moving in a circle of grey, papery noise and flat smacking of wings as they get close to your ears. See pink-lit water and the barrel of a cigar held between fingers upwards and you see three lions of dark metal and turn away and walk seeing a man of stone-colour holding a sword and a column leading down to a rope at its base. See the beak of a pigeon stab a rhomboid crumb of gritty substance and the crumb breaks apart into smaller crumbs. Read CANADIAN PACIFIC. See feet strolling over squares of flat, smooth stone and stones of grey and red. Turn to see a gold sunlight burning bright on the vertical of a clock tower and a moon near to the face of the clock is three-quarters full and yellow-white, with craters of sky blue. See a man at the eye of a camera before a couple strolling and talking together and there are pigeons strutting across the bare horizontal face of a plinth. See a milk-white cow of marble material and the body of a red bus passes before it hiding it for the length of a red bus which passes away and the white cow is visible. See horns of white on the head of the white cow and udders of milkwhiteness

under the belly of the cow. Hear the squeak
and pip-pip of brakes. See gates of iron and
enter a large space. Hear footsteps on
flagstones and up steps of stone and see on
each step a gleam of gold-lit steel like the edge
of a sharp knife. Gold frame of a painting.
Hear, "Far galleries right." Hear, "Okay, bye-
bye." See figures gathered about flowers of
stone at a tomb and a pale blue and grey river
flowing into a sea like long hair in water and
the sea shallow with turquoise in chalky french
blue and deep with viridian in grey. Turn at the
footsteps of a walking man and you see a man
alone on the seat of a chair. A painted blue
garment and figures of cracked paint on a pale
cream-grey. The rug of a sheepskin over the
body of a child and the head of the child with
golden curls and the breast of a woman and the
nipple pink like the pink of a rose and glints of
a blind light like the bluish bloom of an old
cataract. Read The Virgin and Child with Saint
John and you turn to a girl in pink cloth with
sharp eyes glinting and a woman seated head
turned at the ground. See a cross of gold and
the figure of a man stretched out on a blue like
the colour of hot sky and streams of fiery blood
red across the blue from holes in the body of
the fleshtones. Carved stone beyond windows.
Read Crucifix, about 1242 - 85. Pass the
scowling face of a man, see a frown of brown
skin with a crack on the bridge of the nose, and

[225]

a painted hand with a painted book. Halo of
dull greenish gold about a green-brown hood on
the head of a man, and the eyes are red brown
like pools crossed with sun. Faces with green in
the flesh and shadows with green glowing like a
northern light across shapes of dry slopes and
see bare feet afloat, and see bodies painted
among dark painted trees and a flat stroke of
dovegrey with tatter-ends of bristle markings.
Pales of green among dark leaves. See a figure
central to others, and one man is kissing the
face of another and another is holding the blade
of a razor to a man's ear and the image of blood
spews noiselessly and the sky is a golden light.
See gold frames and zones of deep crimson-
scaled black and there is scarlet blood painted
and figures with halos of roundness over their
heads and the image of a man stepping out
from a tomb of violet-grey and brown the
colour of dust, see there are men in a painted
sleep, leaning heads on arms, and arms resting
on shields. See dark-rimmed metal helmets and
eyelids. Pass a painted woman in a striped
cadmium and green-black garment with a pink
garment over the greens and the folds of cloth
painted. See a crowd of eyes among a crowd of
halos and four painted toes scratched with red.
See the face of a man and it nods by the
varnished frame of a door. A man close to a
man seated who stands. Two children holding a
wounded man of smooth paint. See the image

of a book on the image of earth before a kneeling man. See a gold apparition floating above the upturned face of the image of the kneeling man, halo about the kneeling man's face composed of thin spokes of green gold creeping out over rocks. A man's face half turned, a grey beard of wisps and smooth grey hood. See an image of figures gathered at a tomb's dark painted mouth. Read Saint Jerome is shown as a penitent in the wilderness. See painted drops of blood and the image of a hand raised high, holding a painted stone into a painted sky. Greenish sheen on a golden frame reddens as you pass. See an image of wooden floors and you pass a dark painting containing illuminated faces and a greenish-skinned skeletal man afloat with wings above the image of a small child lying still on the image of hay. See thin scratches of gold in rays upwards from the body of the child into the darkness around the floating man. Read Nine cranes stand in a dawn. And look up to see cranes painted and red feathers of their crowns and Indian yellow eyes with black rinds and black captured pupils. A hand quiet and held at the face of a lamb, and you see the painted woven texture of a cloth and the black eyes of the lamb with a dark sheen to them at corners and a pinkish hue to the nose of the lamb and beyond are green trees like a distance in the frame of an unglazed opening. Hear, "Mary Magdalene."

Turn to the image of a man in black garments praying with dark blue eyes, and his face blue with the appearance of stubble. Read and the Meeting of Saints Joachim and Anne at the Golden Gate, about 1500. Blades of painted grasses, painted plantain leaves, ribbed-effect, and green flowers and the key-like leaves of dandelions mingled among stones and dust. Read oil on oak. See figures before a landscape and a folded wattle around a rock. Hear, "Erm ... sixty-one, no, fifty-one." See white crests of paint on turquoise. See brown-green brush-strokes of long grass, green laid over red. Hear, "So that's where your name comes from." Hear the laugh of a woman. See a group of buildings garishly painted on green hills and a blushing sky of rose-pink and painted dark storm-grey clouds in the scene of a skin-pale figure like a child floating on the blue painted distance of a landscape. Turn to a man in a gold frame and a blackness surrounding his image. Hear, "I'm a proper Londonner indeed. I was actually born a hundred yards from the football ground." Image of a lion under the shade of rocks, a man beside the lion wearing a blue cloth, and the beard of his face white and long, and the paint of the image delicately layered. Hear, "My mother was born in Kent." A vulture painted over the image of a man painted into blue cloth, the brown shape of the vulture perched on a bare and spindly branch. Single cross-form of sticks

[228]

bound up rising into a sky strained to all
evening appearances with sky blues floating
through the colour of clotted cream. Man of
paint facing a man of paint. Read Jerome
reading in a landscape. Man surrounded by
rocks, like a man among strangers, and the dark
stars of dry plants at the feet of the man. Read
accompanied by the lion from whose paw he
removed a thorn. And hear, "Traffic, for
example, and get on another bus ... it's too
many miles but I always miss it so." Hear, "Yes,
that's true." Hear, "I don't know, I guess I'm
still not sure." Two men fighting in an image of
woods, strokes of paint softened by rag, and a
small bird larger than the hands of fighting men
composed in woodland greys, and a knife is
held up. Hear, "And I still come back each
time, and in a way I think, well, about ten years
ago." See painted green leaves and the ground is
green. Hear, "You start vegetating in a job like
this." An image of lambs seated in the shade of
a roadside, and the lambs painted in tones of
shade-grey and the shade softened into grubby
distance. Hear, "Life is too short." And turn to
a flat colour-field of ultramarine, garment of
blue paint and the blue eyes of a boy fixed
towards you. Man in a grey suit before the
image of a man, the face of a man hovering
reflected like a ghost of shadow over the
painting of the man's face. Read A man with a
pink. Read was a symbol of betrothal. Eyes of

[229]

grey-blue like urchins of slate in sunlight. See
the look to one side of a painted face and the
suggestion of clenched muscle hiding in the
surface of the skin of paint. Three women
painted above two women in shades of blue,
and one of them with black wings half-folded,
there is a blue flower also. See dark eyes and
strands of golden hair with strands of crimson
and emerald. An image of a bald child with
greenish tones through the surface of baby-pink
skin, the body in two hands, supported by
knees in French blue garments. See mountains
of cobalt blue to streaked cyan and an elliptical
halo of beaten-thin gold on a ground of sky
blue. A woman with dark brown eyes that seem
to move as you pass and her torso dressed in a
pale blue blouse. Four figures before a painting.
Image of a man lifting a pale man wrapped in
lilac and emanation-green gauze from the belly
of a rose-grey stone, circle of black thorns
wreathed and laid on the rim of the stone, face
of the thin man is the appearance of suffering
and lank red hair is falling over bones visible at
his shoulders, in strands of gauzy paint. See
faces half in shadow and a hand raised above
the head of a child seated on a red rock among
dark-leaved flowers pale in their petals, all eyes
dark like the appearance of foreboding. Deep
murmurs of voices from a room to your side
like noises within the shiftings around a cave.
Look up to lights above and see from windows

[230]

into tall grey rooms of an adjacent building and see sky like limestone. Group of young figures. Read THE WOHL. Wax smell of polish and you cast eyes on the reflection of figures. Legs and bodies dropping wobbly and kinked into polished herringbone shapes of the wooden floor. See a stone face bearded. A man breathing fast passes guided by a quick-moving fast-panting woman. Read Venetian paintings of these dimensions. See a gold-turbanned man kneeling. See a woman in blue. And slender strokes of paint under heavy paste-like applications of creamy-white overmarked with flecks of grey and umber like the dapple of a horse and the redness of varnish over the whole. Pass a painted leopard in a garden of leaves and dark branches and a peacock of blues with white ringing the visible eye and the eye's centre thin and black like a hemp seed. Hills of paint behind horses, silent as rocks. Read Saint Jerome in his. Read presumably engaged in his famous translation of the Bible into Latin. A blue hat on the ground with a glint moving over the surface of varnished black paint as you pass. Turn to see corduroys on a woman's legs, the body of the woman and the face stop before a painting of a man and lion. Hear, "Hm." See a sparkle move glinting a face among flecks of light with one hand gloved in pale grey and behind the surface of the glove a darker grey with hints of an umber. Read This melancholic young man holding a book has long been assumed to be a poet. You turn to an arm in plaster and a man suited darkly walks fast and you hear a voice beginning to speak which passes as you hear it, and read is shown as a hermit. You read in the story of the saint's lion as told in the Golden Legend. Read The lion had been charged with guarding the monastery ass; the ass was stolen. River reflecting rocks as pale inverted cliffs the colour of common blue butterflies and pigeon lilac. Dark sea caves and hear, "At those faces." Skull on a grey earth. There is a man on a cross with a brown face and green thorns painted like stitches into the crown of his head. See a crackle like webs of spiders throughout the surface of paint and the faces of women painted serene and seeming content at their mouths, all hands are holding. Read The infant Christ places a wedding ring on the finger. And hear the laugh of a woman. Read SHOP. A glass door is opened and closed at the passing-through of a man. See well-polished floors containing yellow colours of a sunset. Read WAY OUT. Pass a painted battle with a tortured tree and dark, fast-moving babbles of cloud. Turn to read Shipwrecked Fisherman. Three figures at the foot of broad stairs and you descend. Pale illuminated clockface floating ahead in a darkness and a fluted column illuminated into extended black-blue sky like a bruise and small lights of various hues crystallized. Hear, "Thanks for that Paul, there's some good stuff in there, isn't there." The inflection of a word into a question and you feel cool air crossing the ramparts of your face. Chipped black gloss paint revealing a yellowed-white coat chipped to the bare brown flesh of under-iron. Turn to a greenish pediment of stone illuminated with light like the green of swimming pools. Read No access. Lion and unicorn on the surface of a stone with shadows under the paws of the lion. Hear, "That will be fine." And see figures seated darkly on grass and flat shadows like moats. See shadows of figures passing behind and licking like tidewater over your shoes and hands among their own. Two figures pass. Hear the clearing of a throat like scuffed gravel. Cut grass. Hear, "Doesn't matter, what happened." Hear the word 'what' spoken like a concern. Pass cars waiting to move and all cars move at once like a train and the beating of engines very fast is a grinding hum. Hear a foot scrape. Hear, "All the countries in Europe ... I know it's really big in Northern Europe." Two women pass. Hear, "Steak and chips." Hear the laugh of a woman sharp as the cry of a parrot. See a bird flying and one flash of a light and you hear the intake of air into a nose and through a mouth and the exhale of breath leaves by a higher pitch. You glance into the woven darkness of a beard and look up to a small brightly pale moon. Pass a man sitting on a stone with his head in his hands. See a standing-up man waving arms like a man in need, a toothed comb in one hand. Hear, "It'll be alright." See a white-haired man, a pipe's neck inserted into the socket of his mouth, crossing the road. Read THE PARISH CHURCH OF SAINT MARTIN-IN-THE-. See a white stone figure that does not move. Read DEVOTION HUMANITY. See a grey, flecked tweed coat, a hand dragging a red wooden stick, and legs with a tired-like shuffling walk. Pass a man in a chair with spoked wheels, waving his arms and his head like a ship in a storm.

See a blackened church and blacker small windows. Two beeps of a horn. Hear, "He is dead." Read BAROQUE. See scrollwork, see leaves of stone. Black ironwork. Runs of water over limestone. Hear, "What did it say? What did it say?" Read 25 yards. A man with tongs holding a newspaper. Hear, "What is it we are going to see?" Hear reply, "Phantom of the Opera." Two girls stop and smile. "Yeah. If you go down here." See a woman with two bags. And a man with dreadlocks sings a soft song to himself, tenor-throated. Hear, "She does comfort me." See a tongue protrude and curl up to lick a chapped upper lip and the tongue retracts into the mouth like a silent creature. A

woman sighs and turns. Black umbrella bobs
over heads like an upturned coracle. A man
eating. A boy holding a bottle. Chequered coat.
Bottles in a bin. See a collar. Read GARRICK.
Read This Is Our Youth. Hear, "Must
concentrate." See a bronze man. Hear, "Look
through here." See black high boots. Read
HENRY IRVING in gold below a bronze
man's feet. See a red ribbon at the bronze man's
feet. See a man in a corner rummaging, sleeping
bag over his shoulder, on his hands and knees.
Man like an ant-eater. Stacked palettes of cut
granite. Hear, "Do not say anything." Hear
reply, "I think your boyfriend does." Read
HALF PRICE TICKETS. Two men in black
suits in a door's alcove of red light and one
looks into the sky and the sky is dark and the
other looks down to read something written on
his right hand's back. Hear two cheers cried by
a group and the clatter of a knife falling. See a
man's pink tongue climb into the mouth of a
woman. A woman running twists a flash of her
wristwatch. A mouth coughs, blows open to
oval like a boiling custard bubble and shuts. A
woman in a short skirt coughs running. Smell
cooking meat. See an open space ahead with
trees. Smell beer. A green light. Feet walking in
a mass over paving slabs. A strip of blue light. A
girl with cuffs of fake fur over wrists. Two
plumes of smoke exit a mouth and blow back
thinly like whiskers on a catfish. Dragon face. A

girl carrying a rose in a plastic sheath. Hear, "Is it expensive?" A man on crutches talks to himself. See a light flash like a nervous twitch on the surface of all visible surroundings. A woman with white hair. Hear, "Yeah, it's me. How are you?" Hear, "Are we going to get wet here?" Hear, "I like to feel what came out." Hear, "Silly bitch." See bikes parked quietly. Read LK51 WEA N21 FLD. A girl walking under a red umbrella. Read LISLE. Smell of meat. See plants behind glass. Read COME AND GET 'EM! Look up to a picture of a woman's large breasts. A man with pale ears. A man tugs his trousers up onto his hips. Read Your Selection. A girl chewing gum is ruddy at cheeks. Black window frames. Black windows like sheets of obsidian, the black eyes of Indian girls. See glitter moving in a window. A woman walks slowly wearing a turquoise headscarf. Read SMOKE ALARMS SAVE LIVES. A hand puts food to a mouth, holding the food by pale chopsticks. A finger flicks the paper cylinder of a cigarette, ash falls to a glass bowl. See a hand writing. Hear, "I was trying to get the extra stuff." See feet at the top of stairs in a doorway. Read PORCUPINE. See stubble on a man's chin. A man drinking golden lager. Two hands together, tapping eight fingers. Read HENRY PORDES. See an orange telephone. Hear, "Oh, really." Read HOT ORIENTAL. Three mannequins wearing T-shirts out in the

rain. A woman lighting a cigarette sucks in, a
red glow appears. A siren passes crying. Hear
music creeping out from a building through
doors. A sleeping bag being rolled up by the
arms of a shadow. Read OPEN. See a woman in
a phone box, pink paper by the phone, numbers
in black felt pen. Shadow of plants. Red lights
drop down into wet tar and turn to green. Read
DON'T MISS OUT. Hear, "Anything can fall
to ruins." See a photograph of faces like a group
smile. Read EM12. Letters on iron. Read
LOOK. Read CLAPTON. Letters in yellow on
a moving red bus. Hear, "I mean what kind of."
Read ATTENTION. Hear, "Ever seen that
before?" See a mouth say, "No." Read MOOR
ST. A spacious brick wall. A woman rubs her
left eye. A woman rubbing a man's head with
two hands in a doorway. Hear, "Is that true?"
Read METAL MORPHOSIS. Read WET
PAINT. Hear, "Oh, I do know." Read T3
AKA. A big man swaying on his hips in a
doorway. Hear, "It gets a bit mushed." Hear,
"Who wants tickets?" Hear, "Like the heads of
departments, the head of UK, not the head of."
A girl strides over the road. Read UNDER.
Hear, "What do you want, a latte? There you
go." See feathers set in pieces of silver in a
window display. See cakes and fruit tartlets. See
a woman stepping out from a doorway, the
door closes slowly behind her. Hear a
humming. "You know what? I made it, right?"

cries a raven-black-haired woman into a man's ear. Pat of feet walking among feet. Hear, "It makes me absolutely mad." A plastic woman's body dressed in black rubber. See five bras of rubber. Five panties of red and black and blue. A woman in a lilac scarf. A lime green scarf around a woman's face. Hear, "Those look good man." See a room full of men drinking and talking, smoking thin cigarettes where the light is dark. A girl dressed in black in a doorway. A polystyrene carton rolling over the tar road. A woman behind a glass window zipping a coat up to her neck. See red lights like glowing pumpkins. Read ANIS. Three men stand with phones to their ears. Checked trousers pass and an umbrella opens like a mountain over two passing women, a man's face beams between them. Read OCTOPUS. A man drags on a cigarette, a single orange eye of light opens and closes. See plastic skulls. Read BIZARRE in blue letters. Hear a crackly cough repeating itself. Read LJ02 CA1. A man and woman in tense dialogue. See stems of flowers through a window. See a black umbrella open like a flower in a deep doorway and move at man-height out into the street like a dandelion seed. Cry of a scooter. An umbrella opens and closes and opens like a fidget. Hear, "Sorry." Four girls in a row. Smell a sour underperfume passing. Hear, "If you want to go on the interview." A line of figures in black under a brown glossy canopy.

[238]

Hear, "Please money. Please money." Hear,
"Oh eh eh." Man in a broad-rimmed hat like an
eclipsed head. Read SHARP. See two girls with
golden hair. A flat black stone with white veins.
Read NO BILL POST. See two shelves of clear
glasses. Hear, "Many on a." Pass a gas flame.
Hear, "I was touring." Hear, "No, really, if."
Hear, "Roz. The George. Tuesday. Four." See
faces and a beard. See a broad-bellied man. The
road shiny. A girl walking alone. A car speeds
fast as it can. Read £4.50 Jerk Chicken. Hear
howling and football chant. See a couple at a
table. Hear, "I had a glass of wine." Hear, "This
relationship." Next table. Hear, "The publisher
pushed his books." Hear clicking music. See
pairs of black glasses. A man with curly hair
pulling a ringlet between two fingers. Read £15
£20. A black woman sits down. A mouth opens,
tongue like a shovel, and laughs. See the pink
belly hang of a walking man. Sirens approach.
Hear "East London." See an old woman holding
a bag in threads. Read NOODLE. A man
seated on wet stones. A woman stops and holds
out a brown paper bag. A man takes a brown
paper bag in two hands upstretched. A woman
walks on. A man opens a brown paper bag and
looks into its mouth. Read FOODS. See pale
stonework on a red brick building. See a man
on the ground, he is smoking. A man walks
from a dark alley, see blotched skin. See trees
orange at tips with streetlamp focussed in

raindrops. Road jammed nose to tail with cars and red buses. All cars and buses move together. See black windows pass. See silver bags carried. A woman raises a hand and points a direction. Read MAN. See blue lights like stars. A woman grabs a tall bearded man and kisses his lips. See dark walls. Ground freckled with platelets of gum. A girl standing quietly alone. Read 17 YRS DEAD. White letters painted on cardboard held in the hands of a pale-haired boy wrapped in a blanket sitting by steps that lead into the ground.

Dozens of feet run down brass-edged steps into orange shadow. See a wall of violet. Hands to ears with phones. Smell cigarettes. Hear a man saying, "One and then cuts." Places his hand on a woman's waist. Hear a woman's voice, "We just had scones, so." Hear a thudding bass beat. A girl chewing tying her laces. A man eating a floured bap. See floured lips. A bus growls. A hand perched on a woman's hip, the woman hip-held puts a lit cigarette to her mouth and drags in. Air sour with cigarette smoke. See hands selecting slices of pizza with bright steel tongs. See an illuminated wall of trainers in blue light. See a head scarf. See two women holding hands. Herringbone brickwork. A striped jumper of colours on a man passing. A blonde girl running, smell perfume and sweaty

pepperiness. A red pillar box, paintwork
blistered to brown. See grey bags full of stuffed
lumpiness. Read Flurry. Six letters printed on
the wall of a carton. Water over the street. See
sky towering to a dome-like interior in brown
grey like the luminous irons of a trout's skin,
and then the congealed opacity of a river's silt.
Read METRO. See a woman carrying a small
child. See infant leaves, blossom perfect. Gravel
packed down over tree roots. A man of green
light flashing. A girl with black braids swinging
over the tumuli of her cheeks like tarantula
legs. See a skullcap worn. A girl lifting her left
breast up with her right hand. Two men
laughing. Hear, "Hey." Hear, "Yeah." Hear,
"Ok ok ok, a swollen stomach, a white one."
Hear, "Really." A squeaked word. Black buckets
of folded tight tulips like the closed mouths of
fish. See red lights like distant ships. Read
STRUCTURAL ENGINE. See a plastic
woman's body dressed up in a pale satin slip.
Read OXFORD STREET IS COVERED BY
CCTV. A bus growls. Man in a blue shirt
quietly behind a pane of glass reading. An old
man playing a scuffed violin body, notes lifting
and falling like wind through a gap. Two
pigeons fly up, ashy grey, their splayed feathers
visible and shaking. See brushed hair streaked
back. See a white stick leaning against a leg.
Old violin-man's violin lowered in a hand at the
end of a stern chord bowed hard. A wrinkled

chin under a mouth. Hear, "Yeah." Voice to a
phone. See a dark face with white teeth, the
teeth glossy. Mouth talking fast. Hollow steel
clatter of a scaffolding pole. Long scrape-note
of a steel pole sliding. A small swing with a
seated mould-grey rabbit swinging
mechanically. See fake grass matting. A rabbit
with black plastic eyes. See a concrete triangle
structure. An old man standing still as a stone.
Read CAUTION SLIPPERY WHEN WET.
A pair of eyes looking up. Hear two beeps.
Read Lawless. A man in a blue sleeping bag
under cashpoint machines. A queue of people
standing alongside the sleeping bag man. Read
ONYX. Hear, "You know that fucking, I said,
'look, you got a problem.'" A smile on a mouth
speaking hard. See a padlock chained to the
branch of a small leafless black tree. Read
SUCK MY DICK YOU DIRTY BITCH.
Pink letters in lipstick are shaky. Smell dark
smoke. A cigarette put up to pink lips. A sore
nose sniffing. Hear a clicking rhythm leaving a
doorway. Two women chatting. Read CARL. A
coarse weave of blue cloth over a leg. Hear, "I
know I won't do it. I know I won't do it.
Thank you. Bye." Gold plaited hair. See a
picture of rabbits. Lights spark in a bright tree
like beads of lit sweat. Two headless
mannequins wearing closed blouses. A man
opens a car door. Children-sized mannequins
wearing hats on necks without heads. A blue

rabbit under an arm. A girl with a straw in her mouth, her lips sealed around the outer surface of the straw's cylinder. A man shuffle-walks, a newspaper under one arm. See light between legs. Hear, "Oh my god, it's so funny." And a man at a desk writing alone, a room high as a house crowded with structures of erected scaffolding, exposed brickwork and wires like a nervous system. Hear the words, "Temporarily to stay." Hear a man speak in a language you do not know. In yellow letters, read SANDWICHES. The brown moustache of a man passes. See grey fox-tails of catkins. "You're talking like, you know ... two faced," a woman's voice says. The buzzing of a beeper. See two, high, black boots, unworn. A man sitting alone where a phone rings and hear words. See cigarettes in the dark like cat's eyes in a road lighting and fading. Hear, "Isn't he so cute." Small lights twinkle a cold blue white like the colour of ice. Hear, "You don't say, Babanti." Read PORTERCALL SYSTEM ON REPLY. Read ZEBRA. Read SULTRY STUNNING BRUNETTE. A face smiles. See rain beads crawling down a black bollard like dark kittens down a dark tree, a reflected dark making the colour of beads like the darkness of eyes. See a reflected car, silver, turn a corner away from the way the car turns. See many broken chairs like a herd of giraffe with torn orange cloth backs. A man runs wearing a deep, chalky-blue top, see his hands stretched. And see knives and forks laid out at tables and a broad wooden door a blue-topped man opens with one hand. See feet on a carpet of gold dots on blue. See the X of a red, white and blue flag and twelve stars on blue cloth. See small, dusty leaves of heather and three, hand-like glossy leaves of ivy. Hear, "I missed out my house." Words of a man with white hair. See a driver, a grey car, the grey car slows to a halt. See a grey beard. See a thin grey spire of lead like one spine of an urchin. Triangle of a pediment carved with figures in stone. Look to a man four storeys up leaning his shoulder to the frame of a window, see black oval pads of headphones at ears. And see he retreats in the shade of a room set back from the plane of the window. A badge reading PORSCHE worn by a car stationary before a dull cherry-red light, the surface of red light refracted in bright tiny squares. Hear the cry of a car's horn. Two dresses lit from the inside. Read HINDE. See frosted glass lit from an inside. See the image of a single bright flower and a chocolate pushed into a mouth, the lips curling over like an amoeba engulfing its prey. See two figures in a room of clothes and mirrors. A man's back reflected on a dull mirror. See an oak door and a coarse grain of wood like the strands of a river in spate. A man wipes his mouth with the edge of a white tablecloth lifted up from beneath.

[244]

Pass people going in twos quietly. Taxis pass
and you see their black bodies of metal shake
like the jumping of jackdaws. Read WINS
YOU. Three taxis pass in a group. See a scooter
and read 'L' in red. The image of a white,
smooth aeroplane. Look up into dark air and a
speck of rain falls to your eyes like a grain of
sand. Read I like my job. Read 7686 5083. Look
to a man in a shop, absorbed, writing with a red
biro in hand, his head lowered to the page,
marks flowing from the ball of the pen with the
passage of his hand across the page. Pass two
men drinking a blackness with serpents of
white mist rising from the lake-dark ellipses of
tilted blackness at mouths. See a man move
towards the body of a blonde woman, see they
kiss without words, cheek to cheek. And then
sit neat like a body of silence. Flash of a siren
grows to a howl stretched like a drum on the air
of the street. Siren like a dog of air howling up.
Read SPANKING WATER SPORTS. See
stacked turquoise boxes and beyond them a
woman, earnestly projecting her head on her
neck, still as if frozen. Read This building was
opened jointly by The Right Worshipful. See
glass doors dissecting a polished walkway. A
shop of dark bottles, mainly green and soft-
brown and black-green-red bottles are there
like the lacquered shells of certain beetles. Man
biting the nail of a finger, the tip of the finger
inserted between semi-bared teeth, the jaw

muscles clenched and unclenched in rapid succession, the hand twists about on the wrist navigating the nail through the mill of the teeth. Read ANGEL IN THE FIELDS. Hear a light laugh like the sound of a sheet being shaken out. One man walks ahead and a paving slab lifts and drops on opposite corners. Pass the blackened walls of a church with narrow pointed windows like figures with hands placed together in prayer. Read N305 FKJ. See a bottle-green patch of light on the sill of a window. Read 13 on a well-polished brass-plate screwed to a wall. See a polygon structure of lights. Read DURRANTS HOTEL. The faint shadow of a black car slopes on the wall of a building like a thief stealing away. A door closes. Pass a man on crutches and the rocking moves of his four-legged walk are like the run of a dog, very slowly. A leaning-back man in a bow-tie. Read A La Carte Menu Cream of Courgette & Saffron Soup Cream of Leek. Pass a deep red petal detached from a flower. Bright fire of rain falling through light turned to the shadow of sky. Hear, "Yah." A sweet perfume walks. See an ornamentation of sunflowers in plaster relief. One click of an umbrella's mechanism. Look up to the corner of a building's cube. A primrose flower among leaves as green as grasshopper bodies. A woman leaning back on her spine in a long black gown making notes at a table of men and women

with faces turned up towards to hers like the
mouths of fish to a fly skitting over the skin of
a pool. See the brown eyes of one man glance
like a fox running over a field. See the silverfish
greys of lavender leaves. Read CHIC. The
brute elongated box of a fire engine passes in
red. See the figure of a man reading a glossy-
skinned page. See figures around the glossy-
page reader with polished steel scissors
gleaming like smiles as they cut shades of hair.
A low caramel light radiates from the windows
of a black car parked. See dark wooden
furniture behind caged glass. See orange
bollards. The mouth of an alley flooded with
magenta light. Read DANGER 400 VOLTS.
Hear the hiss of tyres over wet tar like water.
Walk under the rigging of scaffolding poles and
a smell of solvents twists up to your nose. Hear
the dripping of water. Read SKANSA. See
hundreds of windows in lattice formation
across the face of a building. Read 27. A grey
leathered camera on a single leg. Air thick with
the pressed-down falling of rain. And through
the dullness of rain see a dry room of tables and
chairs. The darkness of a corner paved with
cobbles set tightly like grey teeth. See men at
black tables, drinking and a woman leans back
on the roar of a laugh. Your sight descends
stairs to a white-tiled basement and windows
are shuttered nearby. Read £370,000. Read
ANA. A black stone facade. Read LEASE FOR

SALE. You walk concrete paving, gritty, with a peeled nectarine sheen of rain damp. Look up to the windows of an uninhabited upstairs. See the darkness of a ground floor, an unlit bar and hung-up glasses catching stray straws of streetlight and a bike's headlamp passing. Four cups of dregs on a round coffee table, two black, one white, one red and white in broad stripes. Black spearheads of railings like the bayonets of guards and beyond are tall towers of wolf greyness in falling rain like the needles of pine. Distant tail lights of cars on the road. Read X90 OXFORD. Pigeon-crooning noise of an engine at idle. See a ground floor wall rendered white and an upper wall unrendered brown as cocoa. See courses of coarse-fleshed brick of black, brown and ochre. The wiper blade of a car squeaks a rubber-blade note and cuts back over the screen snagging three times on a dryness. You pass a clutch of grasses. Lines of moss extend, over mortar lines, the spines of moss brilliantly green in the sharpened headlight of a turning car. Pass an acorn of iron on the head of a railing, about the size of a man's clenched fist. Shrapnel of light through rain. White lines laid onto black road, a black composed of crystals of rose-grey and ochre-grey and shark-grey set into tar. There is a dark garden of trees. Pink blossom erupting from green-throated buds, the tongues of teenagers. Elephant-coloured bark of a plane tree. See a

[248]

distant tail lamp grow more distant and white
lights dull with deep rain. Light floats over
panes of glass and glints happen. You walk
the moss-sealed sieve of a hanging basket. See
unlit streetlamps by the half dozen and rain
falls in lengths like a beekeeper's gauze. Puddles
sprinkled with disturbance puckered as skin is
with hair follicles. Man bearing a screwdriver
places the blade of the instrument to the
slotted head of a steel doorlatch screw. And the
door is open. See a long passage, thin, leading
through to the deep of the house, hear the
strain of a man calling out. See the street is lit
with globes overhead in the haze. See a blue
tarpaulin stretched on the giant bucket of a
scratched yellow skip. Hear, "She hasn't done it
yet." Stone plinth. See the rough and black
inner skin of a banana limp by the taut skin of a
binliner squat on wet paving with a tongue of a
leak. Single thin rip in the pursed body of the
binliner. Purple flowers poking from dark half-
moons of hanging baskets. Pass shadow-figures
in twos, threes, slouching on dark window
panes. See a crisp packet's sharp edge and
crimped closed-end of the packet. Pass a man
looking down to shoes clacking the surface of
paving. A van sitting like a white hen. A grey
taxi passes carrying figures half visible behind
reflections on the mirrorish bloom of long
windows. Raindrops fall slowly and a man
scratches a thicket of fieldmouse-brown

ioustache as you pass through the corkscrewed smoke of a cigarette's smoulder. Raindrops echo in a basement's pit. Read RR X 22 on a flat board mounted on the rear of a large vehicle. Read ROLLS ROYCE. See fishscaled condensation. Read HAND CAR WASH. The star of a fracture. A polished brass door knocker swings on its hinge. A set table for two. A tissue smeared into paving. A crumpled crisp packet and a small blue pen crouched in the cauldron of a flowerpot. Read M as a red car slows to a halt. A man runs out into the rain. Smell the sweet carbon of burning meat. A tall man carrying a bag passes and trails a sharp tang of leather. See one foot angled left to the true course of a body. Leaf buds pinprick like the eyes of needles. See pavement spotted with flat discs of gum. Three beds in a window. Read Over 300. Read FULL. Read TOASTED BIGSIZE. See paintwork coating a stone balustrade and rotund bellies of stone below necked parts of stone. The sweet smell of meat sugar charred. Woman in tight trousers and creases appearing to crease to the bone part the flexing of her legs. See a man in a shop and the shop is called SONG. Man shaving a man's head. Man shoving by shoulder a large box into a van. A boy with a large umbrella and see he waves to a man alone behind glass and see the boy is being led by a man. See the eyes of the boy, brown as dates. Read LORDS. See a man

[250]

in a shop stacked high with card packets. Man
wearing a cloth wound-up on his head stands
like an elm in the rain. Pass a black head band.
Three cars indicate left, and two follow suit.
Hear, "Something like that." Read Smoked
Kippers & Poached Eggs. Dusty deep-throated
purr of fans whirring like moths at the ears. A
green and black stone streaked with thin
whitish veins. Read VICTORY. See in the dim
light variegated leaves shaking in a low breeze
and hear water trickle into a drain wetly under
dry scratches and erratic tickings of leaves
brushing leaves. One beep of a horn, hoarsely.
Read 88. And four chairs upturned on low
wooden tables: the view in a basement. Gold
tulips on green stems in a tall vase. A square of
deep-shaded trees in grubby sky and a car
passing. Muffle of music from the body of a car
as it slows close and speeds up from you and
the dark lozenge of rear window reflects tree
bodies and leaf-hats. Two diffused wedges of
headlamps slur over tarmac and you look to see
further afield two amber circles flashing
unsynchronised and a dark rectangle space dug
into the road and the hole cordoned off by
bollards and red plastic tape with a twist. See a
horse in a window. See a polished brass
letterbox, tiny scratch marks over the bright
yellow brass. Look up to a girl alone in a dimly
lit room and outside the window a man walks
alone bearing a red strap across his chest like a

mark. Read ONE HYDE. Read G329 LRH.
Read EK51 FM2. Pass two figures. Pass a man.
Pass a man. Light crawls over the plated
elephant-leg of a plane tree's trunk and shrinks
back. See an orange ball flashing. Read
BANHAM. Pass white marble steps. Look to a
hand in a pocket in the jaws of a basement's
barred window and see the shadows of railings
spurred over the zone of a flat wall, the bars of
shadow splayed out from the source of its light.
Read 105. Read CATHOLIC MARTYRS
LOST THEIR LIVES AT THE GALLOWS
NEAR THIS. Pass quietly a woman in a pink
coat and a headscarf printed with black leaves
on a background the colour of lemons, stepped
from the building you walk alongside. A door
squeaks shut to blankness. A banana skin
draped over rubbish and stones glistening with
rain and a chocolate wrapper lies curled on its
side like a sleeping man. See the grain of stone
flecked with shapes like grains of wheat
blackened with fungus and cast iron railings rise
planted in stone like the edge of a wheatfield. A
man's head swivels its neck, see the eyes are
sharp like a hawk's. Pass black window glass
like obsidian sheets. Glimpse a dark garden,
dark green and black leaves like carved jade and
slate, lacquer of rainwater, see the opening pink
of a flower. See flowers and faces on plaster.
See a ceiling low over a room, a rose of white
plaster. Read WARNING. Hear footsteps.

Pass lurids of green and a blue bike chained by a fat chain the colour of sardines to railings. A car stopping, a man and woman talk in the room of the car. See bubbling over the surface of a porch ceiling. A man jogging, his movement tense like a sticking ratchet. Pass a man suited with a tie of blood red, he is seated. Pass a pair of bronze hands. Pass a man and woman grey-haired in the space of a kitchen. Two women with umbrellas and a man without. See bottles grouped like a still life with shadows of bottles cast over pavement and a faint hue to each of the shadows tinted by a small quantity of light passing the coloured glass of each bottle into its shadow. Read FIRST CLASS. The red body of a bus draws up and see faces that look down onto you. See the shadow of ironwork, leaves and the coils of wrought iron cast as one shadow. See the flutes of a column, and a dark stripe of shadow running like a vein up one side of each flute, varying bands of shadow-width appearing blue and orange like flames in the shadow. See the head and shoulders of a man alone seated behind the wheel of a black car. Read TAXI in illuminated letters above the curved roof of a car. Pass a woman pushing a bike. See darkness to the left, the darkness of parkland. The shadows of potplants streaked over concrete, the shade of each pot hugging its own base like a shallow off-centred moat about the walls of curved ceramic. Hear the massed scurry of traffic, the hum and hundreds of wheels like hooves in a run as a herd. See crimson roses in front of a mirror. A polishing machine and three shadowed men in a room crouched on their hands and their knees. See the window of a room opened a crack, herringbone of wood. Two round lights and turn to see beads of rain blistered like shingles on the black bonnet of a car. Pointed leaves lit from behind like spires in mist. Headlamps swim over the wet road, undulating roadmarkings. And smell the warm round smell of wet earth, and the mouldy cellar of the smell of leafmould. Pass the wires of a fence. Buds on dark spindly twigs gleam a coated-with-toffee look. Pass the crusty bark of a snapped branch lying on the pavement, curls of ripped wood like thick locks of red hair. Pass telephone kiosks, each empty. A figure walking ahead like the shadow of a bird. Holly leaves black as bitumen. Pass a white car and hear the squeal-pip of sharply applied brakes as sound only. See raindrops hanging from pointed leaves, one breaks like an egg and it falls. See two bins with rubbish to the plastic-lined brim. See a compost heap sectioned by twigs and leaves of shrubs woven by growth, like erratic wicker. See vertical rectangles of light high among trees to your left like the glares of monkeys, and many small lights distant, like a view. A woman walks and the cloth on her legs is coarsely, tightly set over the flesh, with the hems rolled up a hand's height above the balls of the ankles, her steps short and fast like the uneasy pace of a shallow breather. See rags of plastic. Hear the noise of a passing bicycle, strained squeak of a wheel repeating the tick of its ratchet. Read CHARIOT 8. A speckle of rain pimpling leaves, like warts of water. A dead leaf the shape of a dead trout. Read VICTORIA GATE. See the smear of headlamps on wet road, a sheen of many lights straying and then staying-put, and splashy droplets thrown up from passings, and the blades of reflected lights drop through the road and travel like fins of white sharks swimming in pairs. Read COCA. Read CAMEL. See broken twigs like the discarded antlers of stags and a curl of peel like a small canoe overturned. Read NICKERS. Hear voices approaching from faces lurking in shadow. A man and woman draw up and pass on. Birch tree overhead. See lights in windows. A knotted bag. Sign of a liquid having crept over a wall. Blister and crackle of old weathered paint. Read LOOK LEFT. Smell the sweetness of flowers packed as maybloom, rectangular beds of flowering, the flowers soft scarlet and a ghost of yellow, like the nicotined white of sixty-year hair. A house in nearby dark, like a raft on a lake. Foliage of plants among sweet flowers and the business noise of cars and a light wind blowing across leaves, making them turn up and curl and you hear the heavy toad's plop of raindrops falling from leaves and sounds indecipherable but like the rustling-creaks in the shade beneath shrubs to your left. And steps lead down, pale with floodlight, like the light of a dull and orange moon out of eclipse and the steps like the un-squeezed box of an accordion. A single raindrop hangs pregnant at the tip of a handrail. Read 331. Read 330. Read 329. Read 328. Pass a rotted section of a branch and see mothlike squares of furry grey-blue over spongy grain. Light circuits the metal rim of a woman's glasses and you cannot see the two eyes for darkness over the convex of each lens. Stretched oak like an alligator's charcoal-skinned body. Smell the dark brown of burnt sugary meat. A bicycle noise passes and see a long-backed woman pedalling within the tails of a black coat and her hair out from her head like an aura of gold wires. Green frames of windows. Read Authorised Vehicle Access Only No Ent. A rectangle of water. Stationary cars in a row beginning to move. See an oval window set in an oval frame like a moonstone set in white gold. Read JANUARY 1872 "JED". See figures sitting at tables above street level. Cut flowers gathered in a half darkness at unoccupied tables like birds of paradise thrown under blankets. Streetlamps unlit as cars pass and figures walk. Skirt of a woman split along the side up one leg,

and the skin visible within the shutter of its
stride. Man in a lilac jacket and long grey hair
tied in a weasel's tail. Frothlike blossom in
bosses over the body of a tree, like babies in
christening gowns. Long black railings skirting
the boundary of a garden like the hairs of a
witch. See a man's hand running through the
hair of his head like adders through sun-bitten
grasses. Hear a bike rattle. Read N557 O7P. See
a taxi. Read U438 MGJ. See a taxi. A lull of
cars. Hear raindrops fall heavy like fat frogs,
they croak into bits leaping up. Pass many small
leaves. Pass a bin composed of stained wooden
slats bound by two iron belts. Look up to a
gauze of black trees over the ghost greys of sky,
the bleed of orange streetlights radiated up and
swabbed, slow pad of clouds pressing. A needle-
point spire from the black, ribbed bulk of a
church, like the horn of a goat. Flash of a car's
light. A man jogging, each step a stride. Pass a
clot of ivy, the black knot of a red rose in
moonlight. Pass variegated leaves, some shiny,
and some are torn. Pass a black metal grate, the
surface worn to a polished red iron deeply
pitted. See black gates locked by a single wound
chain and clasped by the nugget of a padlock,
see grassland and the dark canopies of broad-
leaved trees behind bars. Glimpse the discs of
plates arranged on a high-backed dresser, and
the room about the dresser studded with dim
light spars. A wide man carrying a striped

umbrella, the umbrella closed to serve as a
stick, walks lumberingly slow. A bicycle passes
and you smell the sweet spice of cologne. See a
wide man stops and turns back and stops again
to turn to continue slowly as before. Read 158.
Read 157. Read 156. See pin-edged leaves of
holly, each leaf a black shield of polished hide
stretched on spine-and-rib-rigging of spear-
tipped veins. A yellow bus passes and the rise
and fall of its turbo squeak-hisses like the noise
of a thousand mice running and crying
together. See smoke exhaled from a mouth like
an eel moving up through murky pool light.
Hear the throat of an exhaust pipe gurgling a
sound like a noose. Black and cracked bark of a
tree a dark shade of brown and red-brown with
edges of orange and blue shadows like lizards
lying in the brown with black shadows
composed of red and green in the black. Hear
breathing and you turn to see jogging calves
bare and tensed with the spring and jog of the
weight on them running, shoes land and fly
with a swish-sound exerted at footfall. See the
shadows of twigs a woman runs through. Read
101. See light puckered to dark tones over the
surface of kerb stones. See a group of stray
holly leaves lying on the base of a kerb stone
where it tongues into the tar of the road. Read
ISL HOT LS. Read Quality Fuels. See large
drums of coach wheels. See a man and woman
staring beneath an open bonnet as into a pit.

[258]

Read 92. Read 91. Read 90. Look up to see dark rooms with wooden doors and sage green walls. See a car emerge from the mouth of a basement, the exit ramped up to streetlevel. See a woman avoids the tail of a car and passes beyond it in three short steps and a woman passing her jogs with a flat silver box in one hand with black wires running to a small flat disc like a boulder across the entrance to an ear, and a wire leading to the hidden side of the head. See a man in tight jeans jogging and the torso covered by a grey hooded top of felt, his head in the triangle-shaped shadow of the hood. Pass a tall cast iron post painted black. See one group of fourteen cars. Four cars drive from a side street. Pass a long salmon-grey granite drinking trough. Pass a black plastic and cylindrical bin. Read THE BLACK LION. Read VDH 40M BMW. See terracotta-coloured blinds and catch sight of a man laughing aloud but hear no sound laughing and hear four handclaps rapidly made. Read No Cycling. Read Parent Care Facility. Read Ladies. See bright poles of new scaffolding. See the figure of a man jogging. A white arrow printed crisply on a clear blue background and the arrow pointing down to the ground to your right. Read Star Tour. See the wink of a green light. See an open space between buildings. Read CITY OF. Hanging acacia pods. Read LIFT HANDSET TO BEGIN. Hear and see a

whistling mouth, lips pursed to a small dark
contraction, the cavity of the mouth blown to a
whistle. Read BLACK LION LODGE. See
brown pods hanging and blown easterly. A bus
stops and a sudden sharp pang of air hissing
from the bus body. Read NO PAINTINGS
ARE TO BE HUNG ON THESE RAILINGS.
A single laurel leaf is wind-dragged sideways
several lengths of itself. See a field of grasses
and the trumpets of daffodils standing like
bugles in the grey grass of an unlit zone. Read
TO YO. Light brightens and dims on the
glossed spear of a railing. See moonwhite
flowers of magnolia. A yellow half-circle. Smell
heavy and sweet scents of blossom in the damp
air. The sugary smell of eggwhite. Pass a pale
pineapple of stone. Pass a whitened stone eagle.
A stubble of cut bamboo. Pass a wall of bricks
sagging, bowed to one side. Abrupt beep of a
car. Black V-necked jumper on a man's torso,
the head of a man speaking into a phone, the
glint of white teeth. Turn to the body of a man
running over a wide road, his head dark with
hair and shadow floating neck-high over the
street. A green hat on a woman's head flashes
like the beak of a bird. A voice talking passes,
you distinguish no words. Look to half-opened
buds of a flower and between two buds a
window lights up three storeys above and you
see the top half of a head and its crown of hair
reddish brown like rye. The soft husky beep of

a horn like the voice of a heavy smoker. The
sudden baby-crying-out of an engine's starter-
motor. Read IN. Read CROWN. Read OUT.
See a street made of shadow through a white
arch. Read Thirsty Skin. A grey circle three
inches across screwed onto a concrete wall. See
a girl with long curls of flecked golden hair.
Thin body of a tree without leaves and beneath
hear the chugging of a scooter's engine, the
scooter stationary. A tall square building dark
like an outcrop of rock the colour of
thundercloud, and the red-black of an anvil.
Hear two whistles like bone shards of sound.
See a blue glass plate the colour of a winter's
blue sky. See the face of a woman applying
pigment to her cheek. See a big man kissing the
face of a woman in the arched lobby of a
church. Read ESSEX UNITARIAN. A woman
on quick steps. See the statue of an elephant in
a laced window, the sculptured ebony of a
deer's head. The oiliness of newly laid gloss
paint. See dark umber bricks of a building you
pass. Read SECOND CHURCH OF CHRIST.
Read FIRE EXIT. Read 102. Read 101. Read
100. A door closes quietly, a light switches on.
See a car move a distance. See a woman walk up
to a car. Hear the click of a car door. A door
opens and closes with a cluck like a hen. See a
car reversing. And a car eking forwards and
passing away and you turn. Read T4L. Three
rows of lit windows and the street is quiet

around the voice of a man talking alone, like
the voice of a dove. See a man and a lit
cigarette. Hear water passing into the cave of a
drain. See red, pointed flowers. See paperback
books put on shelves. Hear the chord of a
small, electric fan's hum. Read MBA. In a pale
upstairs room see moving images leap on a wall,
like the colours of water. Look down to see in a
basement room's window a woman cross-legged
on a carpeted floor among sheets of paper holds
a phone to her mouth and her ear, she is
talking. Read 06 02 PENALTY CHARGE
NOTICE. See two canisters seated on the step
of a door. Hear the creak and slam of a door
and footsteps clearly on wooden boards fading.
Hear the flat cough of a shoe scuffed. Hear the
piped noise of water draining and the ending of
its noise is a glug. See a room containing small
coloured objects. Hear the rhythm of fast feet
walking. A phone to an ear. A bud of blossom.
Hear speech only as sounds without words
behind windows. A cough like the sudden fast
bolt of a horse from a wide open gate. Hear the
wail of a siren moving away. Hear a small, tin-
toned voice from the box of a television and see
a grey-haired woman watching a woman of light
facing her from the lozenge of a screen. See a
barometer's thread in a bone of glass like grey
marrow. Pass a man singing a song, a man in
the company of song. A white triangle. The wet
crunch of a foot stepping on gravel. See leaves

[262]

behind glass, broad and black with minute
fissures of veins like gutters in moonlight, like
old, well-polished leather, like ice cracked by
feet. Read HOTEL. Read HOTEL. Look up
four storeys to a man talking. See the frame of a
window and a car passing softly reflected.
Count twenty-one scooters. Read PAY. Read
06. Pass a man jacketed, the V-necked ghost of
a vest on his shirt, walks with a stick, stops and
he leans hands heavy as a dumb-bell on black
railings and un-leans and walks on, slowly
limping, a slope leads him to climb, see his
cheeks reddened to a mottle like the wings of a
moth, his nose bristled as a moth's body and his
eyes flat like eyes on a moth's wing. There are
trees about like black knives stuck in the lard
white air. A black sugar smell of the skin of
meat cooked. Hear the cry of a moving bus.
Pass a rag of plastic lying down from the
breeze, and a dark wind beats up and catches it,
dragging it like the shape of a fury. Hear a click
behind the blind surface of a door like a small
and metal object dropped onto hardwood. Hear
the high and tunnelled boom of jet engines
passing from roof to roof like a roar's spiral.

See a dark bird flying. Sky's light is a blue grey. XVIII
Hear drainwater and hear cars softly making
the noise of cars. There is a light, cold breeze.
There is the sound of a bird hammering one

note of its particular song, like the clean, muffled note of a xylophone. Hand of a man raised up under the boughs of a small tree and wings of leaves just opening. A black car stops before the man. See a board of buttons, each printed with a number. Read SPEAK HERE. Man in a suit scrapes a drop of brown coffee from the base of a throwaway cup with the edge of the cup's plastic lid. The chord of a bus like the wheeze of an accordion. A plane passes over, sectioned in two by a sharp steeple. See a light winking. See a shop of lights. See a shop of painted tables. See a black cross and four red dots. See painted panels, painted Indian figures aboard the panels. Read QUALITY MARBLE RESTORATION. See elm doors. See red brick tiles. Read ELECTRICITY. See a shop of glass. See the flag of Italy. Read WEIGHT LOSS. See cobalt blue squares of light. See a white man sitting at a big desk. See a black man cleaning the desk with a white feather duster. Read WICKED. See a picture of a man at work. Read MASSAGE. Read FACIALS. See blue lights flashing. See a man slowly walking. Read FAST FAST. See a woman in an orange jacket standing. Harsh green blue lights. Hear the noise of water corkscrewing through the pipe of a drain. See a lone black conical tree. Hear a frenzy of birds' melodies. Box hedge planted and trimmed in a knot. Green shrubs before you, and open sky, white almost yellow near blue. See the orange of a streetlight switch off with a tick. See one light above like a star. A red light. See a large brick in the wall of a building. A man dragging a suitcase on wheels like a puppy away. See the round face of a clock. Hear the woodwind of a pigeon's cry. Pass a wet twig lying arched on the ground. See cobbles like square teeth set round the base of a lamp post. A blackbird flies down. Read GIVE WAY. Hear two chreeps of a single bird. See white flowers shake in the cool air. See between bars of two locked iron gates into empty parkland. Count twelve black cast iron benches. Hear entangled birdsong. Read CAUTION BEWARE OF. See grey kerbstones speckled with black rhomboids and other crystalline shapes. Hear the knife-sharp curled and piercing cry of a gull. Hear the growl of an electric transformer. Hear the roar of a plane shinnying between other sounds. Trees stand still. See a snapped branch overhead. See flint chips in mortar between bricks textured like cracked crusts of bread. Yellow light on a stairway. Shuddering birdsong like notes of a violin. There is a light breeze warping the single icon of a blue flag flying on a white pole standing on a golden sphere of a building. See a man arranging oblong tubs of help-yourself foods in a large room. Look up to the face of a man looking out from an un-openable window, his head dark like a night. See before you a woman walking alone, a red scarf about her head flapping at the tied tail. See closed windows. See a jogging woman, her hair flailing behind her whipping the air. A pigeon floats, closes its wings, unfolds and flaps its wings. See half-unfolded horse chestnut leaves like the claws of insects. See cracked paving stones, damp. See open land studded with broad umbels of trees and arched canopies, and see the emergent regular pattern of planted trees as you walk. See a streak of apricot light in the sky, an oily transparence like unused engine oil around the streak, and like syrup flowed from tinned peaches onto the surface of a white bowl, a yellow stain just above treeline. See a van pass along the side of a bus obscuring parts of the bus in the shape of the van until the side of the bus is wholly visible. Read HOLIDAY INN. Letters of green light. See pigeons moving over paving stones slowly like large pale beetles. Cold cigarette butt in a damp groove between two slabs of paving. A bird whistles three times, a bird cries out of trees and flies itself from a single tree among trees to clear sky. Clatter of wings, a muffled clapping. Cars pass. Read BANQUETING ENTRANCE. Smell a staleness of drainwater. A suited man steps from a doorway and walks with eyes down to the paving, passing without a look up. Hear two drips of a liquid hit a hard surface and echo flatly. Parked cars are quiet. Smell gas, a sharp

smell like the ghost of a stink of a rotting
carcass. Read Slippery Surface. See wrought
iron bars. See the smooth arms of a deep blood
red leather armchair. Look down to the source
of a humming and rumbling air-conditioning
unit, see twin fans inside a grey metal box
attached to the side of a building. See dark
rooms and white jugs on tables. See yellow
shades over lamps. See moving fronds of a palm
and you pass close and hear the whisperish dry,
hissing noise of its leaves touching along
serrated edges. Read DE VERE MANSIONS.
Read THE WALL. Pass between two lengths
of white building to where sky is a lighter
colour of blue. Pass black window frames and a
black car passes. Read TAXI. A taxi passes.
Pass a man with beard and glasses. Pass cherry
and magnolia blossom at full steam. Hear the
sharp, thin note of a bird five times. See the
long shape of a courtyard. See a splash of water
hitting itself like the smack in the bump of a
head as it falls. All windows silent onto a
courtyard. Doors wide as coaches. See oval
leaves of lime green and sets of two hard
bobbles of lime green. The dry chuckle of a
bird. Warped trumpeting cry of a bird. See a
fly, skeletal and floating. See the bearded
interior of a single blossom. Three cheeps of a
small bird moving. Passing-by of a man in green
cloth. Read Syria Early 17th Century. And a
woman rubbing her mouth, see the white hand

at the red lips. See the white mark at the bridge
of a pigeon's beak. There are white flowers
behind glass and you pass them. Pass a doll with
a straw beard. Read CHILLED LAGERS. See
the wings of a flying pigeon turn dark in the
light of the sky. A car door opens. A man
rattles and knocks something plastic. A man
walks. A bus passes. See a man pulling a
sacktruck backwards up a step into a shop. Pass
a man in a cap and a T-shirt, he opens a brown
wooden door and steps through the doorway.
See orange crates stacked like a castle. A man
pulls crates from a shop door. See two men
queuing before a counter displaying pastry
goods. See the mannequin of a woman with red
hair. Read LUNETTE. Pass a waiting car. A
pair of ample red lips and hear music from
walls. Read SCANDIES. Pass a white-topped
man. Read ENG. And read LAND on the
halves of a jacket. Read Phonecard. Read SALE
£1300. Two numbers in brass. Read 45. Pass the
body of a red car, doors closed, six windows
dark. Pass a bike chained without sound to
railings, its front wheel hoicked by the chain
from the ground. Look up to see three birds
wheeling in a sky stained like a bowl of water
with a fish by its watery blood. Read
EXPOTEL. Pass the legs of a grey balustrade
and smell cigarette smoke. Scan five dark
windows above and turn to walk on. See the
tubular body of a fat plane fly and the noise of

the jets bellow like air from the pumps of an organ. Pass red doors and windows and see mirrored walls spangled with lights like darts in a dark smoke. Read FLAT 5. Read AMBASSADE DE LA REPUBLIQUE GABONAISE. See the gate of a black fire escape. Read PLEASE DO NOT CHAIN. A pigeon landing on a ground-based pigeon and a plane's body behind a roof. Pass an arch. See two flashing amber lights on yellow canisters, the dark barleysugar of their lenses. Hear the gushing, sheep's wool curls of a plane's jets roar. Read COOPER. Look up to the butcher's apron of a sky. Read NO ENTRY EXCEPT. Count eight milkbottles empty in a blue crate of scuffed plastic. See grubby, external and peeling, cocoa-brown paint. Read 41 QUEEN'S GATE. A structure of wrought iron, a red metal crane standing above things. Read MARKETING SUITE. Five crows of a bird's cry. See one raindrop on a car. See ornate stonework, leaf-shaped. Read Shepherd. Birds crying up a liquid sound. Pass red and white tape wound about poles. Read WARNING SCAFFOLDING INCOMPLETE. Read THE NATURAL. See mounds of earth and heaps of loose cobbles. Hear gathering cries and a darkening part of sky with gulls. Pass a newspaper folded once in half on a marble step, like a man punched in the stomach. Blue tones of sky darken with height to the sky of colours in a drop of water. Skin of a mackerel uncooked is a building mirrored. Read RED ROUTE. See tall buildings and among them a grey dome the colour of pigeons. Pass the tall figure of a man in stone, carved. Read FOUNDER OF THE BOY SCOUT. Read EDEN. Read TELEPH. Four pigeons clap into flight. An envelope printed. Read FRAGILE. See green leaves, small and soft-skinned and sharp-tipped. White blossom on a black, thin and contorted branch. A double cry of birds. Gold wrought metal leaves, rust like a brown blood across the snapped surface of a stem. Read IT'S HUNGRY. See a single car pass followed by a herd-formation of rushing, private cars. Brown bears of bronze. See a geometric arrangement of bricks. See a group of lions and two snakes. Read LYCEE FRANCAIS. See a holly tree flowering. Pass a dark-feathered pigeon. See the reflection of building tops laid on the quivering meniscus of a thin, black puddle. A pigeon strikes out wings and refolds its territory, shuffling feathers into feathers to an arms-behind-back gentlemanly neatness. Golden lions on railings. Man at a bench packing bags into bags like Russian dolls and you turn to a queue of dark-skinned figures and the queue turns a corner and follows two sides of a building to a broad door quietly with suitcases in all of their hands. See a figure seated on a folding-chair. Look up to beer-gold clouds like

[270]

small stretched fish. Pass a crumpled white plastic bag. Paving stones interlocked. See a double earth-red line at the edge of the road and cars slow. See red brick buildings and a golden obelisk. Pass a short, squat woman, her head dressed in a white habit and a man walks slowly carrying bags that appear heavy. See scraps of glinting litter creeping along gutters like rats of twisted plastic and the scrunched scowl of a crisp packet winced by the air. A pigeon glides and flaps wings. A polygon of water floats up the glint of its whole surface like the moon as you pass. Read EAT AS MUCH AS YOU. Pass the hiss of a passing bus like the noise of a stiff brush swept over rough, rainwet concrete. See a cube of milk-cartons wrapped in a single sheath of clear plastic. Pass a shop of door handles and door locks. Pass a window of chromed bathroom fittings. Read DAQUISE. See a bus driver step from a red bus. Clunk and winding of a diesel engine's start. A blackbird swerves like a paper plane to a hop abruptly twice to a standstill. See the sharp eye of the blackbird and the clear yellow beak before the pollard stump of a tree. Black circles like oxidised copper coins at the ends of short branch stumps at the crown of the trunk's stump. See bright buds among trees. Hear the see-sawing cry of a single bird. See crumpled clear plastic film behind a pane of glass and pressed up to it flatly in places. Read

HOUSEKEEPER'S FLAT. See a door knocker
in the form of a brass fish hinged at the tail. See
a building cut off like a wedge of cheese. Smell
an underground smell. See wooden sheds in a
row. Read RODIGAN'S. Read Images are
being recorded. See grotesque forms of pollard
trees. Black door by a black door in the single
white face of two houses leaning up to each
other. See shutters open, hinged back against
the wall on either side of a window. See opened
red flowers. See black and white diamond tiles.
Smell the dampness of flowers. Hear the hiss of
leaves shaking on a stern tree you pass. The
single click of a something plastic. Pass two
trees without leaves, all stag-wood and leper.
See an orange and white milk float milling its
motor ahead. Look up, hear the hum of a
plane's harmonic. A linen screen hangs at a
window and box hedges before the glass. Pass a
pigeon carrying a white stray feather on its
feathered skull. Pass stone steps wet from being
washed and a scarlet cloth-seated wooden chair.
Pass dead leaves black as alligators. New shoot
of a twig red and green. Pass blocks of grey
granite and look up to lights on a plane and
look down to grains of yellow sand run on the
pavement and smell diesel. Read Nail. See the
street without people. See multitudes of insect
leafbuds and short pollen-yellow catkins
hanging like the tails of sheep from twigs
overhead. Pass a small brick cottage and see

faintly a tracery of ivy shapes ripped from the painted bricks like a house-sized drawing by an irregular pencil, hair-wide suckers like the legs of millipedes without the black bodies. Pass bulging rubbish bags with grey stretch marks on the black surface like stretchmarks in skin, and a damp cardboard box sagging at one end like a man praying with his head to the ground and his buttocks higher than the head. Read JANUARY 8th 1908. See a woman in a long dark coat and the sharp clip of her trot is a clock. Pass a greyish face and a pigeon explodes into flight and you smell fire on a cigarette. A plane appears and passes with a falling roaring. See plastic of black, red and green. Read MODERN ALARMS. A man walks alone with a half-smile like a sand bank at low tide. Hear an echo of birds. See greenish moss in mats like wet countries over the cap stones of wall. See a man driving a dull silver car, the man smoking. Pass small winged seeds of moss on red-veined sap-green stems like small flying machines. Two halves of a cracked walnut open like hands to the sky, like two, inch-long rocking cradles. See the sheen of a snail's track. Read The Countryside Fighting. Two blue socks damp from nightfall. A burnt umber coil of dog's excrement. The grey stump of a tree's biscuity hues within general ashes of bleached sinew. Pass a tarmac tennis court. Read SAINT LUKE'S. Look up to a bloated coagulation of

sunlight like boiled albumen in a hole in the
blotched blue-grey of cool sky. Hear the shrill
breath of a crying whistle once. Two figures
sleep curled in the porch of a church and the
door is shut behind. Two pigeons fly. See beads
of dew clinging to grassblades and sunlight is
snatched into them as you walk and there are
bright flashes awake like children up long
before parents. See a green sleeping bag with
the form of a body. Stained glass illuminated in
a glass-paned door. A bench and a bin and ten
blue heads of flowers, small, and you hear
footsteps passing tombstones. Snake of a coiled
yellow hose. Read OPEN GARDENS. Read
LIBRARY. Read No Ball Games Allowed. Pass
black window frames and pass black and white
tiled steps. Bulging fascia-board of a window
box. Pass a lone pint of milk on a doorstep.
Pass ivy and box leaves with black spots like flat
green ladybirds. See a star of ragwort leaves. A
zone of cut grass. A pineapple flower. Banister
rail of stainless steel. Pass two red vans parked
and a black plastic grille like a rotten tooth.
Pass a man like a thinker on a bench. Read
GENTLEMEN. A door boarded-up. Pass a
man with lank long hair, his forehead sloping
down and jutting above eyes to a thickly-
frowned overhang. Read ANTIQUES FAIRS.
See scabs of chewing gum over flags of paving.
Pass a man arranging newspapers. Hear, "Al
Jesus." Pass a news kiosk. Hear the noise of

[274]

traffic, like the jaws of a river. Squeal of a bike.
A woman sitting in a bus shelter watching a
man and a woman step from a bus. Woman
placing a smooth oval soap into a box called
DOVE. Read THE ROYAL. Read
LONDON'S MOST FAMOUS. Pass two
pigeons. See a clear plastic bottle containing
flowers. Pass a bag of bread. See wax chicks in
rows across a glass shelf. Smell soap. See strings
and beads. See pens and pads. Read IANA.
Pass plastic men with heads tilted back, their
bodies in shirts. Pass fake fur rabbits. Pass
bottles of grey, translucent substance. Pass a
dog of papier maché. Pass a shop of phones.
Cross a street to your left. Pass a shop of
sunglasses and pictures of sun. Pass leather
shoes. Variegated leaves printed in tigerskin-
fashion on fake fur. Pass pictures of old men
and women. Shop of leather jackets, a frosted
glass pane at the rear. A machine with buttons
and greasy green glass. A window shakes. Read
GARDENING. Step over a puddle of sky to
the far shore of the puddle. See a window of
boxes and catch a reflected man jogging. Read
HOUSE WINES. Read HERO. Smell a sharp
warm oiliness of diesel. Pass a man cleaning the
nameboard of a shop with the help of a long
pole of wood. Smell lemon detergent. Pass a
woman's body and a face without details
wearing clothes in a shop. Pass a man without
features of face. A yellow beak utters a

[275]

blackbird's cry and the sound expands from a black tree. Gulls far overhead drop scythes of sharp song which fall like crescents of North wind. Pass stacked chairs. Pass scabby puddles. Pass a rag of wet paper. See a woman without a head facing a woman identically dressed. Pass a woman without head, arms, legs, dressed in a black bra and panties. Three eggs on a box by a feather. Read CLEAN SOCIET. See a straw hat. A hand with wooden fingers clutching a handbag. Pass an image of granny smith apples big as a house wall. Read DO NOT FEED. Read makes the footway slippery and spread. See a pigeon strutting after a pigeon. One pigeon drinking from a puddle of sky and small droplets of water fly up like fleas. Whistle cry of a bird you do not know. Pass a blue can balanced on railings between spearheads. Read TRADESMAN INTERPHON. Read SELF-LOCKING PLATE. See letters in relief on a round cast iron manhole cover. See the branches of a tree reflected on the wrinkled surface of a puddle. Read ILLEGAL DOG FOULING CARRIES FINES OF UP TO. See an empty room and pale carpet within the room. Hear the swat of a car's horn. A silver car passes. Four coos of a pigeon. Hear the rushing howl of a plane. See a man heaving a suitcase and pass. See a chain about a gate, linking gate to gatepost. Pass horns of witch hazel. See boxes and plastic film lining the plate of a

window. Turn to see broken grass, a long, low
brick building cast in a shadow. Read ST
LEONARDS. See twisted black bars of iron.
See four cream chimneys protruding above the
level of trees. See lemon yellow flowers and a
white line drawn onto short grass. Pass dove
grey walls of a corner. A bird flits. Read GRIT.
Read B893 MHN. See a blackbird ripping a
worm from the earth, see the blackbird springs,
turns with the head cocked. See the worm
writhes in two halves. See the blackbird stands
still and with head cocked carefully to the
ground stabs with its clear, yellow beak and
drags up from below a worm folding and
unfolding the limb of its body. Turn to a
woman passing in stretched black leggings. See
a yellow-green stain of copper over pale stone
like a diagram of the Northern Lights. Read
BURTON. See barnacles of rust in eyes of
black paintwork blistered and burst. On a green
car read C JO 1. Hear the up and down siren of
a car and pigeons flocking over grass like ash
landing. See grass worn to red, packed smooth
earth. Clear glass bottle. Read VODKA. Count
nine yellow mushrooms like the humps of
camels. Read Speed Limit 5. See red letters. A
woman with black eyes from a car watches. See
willow trees, graves and daffodils at once. Dust
lifted up into passing air. Read UK DUTY
PAID. See the bridesmaid's dress of a cherry
blossom pale. Sky's clotted greys. On a woad

blue car read A1 7 FEN. See a drop of water falling like a sheep's eye. Read PARAMOUNT. Bright green leaves shaped like cow's ears. Read TO LET. On iron plating read ATM. See squares of water. See dead leaves. See ground elder's black-greenness. Pass linen trousers of a walking man, in creases. A door closes. See an ornate inlay of wood. A woman standing still as a horse on a hill, the red sun makes her hair blacken. Smell honeysuckle perfume. See the beard of a fur coat. A blue car containing white blossom with a woman serious at the wheel. Pass a window displaying wooden stools. Window of mirrors echoes the street behind you in snatches. And two pictures of hens displayed in a shop. Read PEABODY TRUST. See two chairs with carved fish heads for arms and pass five big white feathers. See a woman holding a newspaper down to study silver and glassware in the light of the sun. Naked goatwhite body of a marble boy. See grotesque lions. Read LONDON BOY, 11, ON MURDER CHARGE. Dandelion leaves and see three striped flower buds among them like yellow manes stuffed into closed umbrellas. Pass a man in jeans and blue jacket. Pass two men walking with plastic beakers and you smell the burnt, plum-kernel sweetness of coffee. See one man smokes and the short white cigarette hangs between lips to one side, like a fang. Pass a small grape hyacinth and its fleshy green

parts. A hydrangea and a line of small yellow
flowers looking down. Pass a painting of three
dogs, a violet velvetcoated chair, two stone
lions with worn faces. Read SALE. Read
FERME. Pass a red tie and blue shirt display.
Pass old bricks and a dark room of leather
sofas. Hear into the chuckle of a scooter's
engine to a foot's kick and it roars. Pass empty
offices and the single bowl of a hanging basket.
Read EBURY BRIDGE. See stones pressed
flat into tar and cars moving downhill. See a
greenness on the edge of paving slabs and on
dark brown bricks also, like an algae. See tufts
of moss and tea redness engrained in the green
of moss. See the sun open its blinding hole in
the soapy overhead. A plane whispers. See
brushed-back hair. A train riding lines of steel
in parallel, straddled like two skis. Hear the
curling hiss and screel of train brakes. See two
trains emerge from the mouth of a brown brick
bridge. See fur-grey scabs of scaly hardness over
brickwork, like old, grey rubber mats. The
stump of a leaning lamp post. Feel the moving
air. A woman walks and her hair is dyed blonde
and she smiles to herself. Hear the moan of an
engine. A many-sided building, grey, with
pictures of blue flames on each face. Hear the
scrape of a shovel. A man speed-walks. See
litter brushed up onto the pan of a shovel by a
man. Look up to the dark crusted baubles of a
plane tree and a bus passes and a man in a

yellow coat cycles wearing cobalt blue. A grey
lorry clatters and a single beep repeats as the
lorry reverses. See a man and a suitcase, he
walks alone. See cracked paint on the surface of
the case and the man's coat is brown flapping
wide open at the knee. Pass wire mesh. Read
METHODIST CHURCH. See tall windows
boarded. See window frames of rust brown and
glass the brown-green colour of canals. Read
MONT BLANC. See intense pink of flowering
geraniums. See the stain of water on a brick.
Cherry blossom dark as crows against bone sky.
See chains across a doorway and a fleshy-leaved
plant hanging the height of a house. Pass white
hair, black framed glasses, coarse black hairs
within the shades of white hair like horsetail.
Pass two vans. Pass the page of a magazine.
Read 59. On one side of a porch read 6 6 6. See
a yellow bike and pink blossom above. The
squid's ring of a rubber band. Glass drinking
goblets dusty in a low cardboard box on a
doorstep. Read GAS. Hear the flute of a
blackbird. See pale petals on tar, bruised in
their creases. Pass pollard trees and over and
through the stumps of their limbs see mackerel-
grey sky. Pass a man on crutches dragging three
dogs on thin leads. Read The Art of Decor.
Read FREE. Hear the sound of a brush being
swept across hard, gritty paving. Pass a grey
beard and a blue hat. Read DE QUINCEY
HOUSE. Pass a mute brown sleeping bag

draped over a shoulder, and the shoulder is a
man's. Pass a man brushing down a white van
like a groom at a horse. Read 145. See a girl
dressed in orange cloth on a bicycle. Hear the
chugging of a van driven. See a sunken
playground below the level of the street. Hear a
rattle of small components knocking against
each other in the tiny sack of a pocket. Hear a
cough four times. See rolls of carpet and a man
spits and he blows a streak of phlegm like a
dart from the cave of a nostril. Read PLEASE
RING THE BELL. Hear the scuff of a foot. A
hand wipes a nose. See flakes of tobacco and
smell sweet almondy fumes from petrol. A hand
at teeth. A hand zips up a jacket. See a grain of
sweat between shoulder blades, a darker
diamond of damp cloth. See a long pin-striped
coat and clipped hair. See the sun. See a small
snail-sized mound of red-brown on pavement,
the closed palace of a dog's excrement. See
scraps of newspaper adhered to the pavement
by water. See something kicked and see nettle
leaves, and the serrations of their edges like
saw-teeth. Pass a golden box. See worried eyes
and a red scarf and a body leans forwards on
feet, and four feet pass together on wooden
heels like the sound of the hooves of a single
horse. See a picture of hands in the bangles of
cuffs. See a cap and a ruddy face. Read Lighting
of Easter. See the body of a man rigged up on a
cross and the head to one side. See keys placed

into the slot of a pocket by a hand and left there. Read 7pm. Read COIN-OP. Read INDIAN TANDOORI & ENGLISH DISHES. Pass the still photograph of a girl running and her lips are pursed and turned into a mouth like an O. Pass a red lorry. Read ALL CLEAR. See a man with a black labrador and see one hind leg of the dog in plaster and the dog limps so the rump of the dog rises like a tent and falls with the unbendable step of the back leg. Four rupps of a crow. A long puddle like a liver. Read GUSS. See flinty gravel at the foot of a tree. Pass green iron railings and the smell of paint. A car stops in the road. See a newspaper folded. Hear a cough. Read BESSBOROUGH. Read GI. See leaves pouring through black railings like the arms of convicts for freedom. A flat dead brown leaf like a dropped glove. See rolled-up paper. Speck of rain and you see the darkening of sky. Pass a woman in a T-shirt and red scarf and she passes an orange cable curled up in a coil. A curtained window. See spots of rain, dark like the spots of a Dalmatian. See two burnt matches like the aftermath of battle. Green water moving like a hair on an eye. Green water combed by the pointed feet of a bridge. Read DIVERSION AHEAD. See water flowing brightly into a darker green river. See bankside trees and a green, distant shore. The river is a round smell on the hand of the wind. A girl cycles and

[282]

chews in her mouth. See heads pointed down.
Hear two bumps of car wheels over the lump of
the road. Turn to see water rippled like creased
lead flashing. See three ducks in flight and turn
to see towers. And a green hat of felt and
glasses of blackness over hidden eyes. Read
SPIT. See a flat, gold box. See large rivets. Turn
to see turrets and a pea green spire. See the
owl's eye of the dying sun and you turn to the
clip of the moon shaped like a cat's tooth. And
see amber earrings on dark ears, like the two
triangles of a cat's nightwatch. Green windows
reflecting. See yew leaves dark and cross-
hatched and a woman's face imprisoned behind
the three bars of her frown. A footprint in
concrete and cracked paving thrown in a heap.
Read Sales &. See a figure at speed and steps
falling into the ground. Pass a flat cap and see
hands pulling out of gloves ten pale fingers to
flex naked. See hands interlocked like two
forks, strain like an opened-back book, and see
fingers crossed like a zigzag of stitching.

A sharp stink of urine lurks. Walk out of XIX
ground step by step into a raining air which is
dim and cast over. Pass corners of grey paving.
See a man place two bags on wet ground. Rings
of water spread from each raindrop landing.
One rowan trembles and you look up to the
passing barrel of a plane's body. A bright,

contained splash like ripping and a drain letting the sound of water up from its cavern. A Cinderella's slipper of a car. A blue beer can in the stickle of a potted fir. Sections of fir tip needled, sap-tender horns of leaves from bark like rocks. See four rings of pale plastic connected to each other lying on the earth within the fir tree's pot. Turn to a sound of traffic and see all cars fast at once like a merry-go-round. See faces within the bodies of cars. Read JOB CLUB. Read NO CALLERS PLEASE THIS IS NOT. Hear the slap of raindrops and the growth of a siren. A blue light flashing and the siren dies. A man steps from a doorway. A woman by the closed passenger-side door of a car puts her nose between the thumb and finger of her right hand. A man in the box of a van. The rattle of bottles clinking sharply, you look to the hissing cry and rumble of a train and all traffic stops like a door shut on a noise. Count three men sitting together in a dry room with blue chairs empty around them. See through a window seated long-haired figures in grey and brown clothes, one man bearded at a table in a yellow room, coughing. Cars pass like a chase of motoring dogs. Music within a car beats on the windows of the car like an animal of anger. Pass a green crisp packet screwed-up into a ball of wrinkles and see droplets of water held in creases among the plastic and the entire packet

is clasped between two bars of railings. See
leaves picked up by the wind and thrown high
between blue and white flags which crack and
beat. See a house of brick standing alone like an
island-rock. Smell air full of rain and see the
thin metal hands of a clock read ten-to-eight.
See strips of fabric behind glass. Two men walk
together talking with voices too quiet to hear.
See pink flowers on tables, many chairs pushed
in against the side of each table. The windows
of the room are coffee-brown. Read 101. Read
103. See cracks visible over the surface of yellow
ochre bricks like aerial views of a rocky terrain
and cracks like minute river channels. A hand
runs its back edge across the ridge of a nose.
Pass a black car empty with steamy windows.
See beads of darkness among leaves and one
glint like an eye opening. A train passes over a
bridge and there is a great rumbling and regular
clunking repeated. Pale spots of gum on dark
pavement tar. See windows reflected upside
down in a puddle and the puddle grows
corrugated suddenly with a wind. There are
crimson flowers and a car stops. See a red
pencil gripped between the teeth of a dark face.
Hear a scrape of synthetic fabric and turn to
see a man in a raincoat and hat holding four
plastic bags. And you pass through the shade of
a bridge. Hiss of a car's wheels, sustained and
the knock and thunderclap of rolling stock.
Read CLAPHAM GRAND. Read

Sundissential. Read Hey Hey It's Saturday.
Look up to windows lit and look down to a
splat of white paint across the dark, smooth
surface of pavement. Blue-walled carriages of a
passing train. A bicycle passes and there is a
small breeze like a child crying. See the shape
of a plane and turn to see the un-detailed shape
of a man's face looking down from an upper
storey. Read DAW. See cream and yellow roses
and the petals are large and soft. Look into a
black startle of dull-lit leafless, twigless
branches of trees. Read DANGER Anti-climb.
See letters in red on white. Dark yellow rose
petals bleeding red edges like rims of eyelids.
See the leaves of a flowering currant and no
flowers. And yellow flowers opening like the
beaks of small songbirds. The pale buds of a
plant curled like green larvae. See red leaves
clustered in sets of five, spiderish. Pass two
figures in the shadow of the shelter of a bus
stop, their faces dark with the shade of the
shelter. And a boy with a biscuit in one hand.
See two broken and rotted translucent
mushrooms and the small cuttlefish bones of
their gills. Read Quick Look Barbe. See a man
shaking hairs from a dark blue towel. Read
GLADSTONE. Two women walking beneath
umbrellas. Pass red and white geraniums in
green boxes regimentally. Bricks of fishstock-
grey glass. A car comes to a halt. Hear the
triple click of a handbrake pulled on. Two roars

[286]

of an engine and the fall to snow-silence of an engine switched off. See black leaves reflected in a puddle like the black lilo bodies of crocodiles afloat. See a man in a black shirt shouting words skewed with rage and see he turns to the box of a doorway and stands alone. Hear, "Cheers." Read TEMPLE COURT 1-17. Look up to see cream-coloured towers in a gap between two buildings of brick. See grey flowers the grey of herons and the grey of the yolk's bloom in the hardboiled egg. See an image of road and parked cars on mirrored glass. Read ROYAL ARSENAL CO-OPERATIVE SOCIETY LTD. T S STONE WAS LAID ON 21ST NOV. 1928 BY MR J.T. SHEPPARD TO COMMEMORATE THE REBUILDING OF THIS BRANCH. Read THIS STONE WAS LAID IN THE PRESENCE OF WILLIAM ROSE FOUNDER OF THE SOCIETY. Read EACH FOR ALL AND ALL FOR EACH. See a plastic bag and two leaves side by side like two sleeping brothers. Read GAS. Look up to a dark light of greyness through rain spitting like a downpour of miniature spears. Smell a gas of sewage. Read READY SALTED. See a man in brown accompanied by two women in black. Read EL-HAK BURGER AND KEBAB. A man enters a car and the door closes and the car starts. See a cracked paving stone and one half of the stone is sunken and the triangular trough filled with water to the level of the surrounding pavement. Read COW THORPE. See an image sliding on a billboard out of sight and another image sliding into the frame to replace it. See a man in a lit room and see the room is stacked with glass bottles up to the ceiling. See a man staring into the window of a shop. See dark windows facing the storeys above the shop. Read REVOLUTION AGAINST GLOBAL CAPITALISM. Letters printed in red on white. Read FUNERALS. See broken windows and dark-leaved buddleia shrubs. See a pink doll with grey-blonde hair dressed in knitted pink socks and a purple-to-seagreen shawl. Pass a dark child and see figures at a table in a window. A blue van's rear door swings ajar. Two men at a table and one man with a cap, all tilted up at the face like earth-based satellites to a wall-mounted screen. See the wall is a mustard. A red bus grinds to a stop and you walk. See a black puddle the shape of a slug. See a plane alone like a submarine with wings. See tufts of hair tightly curled and black scattered from snips across a lino. Hear the high, sharp squeal of a woman. See three faces, dark, and there are red-cheeked faces also, blonde hair, spasm of eyes squinted. See a room with screens unlit, a room of flat grey rectangles across the walls. A man in black, black-helmeted, leaning over an off-white counter. Hear the cry of a car's acceleration. Clay

[288]

horned animals. Pass bright glinting raindrops and the rainbow squints once from a sloe-black water. A woman in tight-fitting trousers walking at speed with short steps. See light between legs and see light in a clutched hand, a lighter lit, and the idle flame blown aside by a wind. See the lighter held up to the flat tip of a cigarette in the clasp of a mouth. Read COMMERCIAL WASTE. Pass a picture of an astronaut in space. A chromed padlock reflects in greys. Read GOLDSBOROUGH. Pass bricks dark with water and you hear the cries of a blackbird. A wave driven out from a puddle by the fast-plough tyre of a car and a white surf curls to the kerb with a froth. Look up to a blackbird still on the pot of a chimney. See a spherical object lying on an area of cut grass and two men together. There are seeds and twigs strewn over wet stones. Hear a voice of high singing. Look to a mouth containing white, straight teeth and it passes with teeth set like jewels of white paper. Read CROXTETH. See a face, hooded. White paper, rain-chewed and foot-trodden. Sweet smell of spice. Turn to see men at the counter of a small cafe with a woman, like cows at a gate. A woman emerges from the open door of a car. Her coat is a clear, bright red, drawn in at the waist by a red belt. And she turns and walks into a shop and takes two brown bottles from a brown metal shelf. Pass a face. Pass a tall, narrow, black hat. Smell

[289]

cigarette smoke. Read ZONE ENDS. A tall black hat hiding the upper crown of the head of a woman, and rising from the dark skin of the cheeks in a black way like the beak of a crow straight into air, the hat like the prayer of a hen's tail. Brown of the smell of burnt oil and a yellow smoke in the brown like the flayed chemistry of a polymer. Read DIAGNOSTIC SERVICE. Pass two figures standing in shelter out of rain and see raindrops suspended brighter than sky from the lip of the shelter's flat roof. And one drop breaks from the stem of its water. Hear the word "Prawns" uttered once. A man with short grey half-curled hair like a lamb's. Hear the sound of cotton rubbed against cotton. Double cry of a car's brakes hit sharp. Hear, "You there, eight o'clock, or I go yeah." See a dark shop window and the shop is full of keys hung on hooks screwed to a red board. And each key like a small, particular light, like the teeth of mice. Pass two black gates like the two halves of a rib cage. Read SOLD SUBJECT TO CONTRACT C & A SEWING MACHINE COMPANY LTD. Pass two figures dressed in grey standing close together and a row of dark trees you pass through and leaves blink the orange of streetlamps. Read MATRIMONY PLACE. Read community garden. See a long beard. Hear, "A lot of people, see, they get them hung with it." And a bicycle passes, hear the click of

a chain and the loose, jogged rattle of gears
changing. See a man's arm about an arm. Hear,
"I'll be alright, call." Turn to see a grey tower.
See hands behind glass. Read CARTER,
WHEY & TIPPET. Hear a slight squeal of a
car's tyre. Read ROZEL. Hear a long, alto
droning over you. Pass penny-sized violet
flowers and there is an orange light over a dark-
skinned nose and the face with the nose moves
away. A man steps from a car and you walk and
you read THE MEDICUS GROUP. See two
men entering a car and see bluebell flowers
seeded to brown bulbous sacks like paper
balloons. See the figure of a woman with large
breasts leaving the face of a house. See a man's
face alone, watching something to his left. And
a scatter of voices and the voices diminish. Face
of grey towers like a range of crags. Pass the
curled sabre-fronds of a palm. A window reveals
a sage-green room and chocolate woodwork.
There is the lean hiss of a man's breath. See a
paleness of leaves like parchment. A face
beneath a hat like a shadow under a rock. A
grey dome ahead like the unlit side of moon.
See ornaments of plasterwork. Plane overhead,
pale, and it drags a howl and a diving roar. A
dark face, eyes like a pool black at night. A
scatter of water from the throat of a downpipe.
Read God 2 U is cool thru Jesus A text 4 2 day.
Read America Pool & Snooker. A tin can
balanced on a tin can. And groups of figures.

See two dark hands holding a bunch of bananas.
Raindrops bright over ground, like frogspawn.
A shop of bottles. Pass the entrance to an alley
leading uphill. Read Lavender Hill. See a
milkwhite form of a stone set in the frame of
an upstairs window, the stone curved like a
crouched man or a woman, with a low peach
light in the room behind it. Hear a throat
roughed clear by a cough and a chattering like a
nerviness of monkeys in a sound. Smell exhaust
fumes of a petrol-burning vehicle. Read Wood
Fired PIZZA. See a woman, she is thin, holding
the waist of a man. Read LAVENDER. Read
COMET MINIATURES. Read The Puzzle.
See a schooner-shape of light across the glazed
surface of green tiles. A mouth chewing, lips
glossy. See flowers of blue. A white and wire-
haired woman holding her face, see eyes
squinted in narrow cracks. Orange light over
the road like a film. Blebs of water shaken from
a light by a passing vibration like falling fire in
water from a gutter at sunlight. There are red
lights ahead. Read NEW DISH CHINESE
LEAVES WITH OYSTER SAUCE. There is a
black puddle like a long island the shape of a
liver. Read Halter top £5.99. See bright lines of
water between bricks on the road. See a man in
a green room reading and the mouth closes like
an oyster. Smell stale cigarette smoke. Pass the
face of a tall burnt umber brick hall and long
dark windows lit beyond so the small square

plates of glass within the windows have an
effect like cockle shells. Turn to an oblong
assembly of buildings and the face of a woman
sipping wine from a glass delicately in a room of
subdued light. See mouths opening and closing.
Next window, see a man exploring the aisles of
an empty shop. Next window, an oriental-faced
man carrying two dishes to the table of a man
and woman bent to each other like trees over a
road. Turn to a street of small, black-armed
trees and leaves weeping heavy with rain. See lit
rectangle windows of a train and the line of the
train-windows scroll through the gap in the
wall. Read PLAY. Read Tuman Thai. See
eaters and drinkers secluded at tables. A
woman alone walking fast, dragging a hand up
through the wheat of her blonde hair, dragging
a wheeled suitcase like a dog by a short leash.
Read SISTERS. The mouth of a woman at a
phone and it moves like the eye of a man trying
not to sleep. Hear, "Oh, great." Hear the word
'great' is disappointedly. Read MYSORE. Pass
a green room in the belly of a towered house.
Read JESUS DIED TO SAVE THE. Man with
one finger at his lips and the lips are sealed,
man in a room stacked with bottles high along
each wall. A skullcap of polish on the baldness
of a yawning man. A man bearded about to cry
with eyes winced up like two babies' mouths. A
mouth like a sleeping baby. Figures dash onto a
road like blackbirds awkwardly, with heads into

shoulders. Stream of traffic humming to itself.
And a signal of changing light is amber to
green. Read LAVENDER SWEEP. Pass a long
table, men seated, women seated, on sides like
two teams. Two women wearing black clothes.
Hear, "They'll be, they'll be a." Hear, "Okay."
There is a traffic of footsteps and the noise of
rain grows on the ground. The clicked slam of a
shutting car door. Read WIM. See louvered
shutters behind windows. Pass plastic bodies
arranged standing, wearing tight red garments.
See a dark square space of ground crossed by
figures and shadows and a dog's shadow like a
fox under the trotting dog. And all pass quietly.
A mirrored room and a sweet, flour staleness.
Hear, "Sit out of the rain for a while, something
to eat." Tall chocolate-brown brick and a soot-
blackness to mortar between bricks and
windows ranging the face of the building are
dark without light and one pane knocks. Read
ANY OBJECT PARKED NEXT TO, OR
ATTACHED TO ANY PART OF THIS
BUILDING WILL BE TREATED AS A
SUSPECT DEVICE & DEALT WITH
ACCORDINGLY. Read INSTANT TAN. A
man walks from a building, a door slams like a
snare drum. See rain runs down bricks and hear,
"Is that you." There is a cry-note. Hear the revs
of an engine. Eight train tracks in the broad
gully of a space. See a dark space, a green
signal's light and see the green light conducted

[294]

along the moonbright steel of each track. See
the sleepers. The sky all charcoal. A crane's
steel structure stands with its balanced arm. A
piano fogged behind net curtains below the
level of the pavement. Read AMPHIBIAN
GUARDS. There is a bald-headed man. A man
in shorts and a grey shirt surveying the contents
of a bin. A dark tree moth. See tiger-stripes of
orange over paving. A high voice speaks up.
There are bottles and lights and light through a
bottle like the nose of a spaniel. Pass a stone
the colour of wolves. And look up to the lit
portholes of a passing plane. A light high, sweet
musty smell of wine. Tyres ripping up water.
The hornet of a motorbike going. The dark,
quiet street containing the line of the hiss of
bicycle tyres through water. Read Relax and go.
A space of wet grass glistening with yellow
flashes blue-black in raindrops small as grape-
pips. A face turns in a darkened room to your
left. See a smiling man. A raindrop falls full of
light fat as a dove. See a collar with a copper
silk tie. Three figures pass and two of them
young in the voice. Hear, "I feel very good."
Dark space of trees to your left, leaves flap
against leaves. See rain-glossed leaves in the
scan of bus headlamps, the bus red with
greynesses of red shadow around the cab, the
driver crouched as a crone at a cauldron,
stirring the wheel. Man walking ahead in the
shade of a black umbrella held over the head. A

bone-white cross set into a bone-white circle.
Cry of an engine. Clatter of raindrops like
frying eggs and bacon. Rain smacks down
heavy, accumulated from leaves, and scatters
from paving like a dog pawing. Fine spray
inches above ground of smashed drops. See the
black picture of a bicycle. A woman seated in a
room. Pat of raindrops drums to a hiss. A car
pulls from a sideroad into a space between
moving cars. Look up to see a pale white flower
like a ballerina's dress from below. Looped rags
of a leaf. Rain spits. There are cherry leaves and
you count thirteen flecks of black on one leaf.
An entrance into bushes. See green lights ahead
and black circles composed of three lines. A flat
red packet out on the tar of the road. Dark
bricks of a house. Bulb of a raindrop hanging
from a pointed leaftip. A bridge of concrete in
orange light. Read WANDSWORTH. There
are wet yellow leaves like raincoats and fingered
leaves like skeleton keys, and brain-grey caps of
seeded dandelions. See the heads and necks of
figures in carriages. A green light switches to
darkness. A herd of fast-moving cars slows to
stop. A green man and a bicycle light up on a
black surface. A small car containing four men
revs to a rough clatter like a sheet of metal hit
by gravel and a sound like a roll on a snare
drum. Hear a laugh muffled. Read
TRADITION OF EXCELLENCE. Walk on
and the road is climbing. Read 28 295 C3. Read

tried to hide. There is dark open space, see
cobbles, and then the road arches over a hump.
See an open skin of violet-grey water stretching
like an eel of giantness. There is a metal wall
punched and clasped with rivets. And you turn
to a boat and its rigging moored up. See flares
and horse tail spasms of light over the black
ribs of water. Whips of light. The river curling
through the daub of lights. See distortions of
light into shapes like hens, crows, eels, worms,
an 'S', swallows, mice. And you walk. Rain
freckles the broad of the river. See the curl-
away of the upstream. See scaly patches of
water, and a puddle with horns and a reflected
light buoyant across the shaking water of the
puddle. There is a local quietness and you turn
to an approaching muffled wasp noise. Four
figures on a fast moving boat, and the figures
standing, still as four posts and the wind
blowing back the hair from the flat fronts of
their heads, and you see a wake fanning like the
wings of a black swan and then the wings of a
skate as they stretch and grow dark out of the
scumbled foam from the plough of the boat's
beak. See ripples climb onto the shores of the
river, pull back, and the water continues to beat
the shores and the boat is passing. See the
debris of movement. Turn to a leaning man
carrying a black bag swollen with contents.
There are blue lights and the road descends like
a hill. Read serving our community. Read

SCRAP METAL TOP. See a bone-shaped metal structure of support and a traffic light mounted like a horse's head. Hear, "And I went in there." You pass the voice and words lump together into a speaking sound you cannot decipher. See a man in a grey room lit the colour of flannel. And see the man holds a baby against his bald shoulder so the baby's head looks behind him and one hand of the man pats the back of the baby between the fleshed blades of its shoulders softly and the throat and mouth of the man moves with sound. See a dark church of brick, squat as a fat cat. Read HUGON. Rattle of keys. A woman between black open doors. Read 300. There is the strong smell of sweetness of cooking, and the smell of ginger. And you pass through the smell of cooked bacon. Read WOOLNEIGH. Scaly green and black of the bark of a tree and the lines upwards on the tree are the double helix of a rope. Bark-flakes on the ground. Lights from a plane passing, a livid violet-grey sky in an aura for the split-duration of a light flash on a plane's wing. Gloom like the cave of a closed mouth. A woman pulling a top over her head fogged in net curtains. A howling voice behind wood panels of a closed door. Hear, "Halloo." See a naked plaster man, grey in streetlight. A woman standing still, opening the skin of an umbrella to a portable tent on a stick overhead. Hear, "About ten, smart." Read TINDLE. See

more than twenty lamps. Read TINDLE TOO.
See more than fifteen lamps. Pass buckets of
two skips, each covered in blue tarpaulin. See
carpets of colours and one light is on. Read
CLANCARTY. Read SANDS END
LAUNDERETTE. Look up to a window, a
shelf racked with files, a man with a key ring
shaking a hand. A door of glass panels being
unlocked. A heap of grey bags and sacks of a
woven material. A car slows to a stop. Pass
concrete pineapples. Read REAL MEAT
NATURALLY FED. Two figures walking with
shadows like crows. Pass through a shadow like
an elephant's leg. Shadows like small monkeys
moving among dark canopies. See eye-cracks of
leaf light. A figure alone. Shadows like cats. A
low and pale shrub. The glow worm of a flower.
Lights of two cars passing and you turn as they
pass to see red tail lamps like birds in black
hedgerows moving away. See a man at a kitchen
sink. A dark man on a doorstep head crouched
down to the chest, arms folded close to the
heart, a phone snugged up between a shoulder
and an ear. Read SURGERY. Letters in red on
white. Pass a man walking. A stooped figure. A
man in the tent of an umbrella. His eyes meet
yours and flick somewhere else and you pass. A
greenness of lights. Pass two dogs and a stream
of cars makes a noise rising and falling in
volume like the noise of sea beaching land after
dark. Hear, "Pay out the bills man." Pass a dog

with its tail lifted. Look up to a red light deep in the sky like a splinter in a hand. Yellow sewing machine at a table. A large black puddle perforated by drops of rain falling. The fading drone of a plane's engine. A rubber band the colour of a camel. Pale leaves like canaries. Look up to a man's face looking down to the street. Read BLAKE. Flowers grey with dust are growing in darkness. See a wall with many small frames hung across its white face. A brown kettle and a box on a sideboard. Two figures ahead. Rust red hair of a woman caught like a fox by a car light and the hair blown backwards over the ear by a sharp wind. A singing voice under an umbrella. Hear, "Must be really catching." Pass a voice singing from the cave of a hood. Two hands withdraw from pockets. Bare legs in the window of a room. Beating chunter of a sluggish motor. The grating whine of transmission and a clunk three times. Read OPEN. Four letters in red light. See a woman's hand extend its index finger and press a white button on the frame of a front door. And see five thin men standing against a long wall of shade in a row like guns in a rack.

See four girls. An old man with yellow hair   xx
kisses his right hand's finger and strokes it over
the hair of a girl's head. One by one he kisses
the four girls. See the red eye of a lit cigarette.

[300]

Hear, "Down on the floor." See a blown-out pale rag of smoke from a mouth. Hands in the pockets of trousers. Hear, "Okay, well." Hand to a phone. Boy with a newspaper folded, his hair short. Girl's foot over a railing and she leaps down. Eyes of a woman closed and her navel visible. Man ahead moving slowly. Read ALBION. See two fingers of a girl's hand in a front pocket. A square-shouldered tower set into deep black blue luminous sky. Hear, "Bunch of cheap flowers or something." Turn to hear voices and see the red tail lights of a vehicle moving away. Two men pass in another language. Arm swinging by a hip. See an eye-shaped window and shoes with holes punched-in and stitched with black cord. See a trussed piece of meat, uncooked on the pavement, bristles up through the skin of the flesh. A red-haired woman yawning aloud. Hear, "See you later." And softly you hear, "If you're going to be out Sunday night." See a varnished wooden bar and a carpet of red and green and grey and orange in patterns. See two figures stumbling into arms bent before bodies with hands spread at the fingers and turn. Sky with greys. Blue binliner. Man in a car, seated, one first finger sucked in the mouth. Cry of a phone. Murmur of a voice answering. Jeans bright on the legs of a woman, she walks with a man. Bright scrape of a shoe. Hear, "No," seven times. Knocking of bottles. See a young girl dancing. See black wires to ears. A hooded man, face dark in the shadow of the hood and his foot kicks a stone the length of a stride. Read HAR. Read LEM. Three letters on two sides of a chest. Car. See the eyes of a man. See green leaves in dark light and the sky black with shadows is movement. See many black spikes and turn to the moon in fragments behind black shadows and turn to the moon reflected on cracked glass. Read LV02 AZZ. White-haired man driving and see black windows of an ochre brick building and a flash of diamond-shapes red and gold as you pass like apples in trees. A brass handle gleams. Hear a car manoeuvring. See three lights in clear bulbs of glass. Smell cigarette smoke. And quietly, two men eating chips. Hear chewing, tiny 'ack' sound of food between teeth or tongue and a palette. Smell of hot vinegar and see strands of steam rising from the fingers of a man. A mouth opens in the face of a head, tilted back with three fingers and a thumb held above, one chip falls in. The shine of a tooth. Hear footsteps. You pass. A blue light ahead and a shadow of scooter. Leafless twig. Curtains drawn and a window is dark. Long baskety shadow of a tree's cage. See the flat, ragged leaves of gingko shivering. Hear, "Are you likely to come along." Hear, "Look, I'm walking down Northend Road, so yes, alright, okay, bye." Red lights of a car. See a man in a bed behind slatted blinds. White lights of a car. Five figures pass and three join three to make six of which three joining one make four figures along two steps who turn into three joining three into six and one goes alone. Hear, "She's got a." Hear reply, "And I could bring the sweat up and I didn't even feel wet at the end ... and it's got long sleeves." Shadow of a tree, see the shape of the horn of a goat, see the shape of a ram. And the wind makes a sound, like cattle through bracken, in leaves. A cough from a black door. See a horned moon crescent. Keys thrown to the ground. Man looking up to a woman in the face of a window. She has long red curls of hair with a light behind her. See dark-leaved trees in the dark like still, horned animals. Hear the shout of a man. See the long hair of a figure ahead, frayed out. A patch of damp wall split into two. A man alone. Sheen of a shaved head. A vehicle parking. Hear, "That's basically the strength of it." A leak of oil glints like a cat's eye in the shady streetlight. Hear, "I ain't got time for this fucking inchy bitch man." Look up. Read BAPTIST CHURCH. And see leaves growing from brickwork and hear the noise of a patrolling car containing two men with careful eyes passing through the street and see a shop of bath tubs. Chatter of two or more voices and you turn. Hear, "I can hear the difference between." And hear, "Do you have a ... I'll show you some digital stuff." And hear reply, "What now?" And hear, "I'll have to finish this

quickly." See a cigar-end glow in the dark, flung
down to a foot and pressed out. Double shadow
of an ivy leaf on gloss paint and the single
cough of a man. Behind net curtains see a
white-haired woman in an armchair and a black
cat and see a reflected change of colour from
green to pink to a blue-grey on her face. Turn,
see the frame of a television screen behind net
curtains. See clouds and dull mute tones, an
almost unseeable copper cross on a spire's tip.
Electric light filtered through leaves to a man
of illuminated shadow. Read TYRES TYRES.
Read Entrance to Beer. A boy pulling up to a
phone in a phone box. Short hair. A sockless
man walking, brown jacket thrown armlessly
over his shoulders. Blue shadows beneath the
nipples of a woman like yawning smiles and the
nose of a man and the chins of both. A laugh
like a cry. Hear, "It's really, really red isn't it?"
See a dark red light and in that light the image
of a man made of white rings. Hear, "You
fucking can't." A laugh. Hear, "You know what
I mean." Hear, "Do you know why I'm called
Harrier." And you hear the opening of a door
and the starting of a car and the deep crunch of
gears. Brown bottle on a black shelf by a phone
in the brown dark of a room. Scrape of a man.
A boy moves with his feet. And you turn to the
dark evening flame of the sky with a moon's
cataract set in the pink clear as water. Roof of a
building blackened with sky. See the body of a

woman in bright clothes within the square of a
window dancing with hands above her alone to
herself and the light of the room is yellow like
saffron rice. Clicky whirr of a bike and the
clatter of plastic. Towers stand like men at a
bus stop. Hear the squeak of a door. Hear a
walking woman and a talking man. Sharp clang
of a bell. Smell the smoke of leaves burning.
Read PAY HERE. An oily grey room with
columns of tyres. Hear the tin, crackled voice
of a radio presenter. See a car jack on wheels of
pale blue rolled by a man under the body of a
car. Blonde woman pushing a pram. A blonde
baby yawning. Silver paint on railings. See cars
in a row. A man with wet hair. Read
ULTIMATE CONTROL. See flesh above the
waist of a pair of jeans. An arm rises and waves
and falls. Hear repeating bell-clangs. A woman
steps into the lung of a church of brown bricks.
A piano played in the church and a song of
voices. Black locked gates. Black iron railings.
See graves and three children running among
graves dressed in blue, they stop, turn and run.
Man and woman walk together. A black door is
opened and voices grow louder and quieter.
The black door is closed. Hear the voice of a
man talking loud and voices of many together.
Seeding grasshead. A door closes hard. A stone
woman stands. A blackened stone woman and
child of stone and a bower of stone sunk to a
leaning position. Three children in blue clothes

enter a house by a black door. Grey sky and
three claps of hands and 'gloria' spoken by
many. Claps in succession and see hands with a
white page and a head down, and a woman in
dark clothes without even a flint's spark of a
smile and a man in a car singing alone with a
smile and you hear the cry of a scooter
accelerating and the cry of engines slowly like
the chanting of Buddhist monks backwards.
Hear, "Student, finished yeah." See a
downwards arrow reflected without sound on a
puddle and look up to a herd of passing clouds
moving slowly as whales over dark sky to the
East and footsteps move close and pass. There
are stars. Hear, "Where are we going to go ...
down here, or?" A yawn exists. The clap of a
tripped foot. Hear, "Oops." And hear, "You be
alright? ... lovely seeing you." Hear, "Night."
Footsteps start and their volume grows small
and a man watches a woman walk from the post
of a gate and you pass. See a man ahead
running. Mouth with a grey tooth, hair like
fronds moving and a man in a car with a head
slipping back and a right-hand thumb and
finger drawn over the neck of a woman and the
hair of the woman is grey gold like late summer
wheat. Man with a black stick over his shoulder
and the fast blade of a cyclist cutting the air of
the road in half. See a woman's face turning and
the head of a man with sunlight in creases.
Leaves mazy with wind and you hear the song

[306]

of birds scattered like a seed of sharp cries and
a man broadening, squaring-up shoulders as he
walks and a chest barrelled as a pigeon's and he
coughs and you see pale cheeks bellow like
sheets out to dry and a biscuit of spit hits the
ground from the mouth and the square-
shouldered mouth is made small from the
spitting. Man lifting a black stick and you pass
the two sparrows of a woman's eyes rolling to
one side and the head thrown back. A man
among his reflections over glass before him.
Scrape of a dry, brown oak leaf, which passes a
pigeon. A plane passes low from soft-bodied
cloud as a man's pale hand adjusts a bag's strap.
Read LOVER SHOT DEAD BOY, 5. White
teeth in a dark face, man on a phone, laugh like
a cry, a language of words you do not know.
Read MUSLIM FUNERAL DIRECTORS. See
plants on a windowsill, thick-fleshed leaves.
Man lifting a pack of grey papers. Web of grey
cracks over a windshield and a man's face
behind. Closed green buds of lilies like pelican
beaks, the stems trussed, the bunch lying flat
on a glass top. A man's jacket dragged from the
shoulder by the weight of a slung bag. Vertical
strips over shins and black wires to ears and see
silver discs. Woman with a tea cup held to her
lips by finger and thumb. A man lifts a briefcase
up to his ear, walking, and the first finger
extends to scratch the ear on the rim of the
lobe with the whole briefcase shaking on the

scratch. Man with a face. Man with a face
pinched-in as he swallows and you see the lump
in the throat glide up and glide down like an
egg. Man with grey hair brushed back and
furrows of a frown and a white cigarette
jammed in the mouth. Man with a head like a
wave, with a beach-brown suede jacket and a
curved nose in profile, arched like a castle of
surf. A man smiles sideways. See a woman
lifting a bottle in one hand and leaning
forwards. Four fingers of a hand stretched
spread out over the rim of a car's steering
wheel. Damp blonde hair clumped into limp
eels on a woman passing. And walk hearing,
"Sorry mate, have you got a pound coin on
you." And you see many rows of gravestones.
Hear the rattle of an engine near pads of moss
with small red seed-like heads on stems like
fine iron wire. Red car parked. Man in a blue
shirt in the seat of a car. Black seat. Cry of a
bird. See a woman folding her mouth in. A
blackbird flies up to stand on a stone like a
Roman emperor. See light wink on a glass and
the body of a small black figurine is leaning
alone. See glossy leaves. A black car parked.
Black seats and a passing cyclist. Hear the
'clack-a' sound of changing bike gears. Woman
and man walking both with smiles and see the
woman stops smiling and shakes her head with
its ears and eyes like the small cymbals of a
tambourine. Blackbird running fast across

flagstones. Two amber lights turn on. A woman circles. See an empty room set with tables. And a rose of black iron. Woman brushing her hair back wears flowers on fabric and her chin trembles. See a redness faintly in green leaves like sunburn. A man walks with shoulders squarely and eyes fixed ahead and you hear the scrape-together of the fabric of jeans between legs like the sound of a zip closing and opening, like the fit of a fly's buzz. In the walls of buildings see windows' reflections of windows in the walls of buildings. Two men and the tongue of one rolls over its top lip and retreats back into the mouth as bulldog to kennel. See a dog of pale hair with its head hung low in the noise and rattle of an engine mis-firing. Music from the closed body of a car radiates. See a star of leaves and purple flowers and a plastic machine in the colour beige. Read FOODLAND. Hear, "Yeah, I do." See two men in identical shirts and hear plastic bags rustling in the hands of a woman as she walks singing softly under a breath like the crooning of doves. Two men pass and you hear the breathing of one. Man and woman at a table eating. Click of a bicycle passing. A steel slide and three boys sliding and climbing to slide. Hear, "She must have turned back to this brother who's, yeah." Hear, "That table's so small." Cluck of a bird. See the hands of a couple unclasp and clasp back. See a man lift a bag from the arms of a woman and the woman arranges her hair with a brush. Hear, "Blimey." Hear overhead voices and the stretch of a yawn from a high open window. Hear, "Same every weekend." Hear, reply, "I know." Clearing of a throat. Dark cross of a plane. Pale petals of a vine's flowering. Black, long-bodied car. A shaved head saying words. Hear, "He's a nice guy." Hear reply, "I'd get on with." Pale yellow blossom and the shady square of the back of a van. Dark oblong of opening door. See legs running are flushed pink in shorts. Two eyes in black frames look from a window and meet with your eyes looking up and look low to the right and you read KING COME. Car passes. Read THE PUBLIC ARE PERMITTED TO WALK IN THE CEMETERY DAILY. Mouth of music barks from a car with a drum beating. See a finger pushing buttons on the face of a small phone. Tree hiking upwards by growth. A foot kicks. Bricks in a row, and row upon row of bricks as a church-shaped building. Quill carved on a stone. Read CHAPEL. Read S N. See a green bird of metal. Red tail lights ahead and see large metal books. Two men exit. Woman jogging with the small lit eye of a cigarette swinging in one hand. A man walking fast and you see pink feathers. A red glow in an empty room. Two women and two perfumes at once. An iron girder and a squat bolthead snug as a babe in a cot. Screen of a television grey

and unlit. Read Closed. A bottle raised up to a
mouth tilted. Hear, "What's that word." Read
the FULL-HAM sandwich. Read DON'T
DISPLAY. See the gleam of a nose ring in the
pink light of sundown. See spikes of metal
bolted to a wall of bricks. Small brown
filaments risen from cushions of moss over a
brick wall and read PEDESTRIANS. Cry of a
small bird. Green needles of fir. Hear, "No, but
no, it's not like that." See a man's solitude in
grey clothes skipping alone on a rooftop, and
see the grey rope exerted out into half a loop.
See a room below the skipping man's rooftop,
large-windowed, with many meet-for-a-drink-
after-work women. Read OFFICES. Shelves of
folders. See a brown packet. Read GALAXY. A
car reverses and turns and drives away forwards.
A head is craned up, turning right slowly to
look over a shoulder backwards and you see
round glasses and eyes behind them. Shriek of a
voice. Flicker of light sharp as a squawk. Hear,
"Do it when you get home." See a man
scratching. See a scratched shin kneeling at the
side of a blonde woman sitting on slabs of
paving with a blue blanket over her legs.

Turn. Read NO CHILDREN OR PETS
THANK YOU. See a man with a box on a
strap at his chest. Stubble rubbed with a palm,
hand of a man to the chin, eels of hair gluey

grey on the head. White dog led on a plaited
leather strap. Hear, "She changed it." Read
CEDORNE. See a man shaving a man's head.
Figure on a step, man on a step. See a white
moustache. Read REMOVAL of Abandoned
Vehicle. See a smashed windscreen's buckle,
the dent of a giant fist. Dark hole in smash-grey
glass. Walk under jittery leaves of an oak, and
see terraced houses. Three windows open. A
bike chain. Hear, "Two twenty-two," from a
passing man. Milky green bead on a dropped
leather strap. Clack of a fork on a plate. See a
red cross on a white flag, pass six steel drums
the height of a man and see rubbish in each.
Finger in a man's mouth. A woman biting her
lower lip driving. Two women in a shop. Read
HAROUTUNIAN. Read HAL'S HOUSE.
Three men in a room, four men in a room as
you pass. Read HOT IDEAS LIMITED. Man
in a painter's overalls. Read LORD ROBERTS
MEWS. Car passes. Read FORMERLY THE
SITE OF THE LORD ROBERTS
MEMORIAL WORKSHOPS 1983. Hear,
"Erm, and they, you, you, right, that stupid."
See purple leaves. See a woman lighting a
cigarette. Read BEWARE CAR THIEVES
covert police operations in. Two men talking.
Dried geranium flowers like chapped lips. Two
women ahead pass a single woman and you see
a tight T-shirt and a man carrying a metal bar
and a woman hunched eating with eyes looking

[312]

up. See red crosses on white flags. Sound of the mouth of a woman chewing. Red bloom over leaves. Cherry leaf toothed like a saw. Click of a bike changing gears. A long, black car and a stream of exhaust. Dry bark of a dog. See an insect passing. Flight of a pigeon. Peal of chatters and you turn to see a round cage of steel girders above a cylinder rusting. See pointed grey thorns. Street of small trees with furry, bobble-shaped fruits. Man parking a machine. A room containing toys in heaps. Read NO CIRCULARS. A yellow insect walking a window. Red, black and red leaves of roses. A woman washing a car's body and see suds of soap on her arms. Hear, "But not everybody does I don't think." A man passes and you hear a small huff. Shop of lights. Water in a pool. A rusty and huge cylinder bigger than houses, grey and rusting in streaks horizontally like lines on a desert. And turn to a red bus mincing the growl of its engine. Two men drinking from bottles, one orange, one clear. A shop of wire bird cages. Two men eating a substance laid flat on an oval white plate like a lung. Man leaning on a black car bonnet. Back of a thumb wipes a nose. Hear, "To er, come again." Hear, "You know last time." Cry of a sharp whistle sound. Stubbled man scratches an ear. Two beeps of a horn. Dry smell of exhaust fumes. Squeak of brakes and a 'pip-pip' sound. Read CHUTNEY MARY. Hear a rumble

passing like a large machine at work. A hand
with fingers splayed wiping a nose. 'Zip' sound
from a bike and 'tic-tic-t-t'. See a building of
brick and carved pale stone and hear a noise of
keys in a passing man's pocket. A pyramid of
green gold. Two men sitting and quietly talking.
Hear a voice speaking words whisperishly. See
many leaves hanging and a stretched car
reflected on a convex mirror. See a fingernail
passed in a groove between two teeth. Dark
skin of a man, smell turmeric and cumin. Read
BEEP. Letters in mint green. Man at a bus stop
under a picture of a reclining man and a smell
of warmly dead leaves and look up to see many
leaf veins like thin bones. Dust from the road
swept onto a shovel. Read HORTENSIA.
Shiny leaves with curved tips. Read Vandalism
costs more than just money. See a finger put
into an eye. Man with a grey sack. Read
GUNTER. Tick of a bicycle. Three-wheeled
pram pushed ahead. Apple core of yellow flesh,
brown crests like the peaks and ridges of
mountains. See a woman rolling a white
cigarette, she stands on the oval of a traffic
island. See traffic pass. Read FOOD - OFF
LICENCE. A long cigarette in the lips of a
mouth. See a can of beer on its side in a bush.
Noises of small birds like wheels of squeaks
within a low bush. Car and many cars stationary
with figures inside. And three cars creep a
grunt of traffic and more follow suit. Yellow

signs with red letters and a wind passes. Cracks
over paving and leaves with veins like the ribs
of parasols. Light bulb in a dark room lights up.
Dust on the body of a car. Man stooped,
scratching a bald head in the sirens of a plane's
jet-noise truncating. A girl walking, hand on
buttock. Path leading to a shady door and see
many small leaves dried-up and curled, and
dragged by wind along paving stones. Read
TRESPASSERS WILL BE PROSECUTED.
Blonde woman in pink clothes. Man and
woman beneath a sign. Read FOR SALE. Noise
of a car. Purple headscarf. Read S252 RRD.
Letters on a lorry. See the arch of a bridge and
a small man in black with a cap like a uniform.
Shady windows behind a man cycling with a
newspaper clenched to a crumple against
handlebars. Woman hoisting a bike against
railings and she turns and enters the tiny room
of a phone box. See a grey bridge with gilded
parts over water. Read I FANCY ALL 3. Read
YACHT & BOAT COMPANY. Hear the
squeak of a gate's bolt being passed through its
bolt-hole. See a wall and you look over, down to
a grey slime of mud and green-furred black
barges and big iron chainlinks, big as cats, and a
small gritty beach, and algae-green ropes. Pass
under the shadow of a tree and stand still so
you wear the shadow of the tree and see the
small brown muzzle of a dog leaning out from a
car's open window, and see the car passing, the

[315]

dog's ears bend in the wind. A leaf scrapes once and you walk. Tree bark cracked, black as the soot of a chimney. Sludge of green scum and oily film. Read CYBC on the ring of a lifebuoy. Read RUDYARD KIPLING OBAN VERONICA FLEETSIDE. And you see white cables. See grey clouds curdled. Read CYBC. Read CHAIRMAN. Read JUDITH. A leaf flips onto an eye of phlegm. Read LORIEN. Read MTB 219. A leaf scrapes. Read CYBC. See a gold-painted pineapple. Cream, pink and blue houses terraced. Read SYLVIA PANKHURST 1882 - 1960 Campaigner for Women's. See a yellow sphere and thumb at a woman's cheek. Grunty 'tick' of a diesel van passing. A row of houseboats with flowers in pots. Read THE PAINTED HERON. Car. Car. Read JOHN TWEED. Read K358 XOB. Man's elbow out of a car window passing. A bike and you hear the sound like 'stitch' of bicycle chain. See a bank of river sand, washed smooth. See pebbles and a crushed can. See bars of angle iron, a traffic cone lying on its side like a megaphone and a pipe and a blue flat object and a smell of rivers catches your nose. One sole of a shoe like a cuttlefish bone. See a parrot within the room of a boat, gripped on a perch. Read WALTER GREAVES HILAIRE BELLOC. See a small yellow caterpillar, see the rings of its suckers. See boat decking, table, three chairs, white cloth-covered table and a

[316]

white vase with three cupped flowers. Slouch of
a man. Small boat-mounted bell with a blue
string attached for ringing. Hear the trickling
of water below. See golden scrolls and
ornamentation on the side of a river-spanning
bridge. A two-masted bridge and an expanse of
river curving slow and smooth like a walkable
surface, and a copper green conical roof. Read
WHO KILLED FARHAD. Read U
SMANOV? See alder leaves blackly and a split
scab of bark. Read HOUSEBOAT FOR SALE.
Fluted base of a cast iron post. Three white
metal cranes like a conference. Arch of a bridge
and ripples of water you cannot count. A single
bird cry. Hear a radio's voice and the radio
mounted on the chest of a man by a wide black
strap hung from the neck. Look left to see two
men walking and turn right to see the skin of
the river complex with disturbances like flat
warts and see four cream towers and a mouth
ripping the blade of a fingernail off. Tongue
rubbing up behind a lip and see part of the lip
pinched by a tooth. A child's feet up in a car.
Car and car pass. And the road on the bridge
slopes down as you walk. Clouds glowing trout
grey. See the chain of a bridge and the hexagon
pattern of a grille on the link of each arch and
see river-bits in and between hexagons. Woman
in a car pencilling her lips. A plant dead on its
side without roots. Bus passing a head on a lap
in a car. Smile of a mouth. Woman chewing

and searching the opened mouth of a bag on
her knees for something whilst driving a car
with a baby in the backseat strapped in. Two
men in a car. Red-haired woman on a red bus.
Fingers of a man press a four-button sequence
on a panel of ten buttons next to a door and
the door opens. And the man enters. See a
bronze swan. See a gull and two pigeons
crossing. A bag, fat with the wind, flies. Scatter
of cinders, black and porous as pumice. See a
building being built. Scuff of the toe of a
jogging man's foot. Man with dark marks of
sweat on his shirt like the head of a horned
goat. Read albion RIVERSIDE. Woman in
grey inspecting a white wall. Read S.B. ATRAT
BUILT 1898 AT WIVENHOE ESSEX. Grey
clothed body of a woman. Flash of an eyewhite.
And six feet pass, together a shuffle. Read
FIRST OWNED. Tug of wind on a green
bramble leaf. Read AT GREENWIC. Body of
a woodlouse with sunlight. An ivy leaf moves
back and forth as if sprung. Read THIS
BARGE, POWERED BY 3,500 SQ. FT. OF
SAIL AND HANDLED. Noise of a crane
lifting, and a drilling like the amplified song of
a hover fly's scream. Read BY A CREW OF 2
WOULD CARRY. See an ant running and
turning and returning by the route of its
running. Read CARRIED BEEF FROM
BATTERSEA TO THE MEDWAY
ENDING. The body of a man jogging through

shadows of slats. Read CARRYING GRAIN
TO. A slab of red granite and a white sack of
fibres with red fibres strewn like the rags of a
white hen ransacked by a fox. Barges of
blackness. See ropes and cables and brickwork
and hear the cry of a drill and a man and
woman by the door of a black car talking. See
behind veiled windows the veiled faces of men
and women working among and with plastic
machines, see a model of a tower and a town all
in white. See a man bench-sitting by the space
of wide river with moss underfoot and hear the
pouring of water into itself. Read WARNING
This area is constantly monitored by cameras.
Grey hairs among black of a sitting man's head
and water falling from a crack between two
black wooden gates. See spools and squid
shapes of water falling and see a feather curling
down to the trembling skin of the flow. See
stems of wild aniseed growing from the black
wood of lockgates and a man in a corner in a
cap and scarf eating a chip looks up and turns.
See sky on the shields of his glasses and a chip
passed into his opening mouth and it closes.
See a white stick and walk. See pink panels on a
white bridge and two men are talking. Hear,
"Yeah, that sort of stuff." Man with rags of
black hair locking the bolt of a metal gate and
hear a sound like a 'clang'. Child with hands at
its ears. Read REMOVAL MAY COST A
LIFE. And feet pass in unison. Read IF

MISSING PLEASE TELEPHONE: 020 - 8871
- 6900. See an orange ring of plastic. See a
printed sign. Head of a pigeon and see a crow
turn and its legs walk across the rivershore's
grit. Wet fronds of a plant and a corrugated
cow-brown shield of plastic with deposits of silt
in the troughs of the wrinkle. Tall stems of a
plant, green with leaves and with white flowers.
Hear, "Yeah, in the house." Two women
descend a flight of ten steps. See the white
cables of a turreted bridge and a woman
dragging a wheeled suitcase and you read ALL
TROOPS MUST BREAK STEP WHEN
MARCHING. See a locked gate of black bars
and read GATE. Read PARK
RESTORATION. Grasses high and heavy with
wholemeal seeds and sun glows and five steps
step down into water. See a small thin dark tree
like the ear of a dog and spider webs catch your
eye. Black railings with gold gleaming paint in
flakes. See a crow flying with feathered wings
spanned wide as fingers. And look up to many
leaves shaking at once. And you look to the
small moving body of a wagtail with a yellow
flank and see its long tail lifting and dropping
like a see-saw, it creeps fast over the silt of the
shore. See a pale green padlocked door.
Portholes with vanilla-yellow grilles. Hand
pushing a pair of glasses firmly up onto the
bridge of a nose and see dusty corners of paint
and a van with exhaust-sound burblings. Look

down to the blood-brown curls of the river-
ripples riding mats of woven wrinkled water on
water and boisterous slaps of a wave like a gang
of ripples beating in slaps and shoves the woven
mats of frowned water under. Man with a
shaved head passes. See a pregnant woman and
a clenched brow between the eyes of a man.
Read OPENED 1874. Descend steps by six
pigeons crouched in the midday shade like tired
old men. A woman ahead in red and blue. And
you turn left to see a metal boy helping a boy of
green metal up and a spiralled trumpet
brimming with fruit and a torch like a cone
with a green metal flame held in one hand.
Read 1874 LIEUT. COL. SIR JAMES
MACNAGHTEN HOGG K. C. B. M. P.
CHAIRMAN OF. Picture of a man kissing a
woman. A pigeon flies. Head of a man walking,
see the girdle of stomach. Dead leaves like
sloughed-off snake skins picked up by the wind
and they fall. See five red lights. Read via
SWINDON. Read JAMES HOYLE & SON
BEEHIVE FOUNDRY HACKNEY. See
black lion's claws of painted cast iron. A straw
on the ground. A lorry of timber. A heap of
traffic signs left by the road. And a woman
pushing a pram. See the length of the pavement
is empty of people and see many benches with
the heads of women on the arms staring out to
the river from metal eyes. See the figure of a
woman and her waist is small in relation to

hips. Two wheels of a pram, one flat, one buckled. Tail of blonde hair from a head and there are pink strands through the blonde. See graves. Towers. Cream chimneys. Arm scratching a rib. Woman with a long, grey, rough-haired dog. Cry of sirens. Three lion's claws of feet. And a river smell. Woman leans on one leg. And stops to read one page of a book in her right hand. Read LONDON. A child looks up from the bucket of its pram. Read SWAN. Sulphur-yellow mats of lichen on a wall and you see the river. And the river falls below the face of the wall, and floats up as you walk. Gold earring of a woman. See a flash like a gold tooth in a man's mouth. See a grey pocket on the back of a buttock and see dimples at elbows and see the number '8' between two shoulders. Look up to the black of reflecting windows. A scuffle of leaves and the chunter of a passing lorry. Read OLD FERRY HOUSE. See a hand pull a pink top down to a belt and the top retracts up from the belt like a snail from touch. Black painted faces on a leg and the foot of a child. A man climbing a ladder up from a balcony onto a balcony. And a bike overtakes a van on the inside. Read MANAGEMENT. Glugging groan of a passing red bus. Read The Original. Hear sirens and see a red light pass like a hole in a windscreen and over the face of a man in a car. Heap of leaves. Turn. See a huge golden figure sitting cross-

legged on the far river shore and a blue-hulled
boat moving upstream and crests of water
carved by the plough of the boat's bow. Man in
an unbuttoned shirt climbs three steps. Sudden
cry of an alarm. Read SECURITY NOTICE.
And see a small square of paper torn at an edge
to fibres. Black shape of a cormorant flying.
Waves ride up on the shore and see one figure
ahead of a woman wearing grey and a pink T-
shirt pushing the cart of a pram. Read
DANGER strong currents. See an obelisk
bearing names cut into its visible faces and a
golden ball seated on its tip. Man in a
wheelchair, the chair on a mound of grassland
like a long barrow and the man wearing a black
cap like the cap of a pilot and see a flat sock
lying on the ground. Dog-end of a cigarette.
Read T. C. S. V. EN124 B125 R+B UK JT
DUCTILE. See a pediment containing a clock
and a crown-arrangement of planted flowers
and read DALTONS TRANSPORT. White
letters on the red ribbed side of a lorry's
container. Crumpled white tissue speckled with
red drops of blood. See a ramp leading into
river and the river flows flat. See an orange
plastic spoon on the grey shore containing one
spoonful of silt and see a white neck and head
of a gull. See the yellow leg of a gull take a step.
Shadow of a plane passing over the flutes of two
chimneys glides up the wide, flat vein of the
river. Hear, "Buy ... went on." Leaves fly. See a

woman in a yellow top locking the lock of a
gate. See an old couple from the East. Black
railings with images of urns. Leaves of plantain,
ribbed, long and the urn-shape of a dandelion's
hub and dispatched seeds caught in the sticks
of neighbouring plants by the beards of their
flying apparatus. See the wrinkled skin of
dandelion leaves and see the hand of a man on
the eye of a man and see flecks of water jab up
on the river from a passing boat and see white
crown-forms of flowers and columns of brown,
flat seeds like tiny clay pigeons and ribbed
green stems among dusty leaves like old arrow
heads. Pink bindweed flowers and one picture
of a red rose. See smashed glass. Read 26c
Church Lane 0208 205 2946 Kingsbury. Letters
on a scrap of brown paper. Sirens ahead and
white mould with brown cups over the
branches of hawthorn and green waxy berries.
The edge of a leaf scrapes the edge of a leaf.
Ribbed paving stones see-saw underfoot. Car.
Read 13.5% EXTRA FREE. Rough shadow of a
leaf on painted rough iron. See light on a
twitching leaf. Hear the anger of a car's horn
cry. A car's horn replies. See a cobweb heavy
with grey dust. Read THE LIST ER. Two men
on a bench in a sleep curled like boys foot to
head. See a pint glass by the leg of the bench on
the ground and a rag of plastic. See a white bird
turn, touching the far shore of the river. See a
clipboard left on a wall and read FOR

[324]

FURTHER. Two men in the back of a taxi and
two benches of wooden slats. Stink of water
and see ribs of white arches and a baby asleep
in the cup of a pram. Hear, "That's funny,
yeah." See a two-pronged black railing head like
the horns of a cow. Read WARN clean after
you dog war. And two women pass with their
white hair and see faces of pink mallow flowers
shaking delicate parts in the passing of air and
smoke from the chimney of a long-backed
barge and the barge is tar-black. Read 3170015.
Small green body of an aphid and a brown
bottle tipped on a ledge of concrete and one
glint of a long puddle shaped like a flint axe.
Turn to see white geranium flowers in grey
stone troughs. Seedhead of a tall-legged brown
weed and turn left to see five trains parked very
still. Two trains crossing a bridge of grey
girders. Huge body of a brick building, house of
a giant. Read LUPUS STREET. See letters on
the far shore. Read To do so will result in a
prosecution with a possible. And read an
additional daily fine for non-compliance. See
sun burning on glass and three cormorants fly
upriver almost on water. Two grey wharf cranes
on two tracks big bodies rusted. Huge body of a
building without roof. Look down to poles
dropped like spears onto gritty shore. Shadow
of a gull's beak across its feathers. Wet stones
dark, glinting like well-mouths. Two pigeons
step. Read CELEBRATING. See four fluted

columns, two wings of brick. Read SPOTLESS
YEARS. Blue plastic bag curled between two
wooden slats of a bench. Sunlight slams down
onto water and crashes up as a blindness to eyes
and you turn to curled glints like shards and
folding-up glints. Read Introduction This
booklet. Read Homeopath. See the body of a
duck groomed by the greenish yellow beak of
the duck. Head of a floating duck dipped
underwater. Read POOL & DARTS. Boat
passing slowly. Body of a plane's shadow passing
on far shore. Yellow-shirted man at the wheel
of a boat. Read Y335 HUD. Yellow markings
on a sycamore leaf raised up like bumps. Turn
to see a tall cylinder of glass and beyond a
single stone spire. Read FIRE HYDRANT.
Turn to see waves of the wake of a boat lap up
on wet shore and one silt-grey cylinder head,
one six-celled silt-grey battery. Count six
pigeons moving like cockroaches. Stem of a leaf
with its foot curled like a red concave sucker.
Read RUSS'S GREY HAIR FUSS
OVERNIGHT SENSATION. Read off. Read
ZONE U. Read TELEPHONE. Man in a
purple jacket holding a leaf and a stick. Red
cross on a white flag and read RIVER LODGE.
Ball of screwed-up paper. Fly on a leaf. Group
of figures at a building's corner. Read OUT.
Hear the cry of a horn twice and the second cry
is sustained. Silk-like scarf. Fingertip cut from
the finger of a glove. Read Warning Anti climb

paint. See grass and gravel and a far shore
shines. Read GLASS BOTTLES AND JARS
ONLY. Read TOSCANELLI. See a small red
hard-bound address book lying open. Read
07055 32128 MIREU LEITON 172 PRZEZUT
604370613 TADEK SARKIK 079 57125 913.
Read DINNER & DANCE. See a bracket
fungus, all cream and cocoa. Read NEW
TRAFFIC SIGNALS AHEAD. See a solitary
man of stone standing in the shade of a green
space, one hand at his head, one at his side, and
the body dressed in a stony tunic and his head
hung. A group of children in red to your left
with a woman walking before them. Read
PARK MANAGER TEL 020 7641 5264. And
hear the bright scream and the pitched laughs
of children. See a girl in whites kicking a tree.
Hear, "Much more exciting." Red car. White
car. Red car. Grey car. Yellow spots on green
leaves. Children in blue and white clothes and
girls in straw hats. Hear, "Come on." Boys in
blue flat caps. Smell of fresh paint and see three
children pushing another to the ground.
Woman dancing star-shapes in blue jeans and a
white blouse and you read DISTRIBUTION
OF FREE LITERATURE. See a boy chasing a
girl bigger than him. Three women talking over
a pram, a child's head visible as you turn, a bald
baby in a woman's arms and a bottle held with a
towel levered up to the mouth of the baby in
the shade of an umbrella held by a standing-up

woman. See a wetness around the base of a
lamp post. Man smoking. A root like a stag's
head going into the earth. Voice of a woman
behind a hedge and a motorcyclist by a bike in
black leathers, sipping tea from a cup filled
from a brushed steel flask. See a map on the
seat of a bike. See a newly-washed church of
stone blocks. Man carrying timber batons down
into the basement's dark of a house on his
shoulder. Hear the two-tone cry of a phone.
Small brown beads like mung beans sewn onto a
woman's tunic. A coach-noise passes over the
sound of sandpaper at work. Read FINE
SHARP. Read NO DUMPING. A powder-
coated hand sandpapering a column. Flecks of
dust flying. Three women talking. Read This
Property Protected. Hear, "Under so much
pressure ... safe journey back, better get
someone to repair ... take care, bye." Car
turning right. Lean, brown-haired woman
frowning. Brass doorknob, the sun like a bright
fish curled on the brass. Magenta flowers like a
clown's wig, and like a shade in a flower's
mouth is a brown bee. Two men smoking.
Woman in a red shirt, crimson as she gets
close. She is blonde. Read ILLEGAL TO
DEPOSI. Man eating carries a bag. Man in a
long chair reading and see an open window, a
table within and a fly slams into the pane of the
window. Building on a street corner stripped of
its paint coat. Man cycling is a sharp wind

passing. White-haired woman talking alone. Man with black trousers tucked into black boots carrying a heavy book under one arm. A boy's face in tears and you hear cries and see the boy crying up to a tall woman's face and a groan, hear, "Daddy won't buy it, he won't buy it." Pass a shop of foods. Read SEAGRASS COIR SISAL JUTE. Read TILES AMTICO ALTRO POLYFLOOR. A door opened. A man walks barefoot over the asphalt of road. Read HUMIDIFIERS DEHUMIDIF. Hear, "Yes connect, yes and I'll come and see you at ten o'clock in the morning ... well this time I'm just coming to sort out the medication." Read AIR PURIFIERS AIR CONDITIONERS. See a woman writing. See a laugh. A bowl of leaves. A woman chopping onions on a brown board and sunlight on bare legs. See three men with blue shirts and ties. Hear, "I watched the first ten fifteen minutes of the first half." The freckled face of a woman with red lips. Hear, "Movies, actors." See faces in a dark room, figures at tables with food and drink. A man unsteady, walks like a man with a weight on his head. Man walks with a stick, one hand behind back. Hear, "Of course we had it tough, we had to get up half an hour before we went to bed, it's one of those ones." Man waving to a door with a closed umbrella, see a beard and short hair and a shirt open. Read NO PARKING DAY OR NIGHT. Bluster and bluffing of a

pneumatic drill. A bee flies through the path of
a slow moving lorry. Rip in the shoulder of a
man's shirt. Hear, "Course I did." Clunk of a
rocking paving slab rocked by a footstep. Peal
of a woman's laughter shaking a woman's chest,
neck, face, out of the mouth. Hear, "You laugh
but there's fifty, sixty, in there." Hear, "They're
an age." Man leaning on a man. Shop of wooden
tables. See coral-red lips. Dark dusty windows.
Hear, "I got best." Shop of green clothes.
Woman's chin with white stubble. Hear,
"Everyone I know." See figures at a desk.
Woman steps from a building with two plastic
bags. Woman in tight black trousers. Read
Over 800. See a man in a taxi, hair like the tail
of a black pony and a man and woman at a
table with drinks. Read SCHOOL BUS BOMB
HORROR. And hear, "Believe it or not." Kiss
sound from a man taking a drag on a white
cigarette. A woman lifts up a carrier bag and
you read BOMBAY DREAMS. And hear
words in French. See many pigeons and see the
body of a sleeping man curled on the ground.
Hear, "It is yeah." Mottled head of a short-
haired bus driver. Grey soles of sleeping man's
shoes, pads worn each to a hole at the heel and
see the small suckers of the sole's tread. Green
blanket over the sleeping man. See a man with
brown pitted teeth, and turn to a stall selling
fruit. See blonde hairs on peach skin. Read
Roast Lamb £8.90. Turn right, read KISS ME

[330]

KATE. Left, read FLAME GRILLING JUST
TASTES BETTER. A man in a cap stumbles
and you see the cap frayed at the rim of the lip
of the cowling over the eyes. Hear, "In spite of
what?" An elephant's trunk and a shark's jaw of
stone. Man holding his neck with his left hand,
you read THE HAPPIEST SHOW. Read
WIG DESIGN BY PAUL. See a woman
stumble and regain rhythm and she walks on,
brisk-toed as a piglet trotting. A red-haired
woman pulling a dress from a grey mannequin
turns the dress inside out through its neck. See
a woman's finger and thumb place a grey strip
of gum in the mouth and it buckles back on the
platform of the tongue as she pushes her fingers
and it folds in half and the fingers move out
and away and the mouth grows closed and
chews, her lips pale. Pram without child. Blue
eyes of a woman looking ahead. See a red folder
in the open mouth of a black bag. Blue glitter
on a woman's top and a fingertip of a woman
between finger and thumb of a child. Hear,
"And then this solution right here." Dark eyes
and flowers on fabric. Hand smoothes the hair
of a woman passing and you pass also. Letters
on a red folder. Hear, "I think that, erm." A
woman smoking. 'Z' of a scar on a woman's
cheek. Woman blowing her nose. Read OUR
SHIRT STOCKS. Short tie and a glinting
jewelled stud in the ear of a schoolboy. One
beep of a car's horn. A woman's wrist in the

grip of a man. Two hisses of a passing lorry.
Read Fute bol. Read Luberon. A limping man
laughing and shaking his hand in the air like a
fin. A man laughs aloud turbulently. See fingers
pull the rip-pull of a can lid. Pink eye of a
pigeon. Hear, "Hurry up, this won't stay open."
Read REGULAR HALTER NECK
STRAPLESS CROSS OVER ONE
SHOULDER. Hear, "Was saying." Hear, "It
was rosé, just rosé." Hear, "On the opposite
side of the road." Read CUSTODI DOMINE
CIVITATEM. Read Pay before you board.
Hear, "He couldn't do what he wanted to do."
And see a woman's mouth nibbling the rim of
an ice cream. Laugh of a man. See five petals of
a buttercup, and the star of a daisy shakes in
the wind. A paper floating through air finds a
road in the wind and flies. Tick of a passing
bike. Hear, "Oh, three weeks." Hear, "That fact
long rolling." Hear words from a running man.
Throb of a helicopter. Man with a cup. Pale lips
of a woman and the long excrement of a dog.
Read SMOKE OUTLET FROM
VENTILATION PLANT ROOM 2. A pigeon
flies up in a circle. See a glinting mineral of
polished stone. Man all in orange. Two women
with cups with eyes of black coffee like Turkish
men at a table. A shop of keys. Man with a
glossy magazine. Read THIS STONE WAS
LAID BY WILLIAM BINGHAM. A girl
passes wearing a grey pleated skirt. Read

[332]

EVEN MORE NHS BLUNDERS and see the hand of a man holding a moneybox. Hear, "I can probably get." Hear reply, "Okay, thanks ever so much, bye." And the thud of a door, the sharp neat steps of a man and you hear, "I think there's a different spirit." And you pass a nun wearing a habit and a man leaning onto a wall near to a bronze man and one woman places an index finger into the slit between two buttons of her shirt and you hear from her mouth, "I still can't play golf." And a man says to himself, "oh fuck." And you pass hearing, "Your right hand." Pass and you hear, "The arm northbound is closed off due to a serious three lane accident." And pass into hearing, "You know what I just did." And you look up to grey smooth columns of granite and down to see figures consulting a page. Hear the sound of a thump on a window and a bag creeps over the pavement slowly. Sound of a zip. Hear, "To come back to." Three women pass and four figures are ahead like a square. Hear, "If I look at a." A polystyrene cup thrown to land in the gawp of a bin and you see a man unfolding a plastic bag, uncreasing it by sliding both hands in opposite directions smoothly over it on the counter and you turn to two men, hearing, "And he sent me an e-mail referring." See the mouths of two men brown with smoking. See a smile. A twist of smokes from two men smoking. Hear, "Yeah." Mouth and hands of a

woman eating a pastry, arms articulate up like
the claws of a crab to a small mouth. Flutter of
a pigeon and the grey tail fans. Two men in a
conversation. Two towers of a single building
and you feel a thunder in the ground below.
Read METHODIST CENTRAL. See brass
candlesticks. See twenty-one bikes. A man
laughs aloud to himself. Pass of a car. Clunk of
a drain-cover stepped onto. A paving stone
shifts underfoot like an uneasy horse mounted.
Turn left and you see a black conveyor belt
turning and you hear a sharp screeching. And
you pass reading TRIDENT REFRIGER-
ATION. A car's tyre scrapes kerbstones and
you pass a group of five girls hopping amongst
themselves like hens in a run. See figures and
hear, "And what I reckon." Hear, "No that's
alright, you've timed that fantastically." Room
of bottles, green leather and glossed oak and
see it is a place of golden glintings. Bottles like
gem stones. Hear, "I don't know now." See a
pear-green jacket of a woman and you look up
to the windowsill of a huge hall and see in the
window many glints in the parts of a man-high
chandelier suspended from a rose of plaster by
a dark chain and you see all colours in the faces
of crystals hanging to the height of a man in the
dark space like crumbs of a rainbow and you
hear, "What parks there?" See a pale strip of
stomach smooth as an egg. Face of a woman
smiling and chewing. White pelicans seated on

gnarled rocks. And the rocks are an island.
Figures strewn over grassland and voices like
dark coughs. A man of bronze on a plinth. Scuff
of a foot. Dark image of figures reflected
passing on a woman's eye. Figures of stone
carved in stone and you see many flags and a
low house and you hear coughs of strollers.
Man wiping a nose with the sleeve of a jumper
all threads and you see ducklings pedal and
skate like new spiders. And ducklings preening
and nibbling under tree shade. Four women
ahead and a man with a transparent shirt and
the soles of the man's shoes worn at the heel to
a slant inwards. And a man among ducks and
turn to see the white weeping bones of a
fountain of water rising and falling, like an
empire. Puppy running with a black harness
strapped all over the front of its torso and legs.
See a building of white stone. And a flat open
court of gravel. A single large stone. A terrace
of tarmac with gravel walks on two sides like
sideboards. Turn. See a walking man smiling
and talking alone, making words like a spell
rolled in his mouth and photographing the
place where he walks without an eye at a
camera's body and see two men ahead in dark
clothes with white shirts and the photo-taking
man runs on ahead with a clear plastic bag with
many papers packed and the bag against the
stomach under a hand. See a black helmet on a
man's head. Men in black jackets and white

gloves, many figures with cameras before eyes and see boots of tall black pieces of leather. Hear, "Not many public talents." See black sheepskins over saddles and silver swords and red tassels. See a porch of cobbles and coppery horse dung in balls and a bell chimes and a marching man walks. See a stamp, a stand, and a turn, and see golden parts of a sword raised and a bell cries four times. See reins on horses raised by two hands and a man leads another and the two men are walking at the back of six men. See men in a row, each with red tassels hanging from a hat, each in white garments. See swords by six men placed into sheaths and one sword difficult to fit. See a turn and a stamp of a man. See a marching step. Hear a step and a step and see boots with black triangular parts extending back on the side of each knee. And each marching man enters a building, see limbs swing like clockparts. Walk and read ALL PED CYCLES LEFT IN THIS. Opened window. See a glossy beige room and you read THE PARLIAMENTARY COUNCIL. Two women running, one with a smile. Hear, "Ding-dong." See two horses with riders, an empty side-street. Woman with a velvet torso. Man sitting alone at a table head down. Man in a padded black waistcoat. Look up to a fluted column and the figure of a man on the head of the column like a bird and see the half-circle shape of a hat and a sword by his leg and see pigeons

[336]

below figures passing with suntans on shoulders. See a horse hoof kick over a cup. Hear, "That's King George the First before he was executed, cast in sixteen-thirty-three by a man named Dubert." Hear cried, "Sophie." Hear, "Brazil, yah." See a room lined with shelves and the reflection of a passing figure scans on black glass and the long windows of a shop of shoes and a polished flat stone reflecting feet. Hear, "They look like candlelight." And two figures pass. Long nose of a man and a woman biting her thumb. Two pairs of men in dark suits walking. Read £30,000 BOUNTY. See the puckered skin of a face and a man tapping new cobbles into a blinding of sand. Hear, "They got a thingy ... a wedding." Hear, "Dress." See a woman crouched low searching the shadow of a bag's cave puts a clear blue bottle of water down at her heel. Sharp smell of soap. See a hand on a hip and a cracking laugh. Hear, "Bah, we heard a." Hear, "Had a phonecall the other day, someone said 'You've left one of your gold visa cards.'" And you hear, "The women and the children." A voice darkly snuffs. A woman with a crutch sits. See a man with a black tie. Hear, "Ah, that's her name, I didn't know that." A voice of a man light and hushed. And you look up to carved partly obliterated stone bodies of men and read ZIMBABWE HOUSE. A voice clatters like a tin can, you hear, "This is the

Strand." Man with a grey beard and red nose blinking. See a woman in orange and pass the shadows of a dark, low lobby. A narrow-shouldered figure with black shoes and the arch of the back rounded and the shoulder blades like two sand dunes moving ahead. See a spotted forehead and a smile and hear, "A bit for cancer research." A red top wrinkled at the neck and shoulders. Man with a grey coat and long beard like a fork with two prongs and long hair like the ears of a spaniel. Hear, "He probably got his passport." See an earring on a woman. Hear, "Ticket machines." Woman at a machine. Man standing in shade looks down at his watch and two hands clasp shaking together. Man sitting on a doorstep scratching his head with three fingers and a thumb. Man pushing a big brown sheet of hardboard into the yellow bucket of a skip. Hear, "Excuse me have you got any twenty pee pieces." Woman in a room walks with both hands out towards a wall-mounted mirror. Sunlight on a smooth-headed man. And you hear stringed instrument notes and pass figures to see four figures playing four stringed instruments and you hear music of four strings as one. See music-playing figures take steps to the left and forward, to the right all together. Smell of a brown cigar. See smoke and steam rising from coffee and haze through the air in the covered space of figures seated in music. A small fly passes and a hand

[338]

smacks it out of the air. See a triangle crisp
picked up and dipped into red and passed into
a mouth. Mouth of a red-haired woman smiling.
Hear a mutter of voices kept low among men.
See a woman reading and a woman forking food
up and in. See a mouth close over the tines of a
fork. Man sipping yellow from a round cup the
shape of an apple with its top sliced, in a
spangle of sunlight, see a glass with a stem by
the fingers of a hand. Count fourteen bottles
and a chain on a woman's wrist. And you hear
the last note of instruments struck and drawn
out and the echoey clappings of hands like seals
in zoos and a "Thank you." Many hands clap
and a voice calls another and many smokes rise
from cigarette ends. Smell chocolate. See a
woman beckoning a man and you pass. A man
turns with a dark face and his eyes are gleaming
and you see the front teeth and hear the treacle
of two women laughing. See the ivy of a man's
stare on the face of a woman seeing he is
watching. Hear, "Yeah, I just had ten." And
hear, "In approximately thirty seconds this
balloon is going to burst ... would you." See a
sun flash. And you hear, "Like to give me a nice
round of applause okay ... I'm allergic to latex."
See many figures gathered, like cows at fodder,
seeing the act of a man with his head inside an
inflated balloon. Man with an ice cream cone in
his mouth so the point of the wafer appears as a
beak. Hear a string plucked and a 'twang' and a

large-bodied man leaning on a black bin with
both hands flat like the feet of a gull on the
perch of the bin's lid and his neck like a gull's
climbing into the shoulders. Hands clapping.
Read NAS UWT. Man with red hair. And hear,
"So, they still treating you good." And many
cries sound like rooks at the sundown. Hear,
"At four o'clock in the morning." Hear, "I just
went around." See the shadow of a building and
you pass into it and see moving faces of flags
like fish in shallows and hear a horn's blurt. See
the glint of wet ground and figures in a dark
room. Read SCIENTIFIC APPARATUS.
Voice in a language you do not know and see
eyes sideways and burbling music like a
cauldron's song from the window of a dark
room and hear, "Above Alexandria ... Lon
Calvo, I used to stay there." Hear reply, "Oh
yes." Two voices in unison. Read The very
name of this pub is part of the fabric. Hear,
"And now today." Read hear. And you turn to
see a man on a doorstep and hear, "Ah" from a
woman's mouth, and the woman is leaning on
one leg. See a glint of water. Hear, "We've got a
bit of a walk." A man on all fours like a lion,
one hand drawing a circle on the pavement.
Smell cooking meat like a dark smell with
ember reds, sinew and black charred surfaces of
smell. See many green paper napkins folded,
standing in glasses like party hats. See a
handkerchief pushed down into pocket. Hear

the shrill note of a passing bus braking and a
man with hands in pockets moving on wheeled
shoes passes through the woven traffic of
people like a bird. Man speaking to the
perforated mouthpiece of a phone. See the
stretched ringlet of the phone's cable. Woman
squeezing a part of her face between two
fingernails, you see her reflected in a mirrored
doorway. A man insinuates a 'No' by a wave of
the hand and you pass. Hear, "Sure ... yeah yeah
yeah ... I mean ... I don't know." Pass a shop of
tobaccos. Read ATLAS. Man with a silver ring.
Woman smoking a white cigarette. See hairs
twisted to a point between fingers. Brick wall
of windows and arches of stone on Doric
columns and see brown eyes the colour of
weasels in sunlight and see black glasses placed
over weasel-brown eyes. Picture of a King
Charles spaniel wearing a crown. Glimpse of a
nose, and a man with a green tissue to his
mouth reading, crouched at a table over pages.
See a shop of bright saxophones and you hear,
"I gonna let you smile." See a man with a can,
his eyes turned aside from the face which he
speaks to, steps down into a place in the
ground. And you pass seeing the golden glow of
the face of a man lighting a cigarette up with
one hand cupped like a windbreak around a
sunbather, the lighter flame shifts like the flap
of a hen, like a yellow buttercup held to a chin.

XXII

Pass a woman tucking a beer can into her waistcoat pocket, her head twisted down on a neck of creases like a chicken's, and a hand pulls the flap of her waistcoat pocket over the nest of the can. Hear the sharp cut of a whistle and see red flags. Read REVOLUTION. See a yellow plastic pipe and earth, brick, rubble, grit, rocks, wires, under an opened three-inch crust of tarmac. See crack-shadowed paving. The lone parachutist of a dandelion seed floating up and then down. Hear, "Big copper." Hear, "Hey, how are you doing." Hear, "You drunk man." Pass a black binliner tied. See a finger turn in the cave of a nostril. Two men exit a building and a door closes once. See the exiting men wear black leather. The face of an old woman licking her lips is a face strewn with wrinkles. See a scratched silver disc lying flat on tar and see earth stained with oil. See striations of a rainbow on the face of a scratched silver disc. Sunlight passing through fibres of grey hair. See ovals of blackness on a face around eyes and the muffled thumping of drums among people gathered ahead. There are red flags and many sunglasses worn before eyes. See golden light falling through a thin-stemmed glass of white wine onto a table. See a black shirt filled to a tightness by the chest of a man. Read SERBO. See letters pointed into the cave of a man's pocket. Hear whistles like warnings or

the stridor of seawind through telegraph wires.
See pale seeds flamey with sunlight. Read
STAFF on a man's back. See a man walking
fast, his head only visible among heads afloat
like a leaf on a river. Look up to the bell of a
helicopter hovering like an eclipse. See a
camera held up in the air. Read PRIVATE
BOOKINGS tel: 020 7287 5676. And the patch
of a bird flies and sunlight is grey in the
feathers of its wings, like an X-ray, and see the
wings shrink on the shield of the sun's glare.
Read MOLLY. Read MOGGS. Read Open
your arms. Read to change but don't let. Read
Some like it hot. Hear, "Shall we get a bottle of
something." Hear, "Look at you." And a thin,
inflammable smell of alcohol. See a woman in
white wedding clothes. Sun on the tips of the
pile of a waistcoat. Hear, "Not this one with
the big." Read STOP THE WAR, END. Hear,
"Is he tall ... is he the tallest of all of them."
Hear reply, "Not really." Hear query, "The
second tallest?" See a hand holding a strawberry
by its stem. Hear, "You sure, well I haven't
seen him even." Count forty-four chequered
helmets of black and white. The thump of a
drum starts and cries and whistles leap up.
Read POLICE, spelt in white on black many
times. Sunlit skin. See freckles like tiny stones
under a clear stream. See a bubble of soap fall
to the ground. Man in a long coat reading. A
man's head to a camera. A bubble falls among

heads. See an orange flag among bright pink flags. A man with dreadlocks like a lion surveying the horizon. See a hand twisting a wrist. See an iron grille and below, a hole into ground. See a wheelchaired man wearing a white lizard skeleton giant over his head and a woman dancing and whistles cry up like the heckles of birds. Hear, "Jool has to be." A bottle of water containing five pieces of sunlight. A woman in black clothes, fur of sunlight over her blackness. Seven pigeons beak-stabbing a streak of damp slosh sprawled on the road. A face with freckles gnawing the nail of a finger. Read THE THREE GREYHOUNDS. Black eyes set in white. A voice signals, "Here he is … oh, there's the skeleton." And you turn to a man with a slow walk. A man in orange skips to a window. See a hand at jowls squashing them firm to the jawbone. Scabs of grey gum flat on the tar of the pavement. The pulse of a helicopter beating. Pass a treacly head auburn with sunlight. Read AVOID WAR. A hand pulls sunglasses over two eyes. Hear a language. Lips lit to a redness in sun and a plastic bag caught on the toe of a shoe which stops walking to shake the bag from its toe. See a smear of blue on the lower lid of a man's eye and two red flowers worn in black hair. A bubble floats before faces. Sun brilliantly flickers on skin. A man drops a steel frying pan and picks it up and

[344]

stands with it held overhead. A scrawny man in a white T-shirt whistles and points with one hand to the body of a beer can gripped in the other. See his eyes are cataracts of sea-fog. Man with black skin. A man with freckled skin with red, rough patches. Hear a sneeze and a noise like a war cry. Hear, "The little theatre, I ... just near there." See a glass green bottle lying on its side like a drunk, and a pinkness over the green with reflected sun. Hear, "Are you alright." Pass a mouth chewing and smoke eels upwards. Hear the cough of a man and feel the flung air full of spittle flying. Hands ripping a brown paper bag into tatters. A man with long black hair. The tinkle of bottles. There are dreadlocks a man turns his head about with to fling them to eyes in the head of a woman. See footprints of wetness on sun-grey tar. Flowers stitched to a grey dress on a tall woman's body and the hands of the woman carrying a cymbal. Cry of a horn. A whistle crying and the cry is the shape of a scythe swinging. A grey-skinned hand. Sweet, piercing smell of patchouli and the smell of bananas grows as you walk. Read RECLAIM YOUR DAUGHTERS. There is a dress of crinkled whiteness. Hear, "Doing notes." A spoken inflection rising in pitch to a question. Pass two long pink hairs and blue smoke rises like bonfires at dusk. Look up between walls to a Common Blue's wing of blue sky. Turn to see faces leaning from windows.

Read PATISSERIE VALERIE. Whistles cry down and wolf-whistle in unison. Read MINTY. Read PLAY 2 WIN. Light curled on the cloth of a collar. Read I NEED HELP. A twist of blue smoke like a fibre and then like a nerve. See a row of men in black padding walk through a crowd. A row of men like a linked fence. See a cigarette burning its tip in a hand. Row of men like a set of grey teeth. Hear, "Getting fresh pictures back." Read POLLUTION. A row of men like a blankness advancing. Pink plastic bodies of women dressed in black bras. A figure in white. Read CHILLED WATER. A white mask and helmet concealing a man's face. A football flies heavily into the air and heads tilt towards it with eyes squinted. Read ADMIRAL DUNCAN. A tall matt black top-hat adorned with stars and moons of foil. See a man and a woman with cans of beer and a dog on a lead. The body of a woman wearing a pale blue thong and tattoos of peppermint green and blurred palm trees over an arm, holding a padlock in one hand. Read THE LOVE POSSE. Hear, "You seen us on the telly." A man leaning forwards in brown clothes and walking slow circles. Pink leaflets dispersed and strewn over tar and hear the tick of a bike. Read CARLING. Hear, "oh, okay, it doesn't look like it's going to kick off, does it." Face of a man with soft skin holding a grey megaphone up to his lips and a table spread out

[346]

with flasks of brown tea. Hear, "What's the bloody matter with you all. You want tea, not coffee." The word 'tea' exclaimed. See men in dark clothes carrying many balloons. Hear a shriek. A black beard passes on roller skates. Smell of grease and spice mixed. A dog squeals once. See a man's finger held up with two silver rings. A boy's hand goes into the cup of a woman's big hand. A football smacks down onto tar and bounces up reaching hands. Man barks like a dog. Hear, "How much?" Hear reply, "Twelve." A woman adorned with May blossom and fox fur in her long red hair running. Hear, "Where d'you go from Hyde Park?" Sunlight makes a dog's hair bright like gipsy silver woven in clothes. A woman in red kneels down to stroke a small brown dog with black eyes that shine. Read STREET MEDIC. Hear, "Fuck the police." Hear reply, "Yeah, go on ... go on, fuck 'em batty boy." A football is kicked and smacks down to the slap of a bounce. See shoes. Read ADVANCE WARNING. The spokes of a bike's wheel cast a long shadow like stork legs. Hear the sharp cry of a brown dog. See the silver star of a badge worn by a man and the rims of black hats reflect sun in curls like scythe blades. Pink scar on the chin of a man. See the white frizzy beard of an old man and golden braids of a young man. A woman pushing a bike, fibres of sunlight above her mouth. Black-haired face,

obsidian eyes. Read GERRY'S WINES. Read
& SPIRITS. Read Red. Hear, "I didn't leave a
message because it was just." Police man and
woman and the hands of the woman perched
on the box of a black radio. Pale horns from a
man's nose. A piece of dust turns into a small
fly. Hear the scream of the fly. Clatter of a foot
and high laughter. Smell fish. See the faces of
two crouched men at a table, eating yellow rice
and green peas and the curled pink bodies of
cooked shrimps and the eyes of the shrimp
black set on each bony proboscis of shrimp-
face. Read VICTIM. See a small worm moving
in the matted hair of a man's head. A pointed
cigarette-end of ash. Hear, "She's still going for
it." A gurgling laugh. Hear, "Yeah." A mouth
set in a beard like a cut in a cloth sips from the
mouth of a metal can. Read WE ARE BEING
SWAMPED BY WARMONGER. Smell sweet
and sharp smoke and the rustling crackle of
burning dry leaves, and the minute spitting
noise in the crackle of lit tobacco. See a man
stapling placards to posts, figures gathered
about him with hands out to help. Hear the
snap of a staple gun fired. See a hand hold a
board against a baton. A sequin butterfly of red,
black and emerald. Hear the snap of a staple
gun fired. See yellow glasses on a man's face.
See a plastic woman in a white vinyl bra and
white shiny knickers. A woman's brown hair
from a conical black hat, clasping a black scarf

[348]

tight to her chest. Read 13.5%. See a wooden
pipe in the hand of a man and the hand taps
the bowl against the stern hollow ring of a lamp
post and a slug of tar-black tobacco falls to the
ground. Hear a whistle. Hear, "Hey, how are
you." Hear, "See, they're nice." Hear, "There
are." Read Discover the mysteries under your
skin. The figure of a woman in tight clothes in
the frame of a door and you read above her a
sign of letters flashing, the flashing light
grubby. Read GOLDEN CLUB LIVE SHOW.
See protrusions of the stomach of a woman
above belt below shirt and see large breasts
pointed down at the nipples. Man limps in a
green coat. Hear, "Fucking joking, I'm not
having that." See the form of a thin man with
round blackened eyes like a hawk's, and the
man eating the contents of a bag with the
spoon of his hand. Hear, "You listen to me
right." See the leg of a woman strikes out, kicks
the ribs of a man and the woman hacks air with
a laugh, her cheeks reddened over the cheek
bones. She walks, the man follows with a limp
and a kick in the ribs. Pass a black woman with
ringlets of hair black as squid ink. And she
pushes the man to the ground with the force of
her hands. See a lip of blood run on the man's
quiet face. See two women shout and see the
figure of the man, canary-delicate, remains
quiet and walks round and round with a limp.
Hear, "If you didn't think it had happened, you

wouldn't be standing here now." A uniformed
woman walks up at ease to the shouting
woman. Two police men and women like a
four-cornered ring around two shouting
women. All turn to the man walking limping
and two police lead him into the shade of a
brick wall with blackened mortar. See the quiet
man moves at the mouth. See a notebook
flipped open by the thumb of a hand and the
notebook-man writes without a word spoken.
Hear a gruff shout. A can kicked. See a man
with swept hair, a red face and horns. Read
STAGE DOOR. And hear, "You writing porn?"
Hear, "Disgusting." Read PLAYAWAY
TAKEAWAY KEBABS. Look up to the
thrumming of three helicopters, like red
dragonflies.

Hear, "We gonna have." Hear, "Do we have."
Cry of a siren and a man in an alley reading
alone. Read WORLD SOCCER. Hear a word
in German and two men hesitantly laugh at
once and you pass seeing a hole in a man's
shirt's left shoulder and a woman cries out. Two
eyes meet and turn and you read
ARCHITECTS OF ETERNITY. See a chip
between two fingers of a hand and a woman
wearing a short white apron over black, she
crumples a white page into a ball in the palm of
her hand, drops it onto a tray. A man leans to

the shoulder of a woman. Gaunt cheeks of a
man with a red face. Hear, "Does anyone need."
A woman bent forwards at the back holding a
black stick. Hear, "One for fifteen quid." See a
road's crossing. Men of green light. A door into
shade. Hear, "Yeah but now." And three men
talking. Hear, "I've given." Hear, "Yesterday
you were talking about Japan." Hear reply,
"Okay, alright." Hear reply, "Don't laugh
because you." See a woman with hair the colour
of straw and a man cranes up and waves his
hands in the air and makes an arch of a gesture
with both. Hear, "It's the first time in Italy,
how many time we go to the final in Italy?"
Faces look into faces and hear words harshly in
a language and hear, "Be there for the first
time." Hear reply, "World cup ... world cup."
And three voices talk and the words congeal
and break apart in a language and hear, "Never
been there and I am glad for you." Mutterings.
Hear, "I have to ask my grandfather." See an
unshaven man chewing bread and strands of
saliva with weights of saliva foamed from his
open wide chewing, and saliva milky with the
glue of bread and the mouth makes words and
bread falls out. Hear, "Fuck and fuck you fuck."
Hear, "Jules Jules," cried loud. See shuttles of
spit fly to a near woman's arm. Hear, "You win,
you win ... won about me hundred quid ... you
ever bet, you ever bet?" See a hole in a jumper
and a scalp rubbed over by a wet hand. See

[351]

breadcrumbs in saliva caught in the short hairs.
And you turn and you walk away among many.
There are steps.

Turn and see daylight from sky between
buildings like a river of grey light between walls
of a gorge. See a building of windows. See a
man hanging hooked to a rope, feet flat against
the wall of a building and two men below him
looking up. Hear, "Fuck me, never ask for a
pound ever in your life." See a hooded man
smoking a thin cigarette. See red and black
figures with black hats in the manner of a frieze
of figures printed on the side of a passing bag.
See a red flower on the ankle of a woman's
sock. See a silver ladder. Hear the crack of puff
pastry and see a man biting into a grey sausage
roll. Read TAX FREE. See white spots on blue
cloth. Hear the scream of a drill. Look up to a
man suspended from rope driving the tongue of
a drill into a wall and the drill grinds its
hammer. Read ARRIVO. Read 73. Numbers in
yellow. Hear, "That's right." Smell the ill, acid
smell of hot vinegar. See dark eyes beneath grey
eyebrows. See the dry leatheriness of a black
banana skin on grey concrete. Hear, "She's got
a good sense of humour." See individuals
rushing into a building through an open door.
See the flat lozenge of a phone held over an ear.
Pass a man who walks looking down. Hear the

XXIV

[352]

flat tapping of feet under scaffolding. See a wet road, it gleams in the dark. A woman tightens her scarf round her neck and folds her arms into the slight shade of her breasts as she walks. Read HIFI SOUNDS. A woman exits a shop and twists her arm in the handle of a packed plastic bag. Pass a woman, cross-legged on the pavement, smoking. Hear, "I'll probably go and stay at Colin's." See a man nodding with eyes shut. Hear, "Spare just a few pennies." See a padlock closed about two links of a chain. See the dry skin of a woman smoking. See a crimson tie. Hear, "Yeah, I got four quid ... spend money on it, I'll get sixty." See the hands of a man with coins. See reddened skin. A man holding a shiny blue sleeping bag, a thin white cloth over the ball of his shoulder. Hear, "Sorry about that, I just went in for one minute." See a man dressed in green-black, the colour of ravens, insert a yellow square plastic wallet under the black rubber blade of a windscreen wiper and see a man run up to the car, rip the square from the grip of the wiper and shout. Turn to see sky and a pinkness to it. Read SAINSBURY'S CENTRAL. See a white plastic spoon. See a two-man conversation. The wheel of a bike leaps up over the ridge of a kerbstone. Five trees bearing small leaves. See polished stone and the image of a man passes across. See gravel embedded in tar. Count ten brown buttons on a brown coat. Read UNITED FOR

MAY DAY TO PARTISATION TO WAR.
Pass a girl chewing. Read SPATIAL AUDIO.
See the glazing of the lens of a camera wink.
Hear the word, "Data." Hear, "Try and get it
done." And you see green handrails. See the
Medusa of a woman's hair, like submarine hair
as she walks. Count six gold buttons on an
unbuttoned coat. Hear a sharp hiss from the
body of a passing gold-coloured bus. And the
air is cool. Read pay it off sooner. Hear a sound
like, "Dow-treece." Hear, "You're like gettin'
peed," the word 'peed' emphatic with the 'e' of
the sound brightly stretched. See a hand in a
room with lights. A grey pigeon struts. Hear
sounds spoken you do not know. A man's finger
brushed under the chin of a woman. Hear,
"Not a girlfriend." See the entrance to an alley.
Hear laughter strutting from an open mouth. A
man smokes and bangs on a wooden door with
a fist curled like a shrimp. Read VIDEO
FILMS. See the black box of a loudspeaker in a
doorway, like a square-chested bouncer at a
club door. See fake-fur dogs lined up on a shelf
behind glass. Hear, "Yeah but that's only
because you go ... they got some favourites,
sausages and mash." Two women pass. Read
LIVE MUSIC HERE. See a white shirt with
squares of red marked over its fabric. Hear a
squeak of brakes and a pip pip of brakes. See a
car door open. See the shoulders of a woman
with blonde hair shrug once, and the woman is

walking. Read PIN TABLES in flashing neon.
See rows of screens in a room of black walls,
and images of roads moving on all screens.
Hear, "You'll be fine." Hear, "I will be." Read
MEDIA PRICE. See two hands rubbing a
paper napkin between them around the eight
fingers and two thumbs. Bruised leaves on the
ground like flat lizards. See a shaking woman
helped in the act of walking by the four arms
and legs of two helping women who lead her
into the shade of a doorway. Hear a man cry,
"Two pound fifty strawberries ... two pound
fifty strawberries," and quietly, "yes ma'am."
Hear, "No, that's one." The word 'one' said
with a boldness. See a bearded man sucking a
straw. A man swinging a string of pea-yellow
beads in a hand, and the fingers of that hand
gripped tight on the string. See the redness of
tail lights diminishing. See hair the colour of
red sand and the hair is in curls. Hear, "Yeah I
know ... see you later then ... keep in touch."
See a woman striding, a scarf out behind her.
See a man jogging. See a stall of flowers, see the
pointed large petals of lilies. Hear the beep of a
horn twice. Hear, "In a minute, in a minute."
Read JERRY'S. Read Severe delays until 2004.
Read 85. Hear, "I'll bring, I'll find." See a white
plastic bag containing the shape of an object,
and the bag carried under an arm. Hear
clunking transmission. Hear the squeak of
suspension. See a man barefooted and see small

coins in the palm of a hand, see a finger lift the edge of one coin turning it over to its other face, the head of a woman stamped on the coin's back. See black toenails. See a red blanket over the grey cloth of a shoulder. See long brown hair and hands held open. See eyes look into hands. See the eyes of a man on the ground move left to right. Slabs of square concrete. Hear a shrill siren rising and falling. Blue lights on the roof of a passing white van and they flash bright and dull-away quickly. Hear, "Fucking white bastard." Hear, "Fucking white bastard." Hear, "Fucking white bastard." A woman's hand hoists up a belt at the waist. Read IT'S A SCREAM. Read But you first. Read SWITCHED ON. Hear the grunt of an engine and revving hard is a high metallic grind like the noise of a fly magnified. See coffee-dark glass and figures at tables and the hands of those figures holding their glasses by stems with almost black liquid in each of the glasses. Hear, "Between sixteen and eighteen grand." Hear, "But here's a job, do accept." Hear, "But shouldn't I say to him." Hear, "I'd say whether you want it or not." See a black flag flying at half mast. See grey jumper sleeves and holes in the sleeves and threads of grey at the mouth of each hole. Pass a long-and-brown-haired man crouched and talking to a man on the floor of the pavement. See silver coins in the hand of a man on the ground. See a purple turban wound

round a man's head. See the shrub of a beard.
Read No Access to Euston. See a glass building.
And see trees reflected on towers of glass. A
row of four figures. Read logica. See a man turn
from the window of a kiosk. Hear the word
"Hey" cried out loud. Read OURS TRAVEL. A
woman sits on a red seat. Hear the creak of a
red seat. See shiny black bags heaped and the
bags full and tied at their mouths by thin yellow
cords. Hear, "Yeah but all I know." See five
cardboard boxes. Read Abbey National Group.
Read SOCIAL WORKLINE. Read
RESTAURANT TO LET. Read Thai. Read
ROAD CLOSED. See a tall, slim, round tower.
Hear a cry. Read Boc junction & banned turn
offences. Read BALLS TO CAPITALISM. See
a bus move. Hear, "Don't want you getting all
nasty, you see." Read J37 GMF. Letters and
numbers on a black car passing. Read
CONWAY. Smell gloss paint. A girl passes
wearing a jacket of blue. Read COME IN
AND BROWSE. See the dome of a church.
See four pillars of stone. Read BBC. Blackened
walls of stone and illuminated leaves. A man of
green light. Hear, "Do you like the performance
rolling afterwards." See a hand carrying a pair of
black shoes by the laces. A scrape of metal. A
man holding a hammer in a hand shaking. See a
woman waiting and the wind moves her hair
apart at the neck towards the ear like a cat
stepping through grasses. See men in red

standing. Hear one shout. See ivory white walls
of a building. See two orange lights. See a green
metal head. Read JOHN F. KENNEDY 1917 -.
See letters in gold. Read ALCOHOLIC. Read
SUN 14 APR EAST & CENTRAL LONDON.
See an ivory white pediment on fluted columns.
See round-arched windows of light, windows of
darkness. See dust on glass. Hear the chak of a
blackbird. See heart-shaped leaves. See trees
among trees like a gauze of greens laid on the
low sky. A red bus stops. A woman in a red car
passes the length of the red bus and you turn to
walk on. See pages. Read PARK SQUARE.
The delicate scent of almondy blossom. See
shrivelled yellow flowers. See columns of lilac.
See a lawn of cut grass. Hear the laughing of
men like serrations of air. Pass the sound of a
cough. See leaves, the serrated edges and a red
flower. Read PLEASE DO NOT ALLOW
YOUR DOG TO FOUL. A bearded man as he
walks. See blue, tight shorts on a cycling man.
Read 30. See pink blossom and air makes a
movement like a boat on a swell. Pass two
bright lights. Read PRIVATE. Hear the
winding of a diesel motor. Soft light of a street
of white lights like moonshine. Tick tick of a
bike and a car with a sound like the word
'room' spoken deeply, diminishing on the 'm'
for the length of five cars thereabout. See the
bud of a leaf in parts half-opened. See figures
walking behind bars of iron with heads down.

[358]

Hear, "Absolute agony." Hear, "So, my God ... so that was quite." Pass a grey stone. Read WOUNDED ELEPHANT 1990. Pass a man walking and eating a sandwich. Pass a man kneeling on one knee lifting a child who perches upright on the horse of his knee and he rocks her and laughs out loud. Read HORSE. See a band of pink sky the colour of raspberries crushed and stirred into cream. See four birds flying in the form of a square and the square elongates and pulls at a corner into the squashed diamond-shape of a kite. See a grey path before you and two birds join-up and fly as one bird with four wings and then three and then there are two birds. Pass thick white blossom like a froth and hear the tangle of birdsong from the basket of a bush. Read BOY WITH CALF. Hear clapping distinctly. See empty green benches and hear the bright-dark noise of a fountain. Pass delicately-leaved trees and a daisy half-opened and pining away like a girl for her love. See white petals and shrivelled brown heads four inches up from the level of earth. A flock of bowing green stems bearing the weight of the heads of flowers, the flowers curled back like elephants' ears. See trees of dark olive green like single flames. See opening leaves of transparent flesh, like grubs under stones. Hear the tick of a bike chain. A man walks with long hair. See two glints of amber. See four winged lions with horns of rams bearing between their four backs a shallow dish planted with tulips and the cups of the tulips are dark red. See the open palms of sharp-tipped leaves and a bird cries. See pink sky running over the backs of black leaves like a rose-hued foil. See blue and cream flowers together and the heavy sweet smell of flowers like rose-peach-scented butter. See the thin limb of a jet of water over the ringed cup of a fountain. Falling water and orange big flowers under the trilled sound of a bird like a greenfinch. See a blackbird fly up with its tail fanned out like a hand in alarm. Pass spindly black trees like arms opened out to the sky. A dark bird sinks in the sea of a bush with the noise of a click as leaves meet over its head. See holes in orange petals and you walk an avenue of black cypress trees. Cry of a bird once. A tower of red lights and nine pink tulips. A woman walks fast and you see an eye of white water flung up like a bride's bouquet. See a bubble of foam skating across the meniscus of water in the bowl of a fountain and hear the pat and burble of water glugging to itself. See crumbs of dry earth. Hear the scuff of a shoe on tarmac and a gritty refrain from the motion of feet picking up to speed on. Read in this area are forbidden. Turn to a road of lights. A car's headlamp scans undulating pavement like the body of a skate. Shadow of grit like a small rabbit. See a flashing bulb mounted on the

[360]

front of a bike's frame and the bike moving
close and a figure with legs pedalling is
mounted on the saddle of the bike and the
whole apparatus pauses like a diagram for an
invention. A bird cries hoarsely up and then
down. A brake squeals. See opening flowers,
small and pale and they tremble with the
motion of air about them. Read NO EXIT
BETWEEN MIDNIGHT AND 7AM. Hear,
"I mean I do want to." Pass the scrag of a white
tissue pressed into the rough face of the ground
and the corner of the tissue is scuffed to a
back-of-leather shag. Two chaks of a bird. Pass
a hedge of black branches like bones and leaves
trembling like fingers of a shaky hand. A car
passes. Kneel to smell the cot of a rose and its
scent is soft like the scent of a baby. Rise to
walk on. See figures in human-shaped
containers of black cloth standing about in an
upstairs of dull yellow light. See one figure
bending and placing the empty glass of its drink
on a platform of glass and straightening up with
both hands in pockets on the side of each hip.
Hear, "Do those other things to convince
yourself." See a figure jogging and the figure
passes and the suck of a vacuum passes. See
chalky deposits on the ledge of a stone.
Window-blind illuminated to a glow of grass
green in the frame of a window. Two cries of an
alarm. A man with a walking stick slams a door
shut and you hear the jangle of keys quickly

snatched quiet. Hear the sprinkle of water over a wetness. Humming of an electric fan. See cut-glass cupolas over shining bulbs of light. Sheen on a gloss of black railings. Read CAMEL. Tan letters on a white box. Black paintwork shines in orange. Feel a warm wake from passing traffic. See backs of leaves dark with shade, swipe of light passing, smell petrol. See a line shine the length of a bar of chromed metal. See sets of two lights before you at distance and sets of two lights repeated like many looking at you and car windows half-lurking through dust and the shapes of heads lurking within. See the outstretched hand of a woman push open a gate of iron and she walks. Globes of gold. See a gold dome. Hear the hard clack of heels get faster and a woman running is awkwardly lurched on the heels of her shoes like a boat on the tip of a swell. Read THE DUKE'S HALL. Pass a man with long curls of hair and a beard drawn thin. See a floor of black and cream squares of stone. See a gleam on the dark surface of iron. See red lights and look up to see two thin black hands of a clock. See five figures in black knitting an argument. Read by order of The Secretary of State for the. Dark pediment of granite and feet walking fast on polished stone. Read HERON. A car passes. A car passes. Feet scuff on the corner of a protrusion like a tooth knocked up from the level of pavement. An orange-shirted jogger.

Smell fumes of sweat. Leaves dangling are
shaken. Shadow of a leaf intersecting the body
of a leaf. See thin beams of light over the
pavement like swords. Read GROUP
WAITING AREA. Read GROUP LEADERS/
SALES. See a fog of light on black paintwork.
Pass the length of a long white and black
building. See a man ahead limps and holds up
his right hand and is talking slowly with an
American woman, you hear, by the curl of a
word. Read SENSUOUS AMERICAN. Three
figures under a canopy, like sheep in a cave. See
the side of a nose like the beak of a hawk. Read
LORD ABERCON. See a stone cat's head and
the teeth visible like the shape of a growl. Read
WASH YOUR HAIR IN SUNSHINE. The
slats of a wooden bench. Pass a grid of iron.
Read Cerebral Palsy Helpline. See eyes that
turn down and are dark. A man and red tail
lights of cars are lined-up and cars begin to
move and one car passes at speed. See three
wheels visible of a passing car. Look up and a
star is above you in the blue bloom of the sky.
See the face of a woman chewing and her eyes
look up and to the side through the narrow
coves at the corners of her eyes, are like the
shapes of two fish without tails and you see the
tail of a fish in the red imprint of a triangle-
place on the side of the nose close to one of the
eyes. See unfolded pages of a newspaper on the
loose, twitching and one page curled up. See

curved-as-sabre shadows of branches scattered over the paving. See the interior of a room through the hole of a window. See glinting crystal chips of a chandelier and many colours grow among the glassy bits like the colours of drinks. See pale green leaves against deep reds of brickwork and square windows of glass with pink and red flashes like teeth smacked by a fall. Pass a stone lion seated and one claw is held up. Pass a wooden door pregnant with nails. Pass a black metal lion. See two dark women and they pass. Pass a woman in a long black coat and black hood over the crown of her head making a point. Read PRIVATE No admittance to public. See a rusty iron chain wrapped round the bars of two iron gates, like a bandage on an arm. An arch of stone bridging two buildings. A building fronted by pillars of sage green. A child of iron holding a wreath of pointed iron. See a dark long street to your left under crowns of flapping plane trees. Look up to see triangle leaves against dark blue sky. A red-haired woman walks briskly. See the picture of a woman, her eyes closed. Read HARROW ROAD. Read In Remembrance. See the image of a woman in a broad pea-green hat and a necklace of white pearls over the wrinkles of her neck and beside her see two large-format pictures of women wearing white lacy knickers. Read Sun At Any Time. See a man in black standing beside a black metal chain and four

figures of wood. See thirty-four glasses
containing red wine on a table. See paintings of
figures. Pass two men walking, they both laugh
like monkeys in chatters. See dim empty rooms.
See buckled and warped panes of glass. Read
PLC AMPED. Read WINES. See a glass lifted
to the lips of a mouth and see golden liquid
flow into a head through the urn of its mouth.
Read 28. See a jacketed man. Read e
Nightingale. Black strands of ivy. A man at a
lamp post with a chain in one hand. Hear the
whirr of a fan. Man standing alone, see his eyes
turn up and his whole face hangs like a face
guilty. A woman behind a honey red counter,
like honey spilt, her hand grips about a black
lever pulling it towards her. Smell cooking meat
sweet with a bitterness of a taste like blue ink.
Count six wooden chairs. See a window with
newspapers laid out over the sill. Read
SEYMOUR CLEANERS. A slouching man
walks and the slouch leans forwards into a
stoop. Pass a padlock closed over the bolt of a
door. A wooden crate with paper-wrapped
oranges and the wood of the crate is
unvarnished. A cardboard crate of green apples.
A box of scaly-skinned melons each yellow and
round. A window with brown squares of carpet.
A standing man lifts up a hand. See a red car
stops and the man with his hand raised places
the hand on the door of the car and climbs into
the car. Read EAT IN OR. Read PLASMAS

from £4,000. See a woman in a short white jacket holding a bunch of pink carnations. Three men in grey suits. Hear the cough of a woman. Hear the jangle of keys like a rash of noises. See a tail of dark smoke behind a car's body. Watch a man watching the screen of a television where women are dancing. A smell of savoury spices. A man with a notebook standing before trays of fruit. See a man with grey hair over the dome of his head. See the prickly buzby of a pineapple. The swish of garments over legs on a walk. See oranges and apples and the shape of a woman enters a building. A box is closed by the hands of a man. A red van passes and you hear three tolls of a bell. Hear ticking music like the shimmer of crickets. Read THREE. A bundle of papers tied in a bale. A woman passing with her head down. Read THE LARRIK. A man holding his hand on the part of his chest where his heart lies. See elbows of figures leaning on tables. See a hole to an illuminated basement and you hear the wind-over whine of a car starting and a girl runs from the door of a building. Pass a man and woman in black side by side and see in the hand of the man the rectangle of a white envelope. Read THE CHRISTIAN UNION. A window opens. See a family together, and count three children. Read ANGELIC. The lips of a mouth pursed and hear a hoarse whistle. Hear the cluck of a laugh. Hear, "I

don't understand what that means, hm?" Hear,
"Said ... a fudge-up." See the torso, neck, head
of a thin man crouched over a plate eating
white bread. A man smoking in a room of white
smoke. See two men inside black V-necked
jumpers. Read POLICE. See glinting helmets
on the heads of two men. See a room packed
with men wearing jackets. Read Pharmacy.
Read AL MUSTAPA. Read THE MIDAS
TOUCH. Hear, "The kids are actually
studying." And hear, "Your pretty." See the
figure of a woman and she sits in a chair with
wheels and the chair is pushed from behind by
a man and the seated woman smiles to the
street. See windows of darkness and you pass.
Three men in a window. A figure head-to-toe in
black cloth and only the eyes and hands visible,
the eyes in a slot. See a man wearing a woollen
black hat. See two yellow bags stitched with red
stars. Read A3U ALI. Smell the sweetness of
cooking and there is the smell of charred sugar
and oily fried spice. See red lights lit. Read
FLATS TO LET. Read GIFTS & FANCY. A
glittering red woman's top of sequins. Read
EXTENDED RANGE OF LIVE COUPONS.
Read SELL CASH. Green tigerish-skin of shiny
melons. Read Up the girl. A wall bearing words.
See two women pushing blankets with their
four hands over the body of a baby asleep in a
pram with a hood. Read CLAYS. And the
letters are of blue light beyond the dark head of

a man standing still. Read SAVINGS. Smell the
warm, skinned bodies of fruit you do not know.
See a man with a mouth hung open, the crown
of his head bald and shiny with dark skin.
Fingers tapping the spoon ends of fingernails
on a tall glass. Read HOSPIT. A door shuts
with a clunk and you hear the burst of a car's
engine start and the firing-up to a settled
humming. See a man tucking a blanket over his
shoulders. Hear, "Don't man, you're soaking
me." Man with a red plastic bucket and a red
plastic mop soaking an area of pavement
outside a shop. Hear, "What would you do if
you were in this situation." And hear, "I'd
probably get the coach back to Ox." Hear,
"Well it depends what I was doing the next
day." See a tall and bald man, both his hands
clasped in the hands of a girl. And a woman
with a pearl earring passes. Read
RECYCLING FOR RESIDENTS. See red-
leaved trees. Man walking alone like a penguin.
Hear, "Get cash and then I'll pay it in." A car
passes. See beads of dark substance hang from
the stem of a car's inner mirror. See a man trip
and stumble on a step and his feet pick up the
rhythm of the walk and walk on with his head
turning back to look once. White pillars in blue
light. Read ESCORT. See a small light moving
through dark sky. A shoe of glossy-black leather
the colour of tar. See blurred shadows under
stiff bowed leaves of pond green. See three

shadows of a parked van cast on the road and the kerb onto pavement. A man leans from a doorway and turns in the shade of the alcove, and turns and steps out onto pavement and puts a struck match on fire to the bowl of a pipe and you see smoke rise like a screen at his eyes. Hear a voice in a language you do not know. Read teeth@w2. Read KHAN TRADERS. See three bananas hanging from a hook hooked to a grille of metal and there is a black stripe along the ridge of one banana. Hear, "So I might pop in, yeah ... good." See two eyes sparkle once under streetlight as you pass. See a black car door close like one part of the claw of a crab against its companion. Read CURRY. The hiss of large tyres on the tar of the wet road. Daze of white headlamps. See soft pink skin of a passing face and the mouth smiling, curled up at the corners. Pass a woman alone. See glasses in glass cases lit. Read AVAILABLE. Read D720 LBW. Read commissioners for oaths. See a single orange eye of light ahead. Pass bags full and tied up with yellow cords and heaped in a pile. Pass a crooked mouth. Hear, "Non." Hear a fast language. Hear, "Walk this way." Hear, "Der-dee-der-dum." Leather jacket and see the two toothed strips of the zip do not touch where the jacket is open but integrate at the mouth of the zip-draw and are locked together by the teeth below and the jacket theredown is joined

shut. Read THE IRISH TIMES. Scrape of a
foot on a metal grate. Hear, "Alright big 'un ...
speak to you." Hear, "Alright." And two men
pass.

Read Private Room. Diamond earring winces a XXV
flash of violet, green into orange. Hand with
white leaflets. Man cross-legged on the shore of
a puddle. Hear, "Spare a bit." Read Bar. See
golden pastries in a steel and glass box. Hear,
"If there was." Read Free Bottle of Wine.
Shadow of a fork over a mouth stretched in
chewing. Clack of a man's foot. Hear, "Walk
down here, it's like." Man in a hood. Words
you do not know. Hear, "Trying to juggle
between." Read Non-surgical. And the air rafts
cool over your face among the figures of the
street and you walk. Sky dark and whisked. See
onions netted. See light cast over a stone face.
Black eyes of a girl. Man with a hand on his
belt buckle's eye, the brass of the buckle glows
like a lion. Hear, "I think it was just one night."
Glass gleams in a man's hand and the gleam
shrinks and floats behind fingers. Glass
knobbled like a tray of buns. Man crying like a
screech owl runs into the shape of a woodcock,
flailing his arms like two chains. Orange gem of
a cigarette's light. Ticket fumbled in a hand.
Hear, "Huh." The sound of a flushed woman.
Woman seated and the pavement gleams with

water where it lies flat. And smoke rises from
black lips. A woman's eye turns. See a white
envelope. Heads in a room full of dust in the
light and tables intense with grouped figures
drinking and chatting. See a room in a glass of
white wine and a red glass gleams like jellied
dark fire and a hand waves across it like a stage
direction. See a crease in a man's trouser leg at
the back of the knee. White slats of a blind.
Read TROPHY RAPIST. See grey pavement
crossed by feet and low, creeping shadows.
Hear, "Okay, so over the lights." Bumps in the
paving and gritty lumps of tar. Hear, "La mer,
er." Read THIS ENTRANCE TO. Clear
plastic wrappers. Hand on a heart. Hear, "Don't
know what it's about." See a man and woman in
a black car. Hear, "Maybe get a new pair of ...
like a pair of trousers or something which you
don't wear all the time." Long beep of a horn.
See hazed light ahead and a big voice amplified
and you read No Public Access. Two figures
descending into the ground. Pass a room full of
debris in bags and folded stacked cardboard.
Lights of a vehicle crossing the dip in a
woman's throat. Hear, "And I get tired." See a
hand at a watch and eyes flash up. See the strap
of a bag slung between breasts. See a whistling
mouth and three men in tall sober hats and a
wristwatch is swivelled up into view and is
viewed and returned to hip level. Hear,
"Departure." See many legs running. And hear,

"And I've also written to ... because we can sell them out, so I've basically." Light on a tooth. Hear, "That machine." And you turn to walk back. See girders and rivets inset. See electric lights, see flat polished stones at your feet and long machines parked with small windows and faces with eyes in the shadows of brows. And a man with a woman smiles and she smiles and they both stand quiet in smiles as many walk different directions. Air thick with fumes in a grey. Hear, "God no." A dark hand lands like a clamp on a wrist with a shake. Hear, "Wonderful to see you, is she all right?" Hear, "Great, absolutely." Hear, "Well I think we have actually, it's nerve-wracking ... oh." Hear, "God, well I hope so ... bye bye." Hear, "Bye bye Murph."